Garrie L. Tufford

Principles
of Structural Glaciology

The Petrography of Fresh-water Ice
as a Method of Glaciological Investigation

by P. A. Shumskii

Translated from the Russian
by DAVID KRAUS

Dover Publications, Inc., New York

Published simultaneously in Canada by General Publishing Co., Ltd., 222 Adelaide St. W., Toronto.

Published in the United Kingdom by Constable and Company, Limited, 10 Orange Street, London W.C.2.

Principles of Structural Glaciology, first published in 1964, is an extensively revised version of the translation prepared in the years 1957–1958 and 1960–1961.

The original translation was made by the American Meteorological Society under Contract AF 19(604)–1936 and by the Arctic Institute of North America under Contract AF 19(604)–8343 through the support and sponsorship of the Air Force Cambridge Research Laboratories, Bedford, Massachusetts. David Kraus prepared the original translation and the present revision.

Library of Congress Card Catalog Number 64-15518

Manufactured in the United States of America

Dover Publications, Inc.
180 Varick Street
New York 14, N.Y.

TRANSLATOR'S ACKNOWLEDGMENTS

I wish to express my sincere thanks to Professor P. A. Shumskii for his cooperation in the preparation of this translation and to Professor John W. Glen of Birmingham University, Professor John B. Lyons of Dartmouth College, and the members of the Terrestrial Sciences Laboratory, Air Force Cambridge Research Laboratories, for their valuable advice in matters of science and terminology.

I also wish to acknowledge the assistance of my wife Mary and my son Jon in the preparation of the text and the bibliography.

PREFACE

The main propositions set forth in this work were conceived during my glaciological studies of 1947–1948, when I was first able to undertake a broad study of our northern glaciers. One of the methods of investigation, the petrographic study of snow and ice, yielded particularly interesting results, revealing new possibilities for glaciological research. In undertaking the study of glaciers as a geographer, I became convinced that progress in this field could be realized only through refinement of the physical theory; then the geographical generalizations, for which the present surface morphological descriptions are quite inadequate, would be solved of themselves.

My special glaciological investigations under the unique conditions of our North and Northeast and, in particular, the need for solving the vital and practical problems of glaciology made me keenly aware of the unsatisfactory state of contemporary glaciology. Its components are disconnected and are usually studied by representatives of various allied disciplines which have different methods and specific aims, often too narrow and shallow, and thus are incapable of satisfying practical demands. This fractionation is an historical development; the various branches of glaciology came into being within the framework of other disciplines and as a part of such disciplines. The present needs of socialist construction demand a synthesis of all glaciological knowledge, a synthesis which alone can set the proper pattern for solution of practical problems. In my opinion, the most vital element of a synthesis of the dispersed glaciological knowledge should be structural glaciology, the study of the structure of natural ice types resulting from the processes of their formation.

A large number of investigations, especially of late, has been devoted to individual problems of structural glaciology, but thus far no attempt has been made to systematize the results and to delineate their meaning for glaciology as a whole. In undertaking this difficult and responsible task, i.e., to summarize contemporary knowledge of structural glaciology, I have not intended to summarize all the current concepts, but rather to use the most valuable of these to create a unified theory, based on two fundamental ideas: the genetic classification of ice types, and the zonation of the ice formation processes.

Thus, this work does not pretend to be exhaustive. My approach to structural glaciology has been the study of "permanent" ice types and general problems of glaciology, hence I have not devoted special attention to problems connected with the investigation of saline and brine ice (as indicated by their treatment under a subheading) and little attention has been paid to the structural characteristics of ephemeral ice formations, the influence of vegetation on the structure of the snow cover, etc. I have not been able to form any clear opinion about these matters, because I do not have pertinent data. No studies based on structural glaciological methods have been devoted to these subjects, but perhaps the present work will inspire the introduction of such methods into all branches of glaciology.

I wish to express my sincere gratitude to my assistants in the structural glaciological work, N. V. Cherepanov and B. I. Vtiurin, and to Corresponding Members of the Soviet Academy of Sciences, P. F. Shvetsov and S. V. Kalesnik, who examined the manuscript of this book and offered valuable comments.

The work on the manuscript was completed in November, 1951 and some minor additions were made in the first half of 1952. Since then some of the questions treated in this book have been elaborated further, but this does not reduce the importance of the material treated in the present book. I cannot amend the present text, so I have had to limit myself to indicating the most important recent works in the references.

TABLE OF CONTENTS

Principles

of Structural Glaciology

INTRODUCTION

STRUCTURAL GLACIOLOGY

The most highly developed branch of ice study and at the same time the only branch that has long been an independent scientific discipline is the study of glaciers, which, by established West European tradition, is called *glaciology*. This use of the term is etymologically incorrect, since the Latin-Greek word "glaciology" means, literally, "the study of ice," and, consequently, the study of ice in general, not merely glaciers. Recently, there has been a tendency to interpret the term more broadly, to include all forms of natural ice as objects of study by glaciologists. A. B. Dobrowolski (1923) proposed the term "cryology," from the Greek "kryos" meaning "cold." However, we are not so much concerned with the search for a proper term, as with the need for removing the artificial limitation of glaciology to the "science of glaciers."

A glacier is a mass of ice formed from solid atmospheric precipitation and which is capable of moving independently. This last feature, the movement of the glacier, has been the chief interest of alpine glaciology, which from its inception has been closely associated with the theory of ancient glaciation and has been devoted to explanation of the mechanism of the geological action of moving ice. Glaciers, thanks to their movement and the great mass of material included in them, are the most complex and the most important of the natural ice formations. Nevertheless, the glacier is just one of the forms of ice, one connected in the closest way with the other manifestations of glaciation processes.

The unity of the glaciation processes and the need for studying the interrelations of the processes have been demonstrated by contemporary investigations, which include the study of formations intermediate between glaciers and seasonal snow covers (e.g., immobile snow and ice accumulations of long duration), formations transitional between glaciers and the seasonal ice covers of water (e.g., shelf ice), sikussaks,[1] and pack ice, buried glaciers, icings, fossil ice of various types, and ground ice in frozen rocks and soil. If we

---

[1] ["Sikussak: an Eskimo name for very old sea ice, resembling glacier ice, trapped in a fjord, having a snow accumulation on its surface which contributes to its formation and perpetuation," *Glossary of Arctic and Subarctic Terms*, ADTIC Publication A-105, 1955, p. 73 – D.K.]

exclude the special branch of study devoted to movement, both the methods of study and, to a great extent, the subject matter of the studies of glaciers, snow covers, the ice cover of water, and sub-terranean ice have much in common. This common factor derives from the unity of the material composition and the physico-chemical properties of the different types of ice and, hence, the similarity of most internal processes and processes of interaction with the atmosphere, the hydrosphere and the lithosphere. Extension of our knowledge necessarily demands the study of the glaciation of the earth's surface in all its diversity within the framework of a single science, glaciology, or ice science.[2] Thus, *glaciology is the science of natural ice in all its diversity.*

Before the October Revolution, our glaciology in general re-mained below the level of development in the West, which was due in part to the remoteness of the regions of intense glaciation and in part to the slow tempo of assimilation of these lands into the Russian Empire. Nevertheless, outstanding Russian scientists made an enormous contribution to glaciology and were the founders of major divisions of the science. It suffices to mention M. V. Lomonosov, who first established the concept of the cold layer of the atmosphere, the prototype of the modern crysophere, P. A. Kropot-kin, who, in his work on the glacial period, solved for his time not only the problem of ancient glaciation but the problem of the move-ment of glaciers, A. I. Voeikov, who initiated the study of the snow cover, and B. P. Veinberg, an eminent specialist in the physics of ice and the founder of the modern quantitative theories of glacier flow.

After the October Revolution, Soviet scientists assumed the lead in many fields of ice study. Actually, they founded two sciences, cryopedology,[3] including the mechanics of frozen ground (M. I. Sumgin, N. A. Tsytovich) and the study of arctic sea ice, including

---

[2] The need for expanding the tasks of glaciology was formulated particularly clearly by K. K. Markov (1946, p. 127): "The types of ice formation on the earth's surface are diverse and all belong within the realm of glaciology, a glaciology correspondingly understood and expanded."

[3] ["Cryopedology: the study of intensive frost action and permafrost, their causes and occurrences, and the engineering devices and practices which overcome difficulties brought about by them," *Glossary of Arctic and Subarctic Terms*, ADTIC Publication A-105, 1955, p. 22. I have used "cryopedology" to translate the Russian term *merzlotovedenie* here and elsewhere. Other terms used in English literature for this concept are "study of frost action on rocks and soil," which is somewhat cumbersome, and "geocryology," which has met with considerable criticism as being vague, a charge also leveled at "cryopedology." However, a choice must be made and "cryopedology" has the advantage of being a single word and one clearly defined in the widely used *Glossary of Arctic and Subarctic Terms*. – D.K.]

ice forecasting. These sciences were developed in connection with the requirements of bringing the permafrost regions and the Northern Sea Route into the Soviet national economy. Great progress was also made in the study of the physical properties of ice, the heat and water balance of snowmelt, the regime of glaciers, and regional glacier studies. Academician V. I. Vernadskii considerably expanded and refined the concepts of the cryosphere, its relation to the regions of cooling and its position in the geosphere, and the role of water and ice in the structure and history of the earth. Thus, he laid the foundations for the scientific synthesis of all glaciological knowledge.

The cycle of problems within the sphere of glaciology is very broad. Glaciology is closely related to meteorology, hydrology and cryopedology. The boundaries of these disciplines have not yet been defined. In practice atmospheric ice and the snow cover have been studied by meteorologists and climatologists, ice in the hydrosphere by hydrologists, and ground ice by cryopedologists. In part, this has an adverse effect on progress in the field, because proper methods of study have not been developed and because the various specialists do not have adequate knowledge of the attainments of neighboring branches of science.

The interests and scope of the physical, geographical and geological sciences are closely interwoven in glaciology. If the regional and historical aspects are set aside, the remaining theoretical glaciology still cannot be considered simply a part of geophysics, since the general theory of glacial phenomena is also directly connected with geography and geology.

Theoretical glaciology consists of three parts:

(1) *physical* glaciology, which treats the internal processes, the physical properties and the structure of ice;

(2) *hydro-meteorological* glaciology, which examines the interaction of ice and the atmosphere and hydrosphere;

(3) *geological-geomorphological* glaciology, which studies the interaction of ice and the earth's crust.

With equal justice the latter two may also be examined respectively as branches of hydrometeorology and physical geology or geomorphology. In most cases, one of the latter two orientations usually has prevailed; the former, however, has played only a secondary role. For a long time, glaciers were of interest primarily as a hydrometeorological object (a source of water power and water for irrigation) and as a geological-geomorphological object (in connection with problems of ancient glaciation). However, it was quite evident that these branches of glaciology could be developed successfully only on the basis of a primary, unifying study of the internal processes, the structure and properties of ice.

Physical glaciology in turn may be subdivided into the following:

(1) *ice mechanics*, which studies the elastic, plastic and endurance properties of ice, the distribution of stresses, and movement in natural ice bodies;

(2) the *thermophysics of ice*, which studies the thermal, caloric and radiational properties of ice, phase distribution and transition in natural ice bodies;

(3) *structural glaciology*, which examines ice structure. The relationship of the components of glaciology is depicted schematically in Fig. 1.

Ice structure, as an object of study of structural glaciology, should be understood in the broad sense of the word, beginning with the so-called fine structure of crystals, i.e., the structure of the space lattice of ice, including structure and texture in the petrographic sense, and going as far as tectonic structures.

Study of the structure of the space lattice of ice is in part crystallographic and forms the basis for understanding the physical properties of ice as a mineral type or, more precisely, as a group of mineral types. The problem of the actual physical study of ice is one of establishing constants that characterize the solid phase of water in general; here, the individual features of the sample studied in the physics laboratory are considered to be an unavoidable evil, having some effect or other on the result obtained.

However, pure ice as a crystalline substance is an abstraction. To a great extent the properties of natural ice bodies are due to the presence of other substances in them, and to the structure of the ice as an aggregate of crystals of a particular form, dimension and mutual orientation, while these features in turn are a function of the formation process of the given ice body. Therefore, the physical study of the fine structure and of the constants of the ice mineral is only a beginning, a prerequisite for knowledge of natural ice types, the main requirement being the structural genetic study of ice as a rock.

Structural glaciology is primarily the *petrology of ice, i.e., the science of ice rocks and the laws of their formation.*

Two conditions were necessary for the birth of structural glaciology. First, accumulations of ice had to be recognized as a rock. Theoretically, this is a quite obvious proposition. It was expressed by G. F. Link in the early days of geology and petrography and since then has often been repeated.[4] According to A. N. Zavaritskii

---

[4] See Part II, Chapter VI, p. 79.

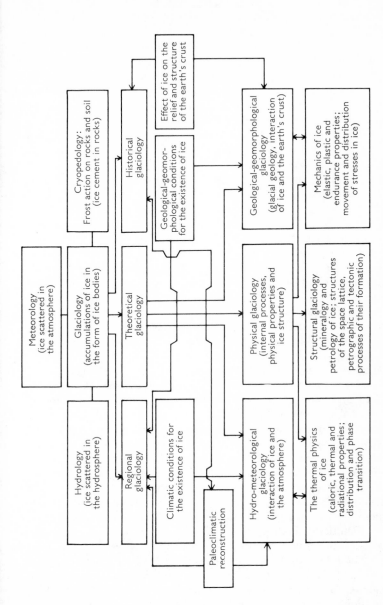

FIG. 1. The divisions of glaciology and the relationship of glaciology to allied disciplines.

(see Golovkov, 1936, p. 5), all petrographers admit that ice masses in the arctic regions and at lower latitudes are true rocks.

Secondly, petrography had to concern itself with structural orientations. As long as petrography concerned itself almost exclusively with the chemical and mineralogical composition of rocks, it had nothing to do with ice, which is a monomineralic rock of the simplest chemical composition. The ordinary task of the petrographer, viz., analysis of mineral species and investigation of the interrelations in the rock, is practically inapplicable to ice, and the differences in chemical composition caused by the impurities give only the most general indications of the origin of the initial material. A truly genetic study of ice, one which interprets the mechanism and causes of ice formation, became possible chiefly on the basis of structural-petrographic features.

The genetic meaning of the structure of rocks was emphasized by J. Dana as early as 1836 and various structural investigations have been made since. However, the significance of structural petrology as an independent branch of study of rock properties with spatial (scalar or vectorial) expression, and of the opposite branch which concerns itself with the actual composition of the rocks, was not completely established until the 1930's, after the appearance of the works of B. Sander (1930) and W. Schmidt (1932), whose procedures were based on the universal stage method of the great Russian crystallographer E. S. Fedorov. Accurate structural-petrographic studies of ice became possible only after a methodology, such as the one mentioned above, had been developed.

Sander (1935) was the first to point out the possibilities of applying the methods of structural petrology, as outlined by him, to the solution of glaciological problems.

Such were the theoretical hypotheses required for the appearance of structural glaciology, but, of course, it was not merely a matter of theoretical hypotheses. Structural glaciology, the rudiments of which were expressed in the middle of the nineteenth century, could have developed independently along with the remaining branches of glaciology if it had not been for unusual practical difficulties, the difficulties of bringing the rocks from the field to the laboratory and the difficulties of laboratory study, which requires maintenance of a constant negative temperature.

On the other hand, structural-genetic study is of greatest interest in application to ice accumulations of long duration, whereas the sphere of human activity was long limited to regions of seasonal ice formations, i.e., the ice cover of water and the snow cover of land. Without the powerful stimulus for the development of science provided by the practical demands of life, abstract theory could not have overcome all these difficulties.

As a result, despite the general acceptance in principle of the petrographic approach to ice study, recognition of ice as a rock was long embellished not so much by facts as by speculations; instead of a petrographic study, analogies were drawn between ice and other rocks and classifications of ice were made on this basis.

Recently the situation has changed. Greater demands for the study of the physical properties of seasonal ice formations have made it possible to link physical investigations with structural data; for instance, the snow cover is being studied in order to combat avalanches and to exploit communication lines and airfields in winter, the ice cover of water is being studied in order to provide better transportation across ice, navigation amidst ice, etc. On the other hand, and this is important, there has been a general trend toward the practical assimilation of areas that have previously been of little interest to man: the permafrost region with its fossil ice, the polar regions and the alpine regions with their ice and firn covers.

This has heralded a new stage in the development of the science of natural ice—the stage in which new data are being obtained by accurate physical and petrographic methods.

At present the structural-petrographic data on ice are still very incomplete; indeed, it may be asserted that in this field we have scarcely begun to fill in the gaps in glaciology. Nevertheless, such an attempt to generalize and systematize the accumulated data is, in our opinion, a real necessity.

THE ROLE OF ICE IN THE EARTH'S STRUCTURE

The specific physical properties of ordinary ice give it a special place in the mineral series. Ice is the *lightest* and the *coldest* of the widely distributed rock-forming minerals; both its specific gravity and its heat of fusion differ very sharply from those of the other minerals, going far beyond the limits of the other mineral series. The laws of the distribution of ice on earth derive from these basic differences.

The main chemical elements and their compounds are distributed zonally on our planet: the heavier are found at depth, the lighter at the surface. The hypothesis that this distribution is caused by universal gravitation is, as A. E. Fersman remarks (1934, p. 292), equally acceptable in any cosmogonic hypothesis, since it may be primary or it may be secondary, because of migration during the late stages of cosmic and geologic history.

According to this law, water in all its aggregate states comprises no less than 8% of the weight of the upper layers of the earth's crust and 75% of the weight of the biosphere (as V. I. Vernadskii [1933, p. 24] conceived it, from the troposphere to the erosion crust inclusive). The H_2O anomaly, i.e., that water on freezing expands and that ordinary ice, being lighter than water, floats in it, is of very special significance, since liquid water and organic life can exist under the insulating cover of ice in a cold climate. Thus, of all the widely distributed minerals, not only solids but also liquids, ice, because of its weight, is the one most concentrated at the surface.

However, the law of specific gravity explains the zonal distribution of only the first 28 elements of the periodic system; the remaining are less widely distributed, often in direct contradiction to this principle. In this connection, the views of V. Goldschmidt and G. Tammann are very interesting; they explain the current distribution of terrestrial matter by the joint action of the force of gravity and the process of gradual cooling of the multiphase system with a subsequent migration of the elements. If one resorts solely to facts and does not prejudge the significance of one or another cosmogonic hypothesis, one must also consider the position of ice among minerals in the thermal sequence of the classification of terrestrial matter.

V. Goldschmidt (1923, 1932), on examining the earth as a single, initially gaseous, physicochemical body, distinguishes four temperature stages of geochemical differentiation:

(1) the division into a gaseous phase and three liquid phases (ferrous, sulfide, silicate melts);
(2) fractional crystallization of silicate magmas;
(3) crystallization from aqueous solutions; and
(4) processes which include the participation of organisms.

As S. G. Parkhomenko correctly pointed out in 1942, *ice formation*, which excludes the activity of organisms,[5] should be regarded as a further, a *fifth stage*,[6] in this sequence. Thus, ice is the last and the

---

[5] Ice formation does not exclude the vital activity of organisms in the sense that the organisms cannot exist in ice; when mineral or organic admixtures are present, not only lower organisms but even some higher organisms can live in and on ice. However, it is absolutely necessary for the vital activity of an organism that the water in it remain in the liquid phase. Ice formation in a living being leads to atrophy and death, and the ability of organisms to exist in ice through evolutionary adaptation to such a habitat is based on the internal resistance of the organism to the freezing of water.

[6] L. V. Pustovalov (1940) examines ice formation as the last stage of sedimentary differentiation. From our point of view, the freezing of water cannot be examined as the formation of a sedimentary rock; however, with respect to the temperature

most surficial mineral, with respect to both specific gravity and temperature sequence, in the classification of terrestrial matter.

The position of ice in the temperature sequence of the geochemical classification of matter, together with the peculiarity of its structure, account for its "purity," *the simplicity of its chemical composition*. According to the general law of geochemical differentiation, the capacity for formation of solid solution with isomorphous substitution of unlike atoms decreases as the temperature decreases, therefore the geochemical separation of matter becomes more and more complete in each successive thermal stage. The separation goes farthest during the crystallization of water, when the substances dissolved in it are forced out by the crystal lattice and may enter into ice only as mechanical admixtures.

Thus, ice is an extreme member of a specific series of minerals and obeys the general laws of gravitational, thermal and chemical differentiation of terrestrial matter. It differs in that it is the lightest and has the lowest temperature and therefore is the most surficial and one of the simplest minerals in its chemical composition, capable of forming great masses of monomineralic rock.

Subjectively, however, from the point of view of man, the main feature of ice is that it is the last stage of mineral formation in the thermal sequence, situated beyond the stage of organogenous mineral formation. The processes of organic life, which require the presence of liquid water, are situated between the stages of ice formation and the formation of all the other, high-temperature minerals. Ice is the medium most alien to organic life, and a considerable accumulation of it completely disrupts the normal course of all processes in the biosphere.

As the last stage of the geochemical division of the thermal sequence, the ice formation stage differs from the preceding related stages of crystallization from magmas and aqueous solutions in that it comprises a comparatively small part of the terrestrial matter. The volume of ice on earth, more than 20,000,000 km^3, comprises only about 1.7% of the total water volume of the earth's surface, not counting the waters of the lithosphere. Nevertheless, as Dobrowolski (1923) points out, ice is the *most widely distributed* of the solid components of the earth's surface and atmosphere. Glaciers alone cover about 16,000,000 km^2 of the land surface, including the entire continent of Antarctica, with an area greater than Europe's;

---

sequence, ice formation and its extraordinary effect on all terrestrial processes should definitely be classified as an independent stage of geochemical differentiation, following the stage of sedimentary differentiation.

ice covers 3.1% of the earth's surface and 10.8% of the earth's land surface. About the same area is occupied by permafrost, which contains ice in the form of ice cement and various ice bodies; almost 10,800,000 km² of this area is in the Soviet Union, comprising 48% of its territory. If we consider the seasonal snow and ice covers, we can say that 30–50% (and part of the year more than 50%) of the earth's land surface is covered by ice. Frosts, brief freezing of rivers, and precipitation of hail in the lowlands are observed occasionally in the tropics, even at the equator (Vernadskii, 1933, p. 33). To this we must add the enormous areas of the polar seas and oceans which are covered by ice the year round or part of the year. Sea ice is distributed over an area of 37,700,000 km², comprising 7.3% of the earth's surface or 11.8% of the surface of the world ocean. If we also consider the area of iceberg distribution, the total drifting ice area comprises 72,600,000 km², which is 14.2% of the earth's surface, or 22.9% of the surface of the world ocean. Finally, there are always suspended ice particles at various heights in the atmosphere.

Thus, ice occurs everywhere on the earth, if not on the surface itself then at least aloft, in the atmosphere. Ice forms a true earth envelope, the cryosphere, as it was called by Dobrowolski (1923, p. 11). It is situated between the high temperature zone of the upper stratosphere and ionosphere and the high temperature zone of the earth's crust. Actually, only the troposphere, with an upper limit 8–17 km above sea level,[7] contains any considerable amount of ice crystals. Thus, the cryosphere reaches a total thickness of about 10 km, but the greater part of it is the zone of fine ice particles scattered in the atmosphere.

The boundaries of the cryosphere change position during the year, and in the regions of permafrost development the cryosphere is divided annually into subterranean and atmospheric parts by the warm earth surface and the lower layers of the atmosphere. In places the cryosphere penetrates 600 m into the earth's crust.

In contrast to all the high-temperature minerals, ice, which forms a discontinuous envelope in the boundary zone of the atmosphere, hydrosphere and lithosphere, seldom finds thermodynamic conditions corresponding to its stable state. Only in the frozen zone of the lithosphere can it be preserved for a geologically long period of time, providing it is not affected by subterranean waters. In the atmosphere, at a steady negative temperature, ice experiences constant changes under conditions of atmospheric saturation by water vapors,

---

[7] Nacreous clouds, at heights of the order of 25 km in the stratosphere, evidently consist of droplets of liquid water (Weickmann, 1949, p. 39).

while on the earth's surface, ice usually is subject to thermal influences as well. Regions of constant temperatures below the melting point of ice do not exist normally at the earth's surface, even at the poles, with the present intensity of solar radiation; these regions are created only by the ice itself, when conditions occur that are favorable to the accumulation of ice, despite periodic melting in the first stages of accumulation.

Thus, the equilibrium in the cryosphere is much less stable; the ice formation processes are replaced more often by the reverse processes than they are in the case of the high temperature stages of mineral formation, i.e., crystallization from aqueous solutions and even more so from magmas. Large-scale shifts of the masses in the earth's crust are required to change the direction of magmatic processes, but the processes of the succeeding temperature stages of mineral formation become more and more dependent on the mobile energy balance of the earth's surface, the climate.

This comprises the last essential feature of ice as a mineral, its *ephemerality*, i.e., its *variability* under terrestrial conditions, which is stubbornly ignored by mineralogists and petrographers. Consequently, ice rocks usually are *metamorphic* to a greater or lesser extent.

All the ice features described here were stated briefly by Dobrowolski (1931). Ordinary ice exists in the cryosphere in the following forms:

(1) as a mineral scattered in the atmosphere and hydrosphere;

(2) as a mineral entering into the composition of polymineralic rocks, in the frozen horizons of the earth's crust; and, finally,

(3) as more or less large-scale accumulations, monomineralic ice rocks on the earth's surface, in the earth's crust or in the hydrosphere.

Our further study will deal exclusively with ice as a rock. Ice cement in frozen rocks will be left to the petrology of frozen rocks and soil, cryopedology. This is a field related to glaciology and touched upon by glaciology in the study of ice-formation processes in the earth's crust.

The ice scattered in the hydrosphere and especially in the atmosphere is of more interest to us, but from a particular point of view. Ice which forms in water and in air may be preserved in a suspended state only because of the movement of the enclosing medium. This state is unstable, and after the ice particles have reached certain dimensions they are inevitably carried by gravity to the boundary between the media denser and less dense than ice; from the air they are borne downward, from water, upward, where they also form accumulations. In what follows, we will examine the ice scattered in the atmosphere and hydrosphere primarily as a material from which ice rocks form, but before beginning the study of ice rocks, we must become acquainted with the basic data on the mineralogy and crystallography of ice.

Part I

The Mineralogy and Crystallography of Ice

CHAPTER I

MINERALS OF THE ICE GROUP

All solid phases of water, whether their structure is crystalline or amorphous, are called *ice*. In this sense, ice denotes a group of minerals, whereas in the narrower petrographic sense ice denotes a solid type of rock without pores, as distinguished from snow, rime and similar formations.

From the chemical point of view, water is usually classified as an oxide. However, as V. I. Vernadskii emphasized, water differs sharply from all oxides in its morphology, chemical properties and its role in terrestrial chemical processes. Preferably, it should be classified as a *hydride*, together with ammonia, hydrogen sulfide, etc., which are distinguishable, under conditions of the biosphere, by the ease of their phase transitions and their exceptional chemical activity.

Natural water always contains deuterium, the heavy isotope of hydrogen H^2, or D, but in very small concentration, on the average $1\ H^2 : 6500\ H^1$ (Fritsmann, 1935; Dorsey, 1940). The physical properties of "heavy water" and "heavy ice" differ from the usual properties of water and ice: the specific gravity of D_2O in the liquid state is $1.11\ g/cm^3$, its freezing point is $+ 3.8°C$ and its vapor pressure is less than that of H_2O. In normal concentration, the effect of an admixture of D_2O on the properties of water is negligible. The heavy isotope of oxygen O^{18} exerts an even smaller influence, evidently having an H_2O^{18} freezing point of $- 0.1 \pm 0.05°C$; the effect of the isotopes of H^3 (tritium) and O^{17} is still completely indeterminable.

According to the data of R. V. Teis (1940, and elsewhere), the solid phase of water generally differs somewhat from the liquid phase in its isotopic composition: it is richer in deuterium and poorer in the heavy isotope of oxygen.

The various mineral forms of the natural ice types cannot be distinguished on the basis of their chemical composition. This may be seen from the only existing chemical-mineralogical classification of ice types, that of Vernadskii (1933), who divides natural ice types into three classes by salt content: fresh (with mineralization of less than 1 g/liter), saline (1–50 g/l), and brine (more than 50 g/l), and

15

into subclasses by gas composition, indicating the probability that ice has five subclasses containing different (still unknown) amounts of nitrogen, oxygen and carbon dioxide. A further breakdown of this classification is made according to the position of the ice in a cross section of our planet (meteoric, surface and subsurface ice) and by the form in which the ice occurs (clouds, the cover of stationary or flowing water, snow cover, glacier ice, cave ice, etc.) or, as Vernadskii himself says, on the basis of "everyday concepts developed from natural observation," which really have no relationship to the mineralogical classification.

If one considers that salts and gases in ice do not form isomorphous admixtures but are always inclusions, it becomes evident that in Vernadskii's classification the criteria for the division into classes and subclasses cannot have the same meaning as they have in the classification of isomorphous mixtures of crystalline minerals, since here one cannot speak of the *concentration* of unlike molecules. However, the presence of inclusions (when they are of primary origin, located within the crystals of the mineral, and change the properties or the appearance of the mineral) affords a basis merely for distinguishing the *facies*, but not the mineral species. Consequently, in chemical composition, the ice types belong to a single mineral form.

Fresh, saline and brine ice are different mineral facies, because when sufficiently salty water freezes, the salts become arranged regularly in layers within the ice crystals; this gives the crystals a platy structure and changes their properties considerably. The chemical composition of the salts and gases is not related to the characteristics of fresh ice as a mineral and must be examined merely as an additional petrographic characteristic.

The picture becomes more complex when the so-called *fine structure* of the ice is taken into account. A mechanically solid amorphous substance and its various polymorphous modifications in the crystal state may differ quite sharply in their properties and represent different minerals.

Ice has always served as the prototype of a crystalline substance, which is reflected in its very name: the ancient Greeks used the word crystal (i.e., *krystallos*, from *kryos*, "cold," and *stellesthai*, "to become compact"—therefore, "having hardened in the cold") for both ice and rock crystal, which the Greeks considered to be petrified ice.

Amorphous ice evidently does not exist in nature. Ice glass without any traces of crystal structure has been obtained only by condensation of water vapor supercooled to a temperature below $-120°C$ (Burton and Oliver, 1935; König, 1944). This form of ice is unstable; on being heated to $-70°C$ it devitrifies. In view of this, all reports of the existence of amorphous ice at higher temperatures are questionable. Beilby (1921, p. 195) pointed out that when fine water droplets are frozen rapidly at $-12°C$, they remain structureless, and crystallize only after light pressure has been applied to them with a steel instrument; he apparently took supercooled liquid droplets as amorphous ice. The natural solid products of the rapid freezing of supercooled water in the atmosphere and on the surface of solid objects (ice hail, ice rain, hail, frost deposit, glaze) only seem to be structureless-turbid or glassy, but actually have crystal structure.

Thus, amorphous ice can be obtained artificially at a temperature lower than is possible at the earth's surface or in the atmosphere, but it can scarcely occur in nature, much less exist for long above the temperature of devitrification. This temperature is so low for ice that it occurs chiefly in the upper layers of the troposphere; at the earth's surface it exists only as an exception.

Crystalline ice may produce polymorphous modifications that differ in the structure of their space lattice and in their physical properties. At present eight *crystal modifications* of ice have been established more or less definitely, each with its own *stability range*; furthermore, at different times there have been indications of the existence of several additional forms, which proved to be problematical or which were disproved by further investigations.

Of the definitely established modifications of ice, ordinary ice (or Ice I) exists under normal conditions, another modification exists at temperatures below $-70°C$ and the six remaining exist at pressures of 2,000–50,000 atm.

A low-temperature modification was obtained by condensing water vapor in a vacuum at about $-80°C$ (König, 1944). This modification had cubic structure similar to that of a diamond, with the same distances between the oxygen atoms as ordinary ice has at that temperature (viz., 2.75 Å). When heated above $-70°C$, this ice converts into the usual hexagonal form; this has been demonstrated microphotometrically. Such ice was obtained in the presence of vapors of organic substances at a temperature of about $-70°C$, and when heated above $-70°C$, it, too, became ordinary ice (Rau, 1944). Much earlier, H. Barendrecht (1896) and F. Wallerant (1908) observed the formation of what appeared to be a low-temperature cubic modification of ice from an aqueous solution of alcohol, but P. N. Chirvinskii (1912), on the basis of Mendeleev's investigations of 1865, showed that these were crystals of the hydrate $C_2H_5(OH) + 3H_2O$ and not of ice.

Of the ice modifications corresponding to high pressures, G. Tammann (1900) discovered types II and III, and P. Bridgman

(1912, 1935, 1937, 1946) discovered types IV–VII. Bridgman discovered ice type IV in 1935, but this should not be confused with the unstable form type IV (unstable subspecies of ice type I), whose existence was alleged by Tammann as early as 1900, but was finally disproved by Bridgman.

The only criteria which allow us to conclude that there is a transition from one modification to another in the high-pressure chamber are the sudden disturbances of the smooth progress of pressure and temperature changes, caused by changes in volume and the emission or absorption of latent heat during phase transitions. Therefore, our knowledge of high-pressure ice is confined basically to its thermal and caloric properties. The most interesting thermal properties are shown in the phase diagram (Fig. 2), which indicates that five stable modifications of ice can be in equilibrium with water; the equilibrium temperature decreases with increasing pressure only in the case of ice type I, in the other cases it increases. Under certain pressure conditions, ice type V can exist up to a temperature of $+0.16°C$, ice type VI to $+81.6°C$, and ice type VII to $+200°C$. These are the so-called "hot ice" types. Ice under high pressure is denser than water under the same pressure, i.e., the ratio of the densities of the liquid and the solid phases of these ice types is one natural for most substances.

Neighboring ice modifications have a considerable hysteresis of transition; each modification, in the absence of a neighboring modification, may exist for a long time without converting into the latter, as indicated by the phase diagram. Thus, at $-130°C$ ice type I is stable to a pressure of about 3000 kg/cm^2, while ice type III is stable to zero pressure (Tammann, 1922). Ice types II and III may be removed from the high-pressure chamber and kept for some time at very low temperatures. Tammann took advantage of this in his macroscopic investigations of high-pressure modifications of ice, and R. McFarlan (1936) obtained x-ray photographs of them.

X-ray photographs of modifications of ice under high pressure are very complex and are difficult to interpret. According to McFarlan, the structures of ice types II and III are the disrupted and more compact structures of ice type I. The great density of ice type VII (1.67 g/cm^3 at $20°C$ and 48,400 atm) indicates that its structure approximates that of the closest packing of spheres (Owston and Lonsdale, 1948).

Judging by the thermal properties of the nine types of ice described (one amorphous and eight crystalline), only one of them, ice type I or ordinary ice, can exist under ordinary conditions on the earth's surface. Low-temperature ice of cubic form can occur only in

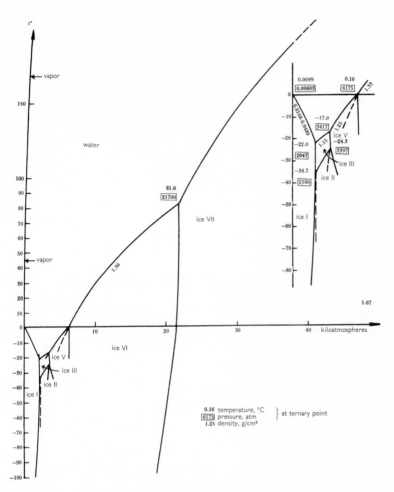

Fig. 2.   Phase diagram of water.

the upper layers of the troposphere. In the macrocosm (in contrast
to the microcosm of the molecules and their components) the conditions do not correspond to the stability range of any of the remaining
forms of ice, because either the temperature is too high or the pressure is too low. For example, the minimum pressure in the stability
range of Ice III can be reached only under a layer of Ice I 22,680 m
thick, i.e., a layer 10–15 times thicker than at the center of the
present ice sheets. However, due to hysteresis, a pressure of 2500

atm is required to convert ice type I into type III, which corresponds to a layer of Ice I 27.7 km thick. Undoubtedly, ice did not reach such a thickness even during the epoch of maximum glaciation. Within the earth's crust under a layer of non-ice rocks, the temperature increases with the pressure at a rate 3.5 times too fast for the "hot" ice types to exist.

Nevertheless, the pressure and temperature combinations required for the existence of types V, VI and VII are present in a thin layer at the surface of solid bodies, with the sole difference that the pressure here is represented by forces of molecular attraction and has an orienting effect on the dipolar molecules of the water. The magnitude of the adsorption pressure is not known reliably, since there are no direct methods of determining it, but on the basis of indirect methods it is estimated to be of the order of thousands and tens of thousands of atmospheres. Should not adsorbed water be considered one of the modifications of ice?

V. I. Vernadskii (1934, p. 260) made such an assumption (namely, that hygroscopic water is a special form of ice) and recently this assumption was confirmed indirectly by A. V. Dumanskii's experiments (1950, p. 319) to determine the heat of wetting. The heat at which different hydrophilic colloidal substances are completely wetted at a temperature of 20°C proved to be 78–80 cal/g and in one case 73 cal/g. A. V. Dumanskii rounded off the result to 80 cal/g and noted its agreement with the latent heat of fusion of ordinary ice. However, the latent heat of fusion of Ice I changes abruptly with a change in temperature: if it is extrapolated to a temperature of 20°C (which, of course, is offered only hypothetically, since it is impossible to superheat ice), it would amount to approximately 102 cal/g. On the other hand, the latent heat of fusion of Ice VI at a temperature of 20°C and a pressure of 8710 atm is 76.45 cal/g and the total latent heat released during the transition of water into Ice VI, and then into Ice VII at 20°C and 21,530 atm is 79.74 cal/g, which quite agrees with Dumanskii's value.

Thus, apparently Ice VII is a monomolecular layer of adsorbed water, as Vernadskii had also assumed. On wetting a solid surface, water freezes at a positive temperature, becoming Ice VII and releasing the latent heat of freezing, which in this case is called the *heat of adsorption*, or the heat of wetting. Generally, the physical properties of "bound water" differ sharply from those of water; in particular the heat capacity and solubility of bound water are considerably smaller than those of water, the vapor pressure is lower and the density greater. According to A. Rakovskii and P. Polianskii (1931, p. 15), the density of the bound "water" of starch reaches

1.28–2.45 g/cm³. Apparently, not only the layer of molecules nearest the solid surface but also the succeeding layers of molecules of the bound "water" are a solid body, modifications of ice under high pressure or their quasi-crystalline analogues. Only the external, less stably bound part of the sorbed layer is mobile and is actually water. In starch the total thickness of the layer of bound "water" still having a shear modulus reaches 8μ, according to the determinations of B. V. Deriagin.

Evidently it is very difficult to establish the structures of films of bound water by normal x-ray procedures, since the structure must change with distance from the binding surface. On the basis of x-ray investigations, N. Kolkmeijer and J. Favejee (1933, p. 602) concluded that an aqueous starch film has a structure similar to a somewhat disturbed structure of ordinary ice, which agrees with McFarlan's data on the structure of ice types II and III. However, as far as we know, this result has not been substantiated by subsequent investigations. Evidently, the question of the structure of sorbed films can be solved by the electron diffraction method. Meanwhile, until this question is answered, we can picture a film of bound water on the surface of a solid body as consisting of a monomolecular layer of ice type VII and of adjoining layers of type VI, and, when the temperature is low enough, possibly also of types V and III or their quasi-crystalline analogues, while the outer part consists of oriented water. As the temperature decreases, the water film must decrease due to freezing from both sides: on the outside the water will become Ice I, and on the inside high pressure modifications or their corresponding quasi-crystalline forms. The part of the sorbed layer which is preserved from within by forces greater than the forces of the hydrogen bond in the space lattice of ice I, i.e., the part which is under a molecular pressure greater than the equilibrium pressure between water and ice at the given temperature, does not freeze.

Thus, polymorphous modifications of ice, corresponding to high pressures, probably exist in nature as thin films and play an effective role in dispersed mineral systems with a large specific area, i.e., soils and sedimentary rocks. The history of the remaining ice forms, whose existence has been assumed by various investigators, is briefly as follows.

G. Tammann assumed that ice types I–VI are not separate forms, but crystalline groups with a number of unstable forms, i.e., in his opinion ice I has four such forms, possibly even seven, and Ice III has two forms. According to Tammann, most of these forms occur by chance, due to causes not yet established, and after a time become the stable form for the given conditions. Of Tammann's ice types, only Ice IV has been obtained more or less regularly in repeated experiments, for example in three of seven tries. Type IV is a somewhat denser variant of Ice I, and forms when the water freezes slowly. The occurrence of such forms has not been observed by other researchers, with two exceptions. In 1904 J. Cox and in 1924 A. N. Shaw obtained ice which was denser than water and which sank slowly to the bottom in water. They obtained this ice at a pressure of less than 1 atm. However, N. Dorsey (1940, p. 396) assumes that these data are erroneous.

According to N. Ia. Seliakov (1936, 1937), when ice crystallizes from water that is supercooled below $-5°C$, a stable modification of ice develops which has trigonal-pyramidal or rhombohedral symmetry with a different crystallographic constant, which he calls β-ice to distinguish it from ordinary, or α-ice. However, later investigations (Owston and Lonsdale, 1948) have not confirmed Seliakov's opinion, and there are convincing arguments that Seliakov erred through incorrect interpretation of his x-ray photographs.

There is also considerable evidence that points to the existence of rectangular crystals among natural ice formations such as rime, ice fog and snowflakes. Some collections of photographs include these types (Dobrowolski, 1923; Bentley and Humphreys, 1931). A number of researchers (H. Schumacher, F. Heinitz, A. Nordenskiöld, and E. Schmidt) used them as the basis for assuming the existence of ice of the tetragonal and rhombic systems. However, the external form alone (without exact goniometric or structural investigations) is not evidence of polymorphism, since crystal forms which at first glance appear to be rectangular can also occur in a hexagonal system, for instance, in intergrowths of hexagonal columnar crystals or hexagonal bipyramids with anomalous growth of faces. However, subsequent x-ray investigations have never revealed such modifications.

Finally, the commonly observed optic biaxiality can be taken as an indication that ice modifications of lower crystallographic systems exist under normal conditions. M. P. Golovkov (1936, p. 31), who observed acute optic axial angles as great as 20° in crystals of Kara Sea ice, left the question open whether deformation or polymorphism caused the biaxiality. In fossil ice, I have measured optic axial angles of ice crystals up to 47°; however, the deviations of the optic angles from 0° to 47° and the presence of a regular connection between the extent of deformation of the ice and the size of the angle between the optic axes [2V] indicate that the causes of this phenomenon are mechanical.

Thus, it has not been proved that other forms of ice exist in the same thermodynamic range as ordinary ice, and the probability of such proof has become smaller and smaller as the number of structural investigations has increased.

Summarizing, it may be concluded that the solid phase of ordinary water comprises a group of nine forms: one amorphous and eight crystalline, of identical chemical composition, differing from one another in structure and physical properties. Of these, amorphous ice can develop and exist only at extremely low temperatures not encountered under natural conditions. The remaining forms probably occur in nature and comprise a group of minerals. Most of them can be found only in small quantities in the upper layers of the troposphere or as molecular films in the upper horizons of the earth's crust, while ordinary ice is the only one that constitutes a very widespread mineral capable of existing in large masses, i.e., as ice rocks. Impurities in ordinary ice offer a basis for differentiating varieties of this mineral, among which one may distinguish fresh, saline and briny ice.

In conclusion, it should be noted that ordinary ice is not the only solid mineral that exists exclusively at a temperature of 0°C and less. Besides ordinary ice, several crystal hydrates [comparatively unstable compounds containing water of crystallization ($NaCl \cdot 2H_2O$, $MgCl_2 \cdot 12H_2O$, $MgCl_2 \cdot 8H_2O$, etc.)] have this low a melting point. S. G. Parkhomenko (1938) calls this entire group of minerals *cryophiles*, or cold-lovers.

In what follows, the word ice will be used to mean ordinary ice, unless otherwise specified.

CHAPTER II

THE STRUCTURE AND GONIOMETRIC SYMMETRY OF ORDINARY ICE CRYSTALS

The properties of ice, as is the case with all crystalline substances, are determined not only by its chemical composition but also by the geometry of its space lattice and the nature of the bond that keeps the structural units of its space lattice in equilibrium.

The problem of the fine structure of ordinary ice has not yet been solved completely.[1] X-ray analysis can establish only the position of the oxygen atoms in the space lattice of the ice. The hydrogen atoms do not scatter the x-rays sufficiently, and at present their position is judged primarily from indirect data. There are bases for assuming that the position of the hydrogen atoms changes continuously at temperatures above approximately −70°C, so that even with more sensitive means, such as those provided by neutron irradiation, only the average structure, determined by the position of the oxygen atoms, can be recorded.

The unit cell of this average structure (i.e., a polyhedron from

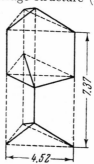

Fig. 3.   Unit cell of a space lattice of ice.

---

[1] Surveys of the first investigations, beginning with 1917, have been made by A. B. Dobrowolski (1933), E. Kh. Fritsmann (1935) and V. Ia Al'tberg (1940, p. 228); the results of more recent works have been summarized by P. Owston and K. Lonsdale (1948).

24

which the space lattice can be deduced by making parallel transla-
tions of it [the polyhedron] along the edges to distances equal to the
lengths of the edges) consists of four oxygen atoms. In the unit cell of
ice depicted in Fig. 3, each of the six corner atoms belongs to six
neighboring cells; each of the three atoms on the edges belongs to
three cells, each of the two extreme axial units belongs to two cells,
while the middle atom belongs only to the given cell. Hence the total
number of atoms in the unit cell is $\frac{6}{6} + \frac{3}{3} + \frac{2}{2} + 1 = 4$. The lattice
of the oxygen atoms, taken as a whole, is depicted in Fig. 4.

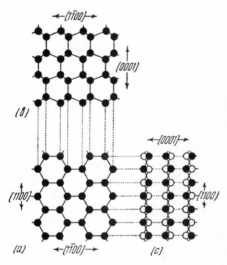

FIG. 4.   Space lattice of ice.

The coordination number of every atom in this structure is four,
i.e., every atom is surrounded at equal distances (2.76 Å) by four
other atoms situated at the corners of a regular tetrahedron, whose
center is the given atom. The most accurate dimensions of the unit
cell were defined by H. Megaw in 1934; after conversion to the CGS
system they are: at temperature 0°C, $a = 4.5226$ Å, $c = 7.3670$ Å;
and at temperature −66°C, $a = 4.5176$ Å, $c = 7.353$ Å (Owston
and Lonsdale, 1948). From this we find that the crystallographic
constant of ice at 0°C, $\frac{c}{a}$, is 1.6223.

The lattice point has dihexagonal-bipyramidal symmetry
$(L_6 \, 6L^2 \, 7PC)$; thus, the lattice has *hexagonal symmetry*.

W. Barnes assumed ice structure to be ionic, so that the nature of the bond between the ions in the crystal does not differ from the atomic (ionic) bond in the molecule. According to Barnes, individual molecules in ice should not be differentiated, the whole crystal being a molecule. Barnes, like W. Bragg, placed the hydrogen nuclei in the center of the space separating the oxygen ions. This is not in agreement with the data on the adsorption of the infrared part of spectra and of the Raman spectra of water vapor, water, and ice, which differ very little from one another. Water and water vapor undoubtedly have molecular structure, where the OH distance in the water vapor amounts to 0.958 Å. Data derived from a comparison of the spectra show that the OH distance in ice should be of the order of 0.99–1.05 Å instead of the 1.38 Å required by the Barnes-Bragg hypothesis. Thus, each hydrogen atom is situated closer to one of the oxygen atoms, and the structure of ice is not ionic but *molecular*.

However, the unit cell of ice would have to be too complex for the molecular structure to agree with x-ray data: 12 molecules for polar structure and no less than 96 molecules for nonpolar structure, which is improbable. There are still other possibilities if a static or a dynamic irregularity of structure is assumed. J. Bernal and R. Fowler made the first assumption in 1933; in their model the hydrogen atoms in the neighboring molecules of ice occupied a different but fixed position. Thus, the ice was crystalline only in the position of its molecules, but was vitreous in their orientation.

In the opinion of Owston and Lonsdale (1948), L. Pauling's assumption that irregular ice structure is of a dynamic nature is the more probable. In Pauling's model, as in Barnes's, there is only one hydrogen atom between each pair of oxygen atoms; however, the position of the hydrogen atoms can change because of rotation of the molecules or because of the characteristic movement of the atoms to a distance 0.78 Å from a position 0.99 Å from the oxygen atom of one molecule to a similar position in the structure of another molecule connected with the first. In this case, a change from a polarized to a nonpolarized configuration takes place continuously in the crystal. This free reorientation of the molecules can be explained by the great magnitude of the dielectric permeability of ice at temperatures above approximately 200°K (−73°C), which is near the dielectric permeability of water. When ice is cooled to a very low temperature, the molecules are held in one of many possible positions, which does not presume the occurrence of a definite configuration without random orientation of the molecules.

The latest technique of x-ray structural analysis makes it possible to study not only the position of the atoms with respect to each other, but also their thermal vibrations. With long exposure, diffuse spots and bands appear on the Laue diffraction pattern along with distinct isolated points. The intensity of these spots and bands is conspicuously dependent on temperature. For ice, this presents a considerably more complex picture than do the simple elastic vibrations and evidently stems from the group movements of the oxygen and hydrogen atoms or from the group reorientations of the molecules. The movements along the principal crystallographic axis [0001] are especially intensive, which indicates the relative weakness of the atomic bonds in this direction.

Traces of the vibrations disappear only at very low temperatures and are still visible at −73°C. The mean amplitude of the thermal vibrations of the atoms near 0°C reaches almost 0.5 Å. Despite this, the crystals of natural ice are relatively perfect and, according to Owston and Lonsdale, are not mosaic.[2] During melting, the characteristic structural picture of ice gives way sharply on the x-ray photograph to the diffraction ring of water.

The basic features of ice structure can be revealed by direct study, hence the question of the *goniometric symmetry* of ice crystals has less intrinsic value. According to Bravais's statistical law, most often the faces that develop on crystals correspond to the space-lattice networks that have the greatest reticular density, i.e., those most densely populated with atoms, which is usually associated with the smallest rate of growth of these faces. As we know, the arrangement of the space lattice does not completely determine the goniometric symmetry of the crystals; in the case of hexagonal symmetry of the lattice, the crystals can belong to both the hexagonal and the trigonal systems, since both combinations of faces are possible in this symmetry. Thus, the question of the goniometric symmetry of crystals of ordinary ice should be solved empirically, independently of structural investigation.

As M. P. Golovkov remarked (see Veinberg, and others, 1940, p. 264), the study of ice-crystal symmetry is connected with nearly the entire history of the development of mineralogy and crystallography. Sketches, descriptions and approximate measurements of the angles of ice crystals, which made it possible to establish their affinity with the hexagonal (trigonal) system, appeared as early as the sixteenth and seventeenth centuries (Olaus Magnus, 1555; J. Kepler, 1611; R. Descartes, 1637; R. Hooke, 1665; and others).

---

[2] However, my observations, made in polarized light, indicate that mosaic structures appear widely among the natural ice types and evidently occur in the presence of external impediments to crystal growth.

However, even today we do not have the accurate goniometric measurements of ice crystals required to solve this problem satisfactorily, because solid (non-skeletal) regularly bounded ice crystals seldom occur and because it is nearly impossible to preserve them. Most investigators have depended on the external appearance of the crystals, the hollows in them, the internal and external corrosion, impact and pressure figures and, only in rare cases, on rough measurements. Meteorologists, having much factual data at their disposal, have often limited themselves to descriptions, without drawing crystallographic conclusions and without dwelling on the essential details. Many investigators have not gone beyond establishing the affinity of ice crystals with the hexagonal system, evidently not differentiating between the hexagonal and the trigonal systems.

Refinements of this technique have run along lines of differentiating between the hexagonal and trigonal systems and of distinguishing the hemimorphous forms. Often ice is still regarded as belonging to the hexagonal system proper, an attitude extant since the end of the eighteenth and the beginning of the nineteenth centuries (J. J. Scheuchzer, 1706, W. Scoresby, 1820, and others), even though the long established and frequently encountered irregular development of crystal faces, which can be defined as hexagonal at first glance, definitely points to trigonal symmetry, which was noted in particular by the Russian scientist R. Prendel' as early as 1890. A fact of equal importance is the broad development of hemimorphism in ice crystals, a difference in the form of the opposite ends, which has been known since 1823 and has been confirmed by extensive observations (J. Smithson, 1823; A. E. Nordenskiöld, 1861; the Russian lieutenant Korsakov, 1862; P. A. Secchi, 1876; G. Hellmann, 1893). In the past decade, the hemimorphism of slowly growing crystals in cirrus clouds has been proved by microphotographing such crystals at their place of origin, from an airplane (Weickmann, 1949).[3]

Thus, among ice crystals there is a wide distribution of crystals

---

[3] We know that hemimorphism of crystals is connected with polarity, i.e., with the difference in their properties in opposite directions. The polarity of the principal crystallographic axis of ice, along with the hemimorphism and the character of their growth, is evidently confirmed by the different rate of evaporation of the opposite ends (Dobrowolski, 1923, p. 143; Adams, 1930). Other researchers reject polarity because of the absence of piezoelectric and pyroelectric effects in ice; in answer to this, the adherents of the polarity point of view indicate the possibility that the crystals tested for the piezoelectric and pyroelectric effects were twins along (0001). Possibly the contradictory nature of the results is due to the lack of an established structure in ice at temperatures above $-73°C$ (see above, L. Pauling's hypothesis).

that have both hexagonal and trigonal symmetry, that have an identical form at both ends along the principal axis, as well as hemimorphous crystals. In such cases the signs of lower symmetry are the determining factors, since the hexagonal form may result from a chance identical development of two trigonal forms, while the absence of hemimorphism may be the result of twinning along the basal plane. Without taking this into consideration and using as their basis unsystematic and inadequate data, many researchers, in disagreement with each other and with the facts, have given the following definitions of the form of ice-crystal symmetry:[4]

(1) Trigonal-trapezohedral ($L^3\,3L^2$) (N. Flerov, 1934);

(2) Rhombohedral (L_6^3) (E. D. Clarke, 1822; D. Brewster, 1834; H. Schlagintweit, 1854; G. A. Kenngott, 1886);

(3) Ditrigonal-scalenohedral ($L_6^3\,3L^2\,3PC$) (G. Abich, 1869);[5]

(4) Dihexagonal-pyramidal ($L^6\,6P$) (F. Rinne, 1917; A. K. Boldyrev, 1928; H. Bader, 1939; H. Weickmann, 1949);

(5) Hexagonal-bipyramidal ($L^6\,PC$) (A. Tutton, 1922), Fig. 5.[6]

The first three definitions do not take the hemimorphism of ice crystals into consideration, the fourth disregards their trigonal symmetry, and the fifth does not consider either. The investigators who considered both these characteristic features of ice crystals (with different degrees of confidence in them) came very close to the true definition of symmetry type (Rohrer, 1859; G. Nordenskiöld, 1893; O. Mügge, 1895–1918; C. Hintze, 1904). The last, conclusive and self-evident step was taken by A. B. Dobrowolski (1902–1933) and P. H. Groth (1906); Dobrowolski (1923, pp. 121–185; 1933) backed his opinion with an immense amount of factual data (see also Veinberg, 1940, pp. 264–279). We are speaking of his preference

---

[4] [The generally accepted terminology for the crystal classes listed is:

		Hermann-Manguin symbols
(1)	Trigonal-trapezohedral (A_3, $3A_2$)	$\dfrac{32}{3}$
(2)	Rhombohedral (C, A_3)	
(3)	Ditrigonal-scalenohedral (C, A_3, $3A_2$, $3P$)	$\bar{3}2/M$
(4)	Dihexagonal-pyramidal (A_6, $6P$)	6mm
(5)	Hexagonal-dipyramidal (C, A_6, P)	6/m

(Comment by Prof. J. B. Lyons.) – D.K.]

[5] The definitions listed are in agreement with L. Spencer's opinion (*Encyclopaedia Britannica*, 1910–1929); he referred ice crystals to this group of symmetry types.

[6] N. N. Stulov (1949) referred his ice crystals to the dihexagonal-bipyramidal type of symmetry ($L^6\,6L^2\,7PC$), but noted that the irregular development of the faces of the "hexagonal bipyramid" may indicate that they belong to one of the symmetry forms of the trigonal system.

for ditrigonal-pyramidal symmetry $(L^3 \, 3P)^7$ over trigonal-pyramidal $(L^3)^7$ in his choice between the two types of trigonal symmetry that satisfy the requirements of hemimorphism (clearly the symmetry of the trigonal-pyramidal type does not suffice for ice crystals, which always show three planes of symmetry along the principal axis).

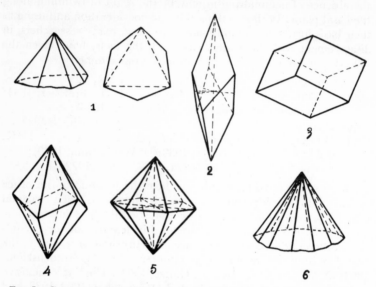

FIG. 5. Common forms of the crystallographic symmetry types presumed for ordinary ice. 1. ditrigonal pyramid and its base, a ditrigon; 2. trigonal trapezo-hedron; 3. rhombohedron; 4. ditrigonal scalenohedron; 5. hexagonal bi-pyramid; 6. dihexagonal pyramid.

Consequently, ice crystals belong to the *ditrigonal-pyramidal* type of symmetry in the *trigonal system*,[8] whose symmetry elements are the triple polar axis and three planes of symmetry. A regular hexagonal form of freely growing crystals is created by the combination of two nearly identically developed trigonal forms (prisms and pyramids), but the latter may develop irregularly, which is usual for the initial stages of growth, and then the crystal will be an irregular hexagon.

---

[7] [The Hermann-Manguin symbols would be $(A_3 \, 3P)$ and (A_3) for these crystal classes. The internationally used Hermann-Manguin symbolism is 3m and 3, respectively. (Comment by Prof. J. B. Lyons.) – D.K.]

[8] [Perhaps more conventional terms would be "rhombohedral system" (physics) or "rhombohedral division of the hexagonal system" (crystallography). (Comment by Prof. J. B. Lyons.) – D.K.]

However, trigonal forms develop only in paired combinations and are never found alone.

According to Dobrowolski, the most characteristic simple forms of ice crystals are the monohedra $\{0001\}$ and $\{000\bar{1}\}$, the two trigonal prisms $\{10\bar{1}0\}$ and $\{01\bar{1}0\}$ and also the pyramids $\{10\bar{1}1\}$ and $\{01\bar{1}1\}$ as mentioned above, always in combination with each other. Depending on the relative development of these forms, the crystals assume a *tabular* or a *columnar* habit.

Two monohedra in combination with two very short trigonal prisms are developed in crystals of the tabular type. In columnar crystals, usually a monohedron is retained at the less soluble pole, while trigonal pyramids appear at the more soluble pole; more rarely both pyramids $\{10\bar{1}\bar{1}\}$ and $\{01\bar{1}\bar{1}\}$ develop at the less soluble pole.

In ice crystals, twinning takes place only along the basal plane (0001). Intergrowth twins are often found among sublimation crystals of columnar habit, where the individuals comprising them may be determined only through hemimorphism, since optically they remain identical. Observations of hemimorphous water pockets around air inclusions in glacier ice led H. Bader (1950) to conclude that polysynthetic twins along (0001) also occur among ice crystals; however, these data still require verification.

CHAPTER III

THE BASIC PHYSICAL PROPERTIES OF ORDINARY ICE

The fine structure of ice determines not only its crystallographic form but also a number of its *physical properties*. We shall dwell briefly on the basic thermodynamic and mechanical characteristics of ice required for an understanding of the processes of formation of petrographic structures and on the optic properties considered in the study of ice structure.[1]

The hydrogen bond responsible for the cohesion of the ice molecules is very weak and becomes fully established only at a very low temperature. Therefore, *ice is an unstable substance, easily disturbed*, but, at the same time, *its geometric structure is highly stable*; this is manifested in its slight compressibility and the need for applying a very high hydrostatic pressure in order to reorganize the structure. The effect of heat on ice stability is reflected in the low temperature of equilibrium between ice, water and water vapor and, when there is an external mechanical effect, in the fluidity and weakness of the ice.

Melting and sublimation temperatures. Of the widely distributed substances, ice has the lowest melting and sublimation temperatures, next to atmospheric gases (Fig. 6). The melting point of pure ice in contact with water-saturated air under a hydrostatic pressure of one normal atmosphere is 0°C or 273.16°K. In this case, the direct pressure effect reduces the melting point by 0.0075°C, while the effect of the dissolved air reduces it by 0.0024°C. Thus the triple point, at which the system ice-water-water vapor is in equilibrium, corresponds to a temperature of +0.0099°C. The pressure at this point cannot be reduced to zero, but is equal to the water-vapor pressure at the given temperature —0.00603 atm or 4.58 mm Hg (the reduction of the melting point due to this pressure amounts to only 0.000045°C).

The equilibrium between the different phases of the substance is dynamic: it does not indicate the lack of transition of the substance

---

[1] Practically all the basic data on the physical properties of ice are contained in résumés by B. P. Veinberg (1940) and N. Dorsey (1940).

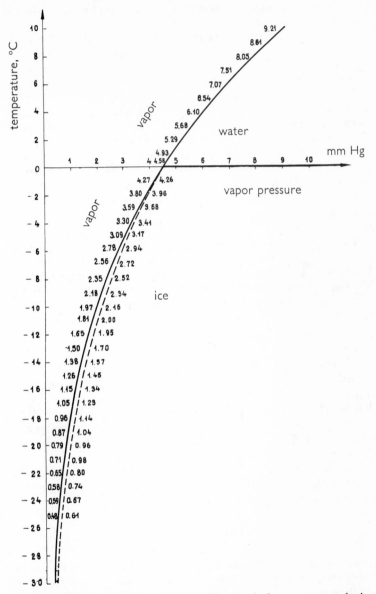

FIG. 6. Pressure of the saturated vapors of Ice I and of water at atmospheric pressure. The dashed line is the curve of equilibrium between the vapor and supercooled water.

from one state to another, but only an equal rate of transition in the two opposite directions.

The rate of transition of the molecules from one phase of the substance to another phase adjacent to it increases as the vibrational energy of the atoms, i.e., as the temperature increases. Therefore, the pressure of the saturated vapor is negligible at low temperatures; at $-70°C$ it is 0.002 mm Hg, at $-110°C$ it is 0.000001 mm Hg. At the same time, the pressure of the vapor which is saturated with respect to ice, e_i, is less than the pressure of the vapor saturated with respect to supercooled water, e_w, at the same temperature. At $-12°C$ to $-13°C$, the absolute difference between the pressure values reaches 0.2 mm, then again begins to decrease while the relative difference increases uniformly; at $-10°C$ the incomplete saturation with respect to water of the vapor which is saturated with respect to ice, $\left(\dfrac{e_w - e_i}{e_w}\right)$, is 9%, while at $-40°C$ it is 33%.

The pressure effect. The melting point of ice decreases under the effect of *hydrostatic pressure*, as was predicted on the basis of theory by J. Thomson in 1849 and confirmed on the basis of experiment by W. Thomson (Lord Kelvin) in 1850. The magnitude of this reduction is defined by the Clausius-Clapeyron equation

$$\frac{dT}{d\bar{p}} = \frac{A\Delta V}{L}$$

(T is the absolute temperature, p the pressure, A the thermal equivalent of work, ΔV the change in specific volume during phase transition, L the latent heat of conversion) and comprises $dT/d\bar{p} = -0.00752°C/atm$ at $0°C$. In a later work, J. Thomson himself (1861) recognized that this reduction of the melting point was the result of hydrostatic pressure alone and did not involve oriented, unilateral pressure.

For the case of *oriented* pressure or stress of any other kind, J. W. Gibbs in 1877 and E. Riecke (1894) showed that the melting point of any deformed body decreases by the value

$$\Delta T = -\frac{1}{2} \cdot \frac{\omega_0 T_0}{ALE} \sigma^2$$

independently of the Thomson effect, due to the increase of potential energy (ω_0 is the specific volume under normal conditions, T_0 the absolute melting point, A the mechanical equivalent of heat, L the melting point of a unit mass, E the modulus of elasticity, σ pressure). The equation is valid only for the conditions of the reversible process, i.e., strictly speaking, σ cannot exceed the elastic limit. However, inasmuch as the deformation of solid bodies is of a complex elastic-fluid nature (they relax after being loaded beyond the elastic limit), E. Riecke applies his principle up to stresses equaling the breaking point. According to his computations for ice, ΔT is 0.0000036 σ^2 (in kg/cm^2) and for a breaking point of 70 kg/cm^2 the maximum ΔT is $-0.017°$C. According to more exact, recent data for ice, $\Delta T = -0.00000485 \sigma^2$; however, on an average, the breaking point of ice (for compression) at 0°C is not more than 30 kg/cm^2 and, correspondingly, the reduction of the melting point due to oriented pressure is $\Delta T = -0.0044°$C.[2]

The decrease in the melting point of ice under hydrostatic pressure is connected with the decrease of volume during melting. As can be seen from Fig. 2, it pertains only to ice I. Therefore, the disruptive force of freezing water is limited by pressure of the order of 2500 atm, occurring in the case of freezing in a confined space at a temperature below $-22°$C, since the spontaneous formation of ice III, accompanied by a decrease in volume, begins at that pressure (Tammann, 1922, p. 154).

Specific gravity and specific volume. Ice has an "open," not very compact structure, therefore it is lighter than water. The specific gravity of pure ice at 0°C and 1 atm pressure is 0.9168 g/cm^3, and its specific volume is 1.0908 cm^3/g (Bridgman, 1912, and elsewhere; Lonsdale, 1950), while the specific gravity and specific volume of water are 0.999863 g/cm^3 and 1.000132 cm^3/g, respectively. Any departure from the above values for ice indicates the presence of impurities.

Furthermore, the latent heat absorbed in large amounts during the melting of ice is expended on increasing the interatomic distances. Actually, the mean distance between oxygen atoms is greater in water (3.0 Å) (Morgan and Warren, 1938, p. 666) than in ice (2.76 Å). How does this fit in with the density increase during melting?

Water has highly developed structure with a tetrahedral arrangement of molecules that is similar to that of ice, these molecules being dipoles with charges at the ends of the tetrahedron. However, as we have seen, even in ice at high temperature the movements of the

---

[2] H. Lechatelier (1882, p. 335), and later J. Johnston and L. Adams (1913, p. 214), assumed that the melting point of ice decreases 12 times more under oriented pressure than under hydrostatic pressure, i.e., by 0.091°C/atm; however, this point of view is evidently erroneous. Attempts to derive theoretically the effect of oriented stress on the change in the melting point were also made by Poynting (1881), Ostwald (1902) and P. Niggli (1915), but G. Tammann (1922) proved them to be in error.

atoms or the reorientation of the molecules lead to a gradual amor-
phization preparatory to melting. In water, the weak hydrogen bond
between the molecules is constantly disrupted and re-established.
Due to this, the coordination number in the structure of water, on an
average, is greater than 4, probably 4.5 (Rodebush, 1949, p. 269),
which also explains why it is denser than ice although its interatomic
distances are greater.

Specific heat and thermal conductivity. The specific heat of ice at constant pressure C_p and its relation to temperature $t(°C)$ are expressed
by the formula

$$C_p = 0.5057 + 0.001863 \ t \ \text{cal/g °C}$$

By other, evidently less accurate, determinations, the specific heat
of ice varies within fairly wide limits and does not vary linearly with
temperature. Figure 6 shows the nature of the relationship between
the specific heat of ice and water and the temperature at a constant
pressure of 1 atm, according to the measurements of F. Simon (see
Dorsey, p. 480).

The thermal conductivity k of the ice with respect to temperature
t, according to the Celsius scale, is expressed by the formula (Veinberg, 1940, p. 163):

$$k = 0.0053 \ (1 + 0.0015 \ t) \ \text{cal/cm}^2\text{sec°C}$$

There are indications that the thermal conductivity parallel to the
principal crystallographic axis 0001, $k_{\parallel}$, is somewhat greater than
that perpendicular to it, $k_{\perp}$. The quantitative data pertaining to this
were obtained by Forbes in 1874 and by Straneo in 1897. According
to Forbes, the ratio of $k_{\parallel} : k_{\perp}$ is 22 : 21, but his absolute value of k is
less than half the actual value. According to Straneo, $k_{\parallel}$ is sometimes
larger, sometimes smaller than $k_{\perp}$ (Dobrowolski, 1923, p. 41):

$$k_{\parallel} = 0.0050 - 0.0052; \ k_{\perp} = 0.0051$$

Some investigators (Trouton, 1910; Barrat and Nettleton, 1929)
hold that, on the basis of these data, one may assume the ratio

$$k_{\parallel} : k_{\perp} = 21.9 : 21$$

Heat content. We know that the absolute value of the *internal energy*
of a body, as well as other of its characteristic thermodynamic
functions (i.e., those that define the state of the system unambig-
uously) is indeterminable; we can determine only the *change* of the
internal energy during the transition from one state to another. It is
convenient to take the zero point of the absolute temperature scale

as the arbitrary zero position in this case. The internal energy, U_0 (measured from 0°K), for solid and liquid bodies in which the difference between the specific heat at constant volume and the specific heat at constant pressure can be neglected, is practically equal to the *heat content* or the enthalpy, χ_0, i.e., to the amount of heat which must be expended to bring the body to a given state by means of the reversible isobaric process

$$\chi_0 = \int_0^T C_p \, dT$$

Consequently, for ice and water at a pressure of 1 atm, the heat content and the internal energy, measured from 0°K, are practically equal, since the work expended on overcoming external pressure during heating and expansion, which comprises the difference between these functions, is negligible.

Figure 7 shows the change in the heat content of the ice and water at a pressure of 1 atm within the temperature range 0°–300°K. At 0°C, the heat content of ice is about 72 cal/g, while at the same temperature the heat content of water is 152 cal/g. The difference of 80 cal/g (more exactly, 79.69 cal/g) is the latent heat of fusion L expended on disrupting the space lattice of the ice with an increase in the distance between the oxygen atoms from 2.76 Å to 3.0 Å. Thus, measuring from 0°K, the internal energy of water at a pressure of 1 atm and a temperature of 0°C is more than twice as great as that of ice under the same conditions. The heat content of water vapor under these conditions is about 767 cal/g, five times greater than that of water and 16.5 times greater than that of ice.

The latent heat of phase transitions. The latent heat of vaporization of water at 0°C is 597 cal/g, while at lower temperature it increases by 0.00537 cal/g per degree negative temperature. According to the law of the conservation of energy, the latent heat of sublimation of ice should be equal to the sum of the latent heat of fusion and vaporization, i.e., 677 cal/g at 0°C and 8.5 times greater than the heat of fusion. The experimental determinations have shown that with slow sublimation, values are obtained that are close to those indicated, but with rapid sublimation the heat of sublimation exceeds the heat of vaporization by only 1.6%. Evidently, the vapor forming during sublimation is polymeric and the further disintegration of the complex molecules with absorption of the remaining heat already takes place in the air.

Entropy and free energy. The *entropy*, S_0, of ice and water shown in Fig. 7 and measured from 0°K is a characteristic function that

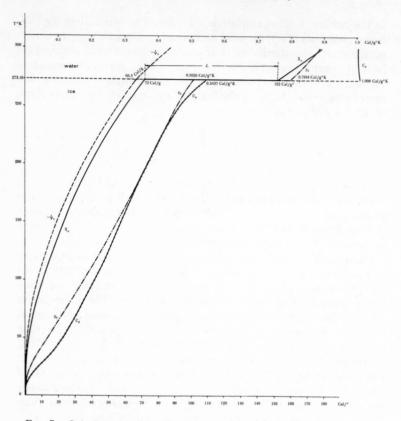

Fig. 7. Caloric properties and thermal energy of ice at a pressure of one atmosphere.

C_p = heat capacity at constant pressure, cal/g °K.
L = latent heat of fusion, cal/g
S_0 = entropy, cal/g °K
χ_0 = enthalpy, cal/g   } from 0°K.
ψ_0 = free internal energy, cal/g

remains constant during a reversible adiabatic process and increases during an irreversible one. Entropy can be expressed as

$$S_0 = \int\limits_0^T \frac{dQ}{T}$$

where Q is the heat communicated to the system in any reversible process in order to bring it from 0°K to T°K.

Entropy can be used to show what part of the internal energy of a system is "bound," "inverted," and cannot be converted into work.

The bound energy is TS. The remaining internal energy, $\psi = U - TS$, or for water and ice, $\psi \approx \chi - TS$ is the *free energy*, work expended on the system from the outside during the isothermal process.

In Fig. 7 the magnitude $-\psi_0$ represents the part of the internal energy loss of ice or water which may be converted into work in the reversible isothermal process. At 0°C the free energies of ice and water are identical, but in the case of ice it comprises 92% of all the internal energy, while in the case of water it comprises only 44%, since the heat of fusion is bound energy.

Mechanical properties and temperature. The mechanical properties of ice in general are governed by the weakness of the hydrogen bond and by the geometric nature of its space lattice. Under oriented pressure, ice, like every crystalline substance, may behave as an *elastic*, a *plastic* or a *brittle* body, i.e., it may deform either elastically or plastically or it may break. The factors that determine its behavior are the amount and type of stress, the rate of increase of the stress, the temperature and, possibly, to a small extent, the previous deformations. The effect of most of these factors is such that they either cause the appearance of the elastic and brittle properties, excluding the plastic, or else the range of the plastic deformations is expanded at the expense of the elastic and the brittle.

When characterizing the mechanical properties of ice, it must be kept in mind that generally ice under natural conditions is at a temperature very close to its melting point. In order to make a true comparison of the effect of temperature on the properties of ice and of other substances, one must compare their *reduced temperatures* T/θ, where θ is the melting point of the given substance on the absolute scale. In such a comparison we find that the temperature conditions of ice at the earth's surface usually correspond to the temperatures of the hot working of metals and to conditions under which most other minerals are found at a considerable depth in the earth's crust. For example, the melting point of orthoclase is 1170–1200°C; consequently, orthoclase at the earth's surface would correspond to ice at a temperature of −220°C.

The lower the temperature, the more difficult it is for the atoms in the space lattice of ice to regroup, the more durable the space lattice becomes, and the more intense are the manifestations of the elastic and brittle properties of the ice. On the other hand, at high temperatures the ice becomes more and more plastic. The brittle hardness of ice at temperatures near 0°C is 1.5 (Mohs scale):

at −15°C 2–3
    −30   3–4
    −40   4
    −78.5 .... 6, i.e., the hardness
                                       of orthoclase

(Koch and Wegener, 1930; Teichert, 1939). In absolute values this amounts to an enormous increase in hardness. Ice has no clearly defined elastic limit with constant load at 0°C or, at any rate, when there is resistance to shear the elastic limit does not exceed 0.1 kg/cm² (Shul'man, 1948; Perutz, 1950). At low temperatures, however, the elastic part of the deformation increases considerably. Even at 0°C, shear does not become perceptible until the ice is subjected to stresses of around 1 kg/cm², so that in first approximation ice may be regarded as a plastic substance with an elastic limit of the order of 1 kg/cm² (see Perutz, 1950).

The relaxation time of ice is 1.5 times smaller at 0°C than at −5°C (Veinberg, 1938). According to Shul'man (1948), the viscosity of ice increases, approximately linearly, by a factor of 3 when the temperature decreases from −1°C to −20°C, while according to Höppler (1941), it increases by a factor of 1000.[3] The viscosity of ice decreases especially rapidly as 0°C is approached, owing to the increased facility for internal gliding and the possibility of partial melting. The crushing strength of ice increases, on an average, 2.6 times in the temperature interval 0°C to −30°C (Veinberg, 1940, p. 202).

Relaxation of stresses. To a considerable extent, the nature of the deformation of ice also depends on the *rate of increase of the stress.* According to J. C. Maxwell, any deformation consists of mutually overlapping elastic and plastic elements, and the magnitude of the deformation is simultaneously a function of the load at a given moment, as in the case of ideally elastic bodies, and of the integral of the change in load with time, as in the case of fluid bodies. If a rapidly increasing force of short duration acts on a body, the deformation will be elastic even if the force is great, while if the breaking

---

[3] Shul'man's data, obtained by the tension method, are apparently more reliable than those of Höppler made with a consistometer (F. Höppler, *Kolloidalische Zeitschrift*, 97(2): 154, 1941.*

* [Höppler's device consisted of a sphere attached to a rod, which was pushed down into the ice, the force being measured and the rate at which it descended being then used to deduce viscosity (which, since it was not a constant, served only to show that the method was not really valid). (Comment by Prof. John W. Glen.) – D.K.]

point is exceeded, there will be a disruption that nearly bypasses the plastic stage. On the other hand, in the case of a prolonged increasing load, the elastic limit decreases sharply, the elastic deformation is overlapped by residual deformation and the more prolonged the loading is, the greater will be the amount of elastic deformation that becomes residual. Therefore, with time, a constantly decreasing force suffices to keep the body in a deformed state. Maxwell called this phenomenon weakening or *relaxation*. The time required to reduce the stress necessary for a given deformation to its eth part ($e = 2.718$, the base of natural logarithms), or the relaxation time, is a measure of the relative roles of the elastic and plastic portions of the deformation. Consequently, a large relaxation time indicates that the reaction is primarily elastic, a small relaxation time indicates that the reaction is primarily plastic.

The relaxation time of ice varies from 8 to 90 minutes (Veinberg, 1938; Donchenko and Shul'man, 1949), depending also on the direction of the deformation. Hence, the ratio of the elastic to the plastic portion of the deformation may change by a factor of more than 11.

Anisotropy of the mechanical properties. All the mechanical properties of ice are sharply anisotropic. In the space lattice of ice, the planes with the greatest reticular density and those farthest apart are perpendicular to the main axis. A disturbance in the basal plane (0001) causes a disruption of only two atomic bonds per unit cell and these are bonds perpendicular to the basal plane, while a disturbance in any plane perpendicular to the basal plane requires a disruption of at least four bonds per unit cell and these bonds are so inclined to the disturbance planes that the atoms bound by them, in projection, are closer to each other than the atoms separated by the basal plane (Owston and Lonsdale, 1948). The relative weakness of cohesion in the direction of the main axis (0001) is also indicated by the larger temperature coefficient of linear expansion (29×10^{-6} per degree along the main axis and 17×10^{-6} per degree perpendicular to the main axis in the temperature interval $0°C$ to $-66°C$, as follows from data on the dimensions of the unit cell of ice) and by the above-mentioned greater intensity of movement of atoms along the main axis. Because of this, long before x-ray studies were instituted, McConnel (1891), using as his basis the reaction of ice to oriented stresses, conceived of the internal structure of ice crystals as an agglomeration of numerous, very fine, durable but supple plates oriented in the basal plane, like a deck of cards smeared with non-drying glue, and the intervals between these elementary plates (planes of densest packing of atoms) were *planes of weakness*.

Weakening is also manifested in a different manner. According to the law of Bravais, the basal plane of ice should be a cleavage plane; however, cleavage does not actually occur because of the incompletely established and consequently easily re-established bond of the molecules at the temperatures of the earth's surface. Furthermore, weakening of the basal planes is clearly manifested in the mechanical properties of ice, in the disposition of the gas and salt impurities and in the distribution of internal melting, i.e., of "ice flowers," along these planes when thermal energy and the indistinct, diffused water films are absorbed during compression of the ice in the direction of the main axis (Tyndall, 1858).

Of the mechanical properties of ice, anistropy has least to do with elastic properties, much more to do with strength and most to do with plasticity.

Glide planes and the behavior of monocrystals. The basal plane of an ice crystal is its only well defined glide plane. The magnitude of the critical tangential stress at which gliding starts is not known for ice, but in view of the very low elastic limit of polycrystalline ice (not more than 0.1 kg/cm² at $0°C$). it should be negligible, at least at high temperatures.

The stress z at the elastic limit differs from the critical tangential stress τ as a function of the angle ϕ between the z direction and the glide plane, and also as a function of the angle ψ between the projection of the z direction onto the glide plane and the nearest direction of glide:

$$\tau = z \mid \sin \phi \cos \psi$$

The directions of gliding in ice crystals have not been defined. In analogy to metals having hexagonal symmetry, it must be assumed that the glide directions in ice are the diagonals of a hexagonal prism $[\bar{2}110]$, $[11\bar{2}0]$, $[1\bar{2}10]$. In Mügge's opinion (see O. Mügge, 1895, 1899, 1900), the basal plane of ice is a plane of *translation*, differing from simple gliding in that the movement takes place with nearly equal ease in any direction of the basal plane; this permits an elastic-plastic bending of the elementary plates with different relative displacement of their parts, and rotation around the main axis. Mügge's experiments proved the possibility of all these aspects of plastic deformation, up to the complete extraction of the parts of the crystal that are bounded by the basal planes.

In ice the magnitude of the critical normal stress ρ necessary to rupture the crystal along the basal plane is incomparably greater than the critical tangential stress at which gliding starts. The breaking-point stress of ice $\mathcal{Z}$ is reached when $\rho = \mathcal{Z} \sin^2 \phi$, where ϕ

is the angle between z and the plane of splitting. The crystal behaves as a truly elastic body until the stresses in it reach the critical value. If the critical tangential stress τ is reached, the ice will deform plastically, without disruption of the continuity; if, however, the critical normal stress ρ is reached at the same time or subsequently during the plastic deformation process, the ice will react as a brittle body and split.

The above shows how the manifestation of the elastic, plastic and brittle properties of ice depends on the direction in which a force is applied and on the magnitude of that force. A force causing *shear*, or cleavage, may act in three main, mutually perpendicular directions:

(1) the shear force coincides with the basal plane. Only translation occurs, the deformation is plastic;

(2) the shear force acts in the direction of the main axis perpendicular to the basal plane. The elementary plates of the crystal bend and, after the critical stress is exceeded, break. The deformation is elastic-plastic, alternating with disruption;

(3) the force acts in the basal plane, but the shear force is perpendicular to it. The elementary plates that are rigid in the longitudinal direction allow only a negligible elastic deformation, which changes to disruption in the case of a significant increase of stress. Ice behavior of this type was demonstrated by the experiments of J. McConnel and O. Mügge (see Fig. 8).

Case I   Case 2

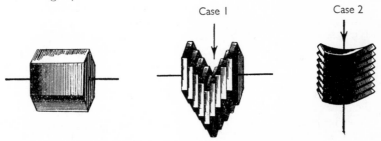

FIG. 8. Sketch of Mügge's experiments on the deformation of ice.

The reaction of ice to tension is generally as above, except that the tangential stress is maximal and becomes half of z with a 45° inclination of the basal plane ($\phi = 45°$) to the direction of the tension. Linear compression differs from tension only in that the disruption (crushing) is attained through the stress of the crystal's transverse tension, which occurs as a result of longitudinal compression.

If the ice deforms more or less perpendicularly to the main axis (Case 1), the slight elastic stresses relax intensively, while if the deformations are parallel to the main axis (Case 2), the relaxation is weaker (Filippova and Shul'man, 1949). In the first case the relaxation time is close to the lower limit (8–10 min), while in the second case it takes as much as 90 minutes.

As the experiments of Mügge and the observations of Hess, Wegener, *et al.* have shown, the elastic-plastic bending of ice crystals under a slowly increasing, small load may reach a considerable magnitude. After being freed from the load, crystals distorted in this manner do not reveal any noticeable elastic aftereffect, thanks to the relaxation of the stresses. Shul'man (1948) is of the opinion that residual non-relaxing stresses are also operative in ice.

Viscosity. The viscosity of ice is very anisotropic. According to S. K. Khanina and A. R. Shul'man (1940), the coefficient of viscosity of ice with a bending force perpendicular to the main axis (Case 1) is from 10^{10} to 10^{11} poise, while under a force parallel to the main axis (Case 2) it is from 10^{14} to 10^{15} poise, or a thousand times greater. Generally there is no plastic deformation in the third case mentioned previously.

Evidently the strengthening phenomenon (increase of the elastic limit during the flow process) characteristic of metals is not observed in ice that is deforming plastically. G. Beilby (1921) explained this difference by saying that a very fine film melts on the glide planes of all substances: in metals this film hardens in an amorphous state, making further gliding difficult, while in ice at ordinary temperatures it crystallizes conformally, leaving the conditions of gliding unchanged. The strengthening (hardening) and relaxation phenomena should only be observed below the recrystallization temperature in ice (around $-70°C$). Recently, however, it has been established that Beilby's explanation does not hold for metals. Tiny disturbances of the lattice during deformation along the edges of the glide plane have proved to be the actual cause of the hardening. Evidently these disturbances do not occur in ice or else they are quickly adjusted.

Strength. Ice strength in different crystallographic directions is known for only one type of deformation, in which the anisotropy is considerably less than it is for viscosity. According to the data collected by Veinberg (1940, p. 201), the *crushing strength of ice* parallel to the main axis as an average of 1246 cases (determinations) is $31–33$ kg/cm^2 with variations of ± 10 kg/cm^2, and the crushing strength perpendicular to the main axis is $20–25$ kg/cm^2, which is in good agreement with the described ice structure consisting of elementary plates in the basal plane. The breaking strength of ice at

$-3°C$ is 16.2 ± 4.4 kg/cm², the tensile strength is 11.1 kg/cm², the shear strength is 5.7 kg/cm². All data are for fresh ice with some impurities and, consequently, the strength of pure ice would be somewhat greater.

Deformation energy. The energy expended in mechanical actions on a crystal converts in part into bound thermal energy, due to which the temperature rises or melting takes place, while the remaining energy transforms into the free energy of the crystal. The transformation into thermal energy is of the same magnitude as internal friction occurring during deformation; consequently, it takes place chiefly during plastic deformations but to a small extent during elastic deformations as well, because they are not completely reversible (elastic hysteresis).

The free energy increment of the crystal due to mechanical effects is minimum during plastic deformations, where it takes place in connection with small disturbances of the space lattice and internal stresses leading to strengthening. When the crystal is disrupted, the entire free energy increment is in the form of the surface energy of its fragments, and the energy is expended on the creation of an additional surface. In the case of an elastic deformation, however, the crystal under stress assumes a large internal free energy, which may be expended on molecular processes connected with relaxation or may again convert into mechanical work expended on overcoming the external forces in the process of elastic aftereffect.

Most processes of ice deformation are of a complex elastic-plastic nature. These processes are irreversible to the extent that they do not lead to a stressed state of the substance, and the kinetic energy expended on them is converted into thermal energy due to internal friction. The remaining kinetic energy, whose magnitude is determined by the elastic part of the deformation, transforms into the free energy of the substance under stress and serves as the source of energy for the processes of relaxation and elastic aftereffect, and, perhaps, is retained in part in the form of residual nonrelaxing stresses.

Optic properties. In some respects the optic properties of ice are as unusual as its thermodynamic and mechanical properties. Ice not only has an exceptionally small coefficient of absorption in the visible spectrum due to transparency, but it has the lowest index of refraction of all the known minerals and has very weak birefringence. For rays of wave-length 550 mμ (center of gravity of daylight) $n_e = 1.3120$; $n_0 = 1.3106$; $n_e - n_0 = 0.0014$; the dispersion of the birefringence of ice is normal and very slight. Thus, ice is optically positive and, like all minerals of average symmetry, is uniaxial, whereby its optic axis coincides with its main crystallographic axis [0001].

Due to its slight birefringence, ice is optically very sensitive to stresses in the space lattice: the slightest stress causes the appearance of optic anomalies, viz., wavy extinction in polarized light with an analyzer, and biaxiality. External mechanical effects constitute the main cause of optic anomalies. The forces of crystal growth, which manifest themselves in the presence of external obstacles, rarely cause optic anomalies. Usually, the stresses are not great enough during crystallization; wavy extinction and biaxiality with angles of optic axes up to 8° are observed occasionally but only around fine solid inclusions at a distance no greater than a millimeter.

Purely plastic deformation such as gliding or translation along the basal plane does not affect the optic properties of ice, since it does not cause stresses in the space lattice. Optic anomalies in ice are always connected with bending of the elementary plates (0001) of the space lattice, i.e., they are due to the elastic part of the deformation. Extinction in polarized light with an analyzer in the case of bending of the elementary plates, according to Tarr and Rich (1912, p. 246), takes place in directions parallel to the bent surfaces. After one of their experiments on the compression of ice, where an ice crystal about 1 cm in size under a stress perpendicular to the main axis experienced deformation on one side but not on the other, these investigators observed a rotation of as much as 20° in the direction of extinction in different parts of the crystal.

In optically biaxial ice crystals, the acute bisectrix coincides with the main crystallographic axis or with a perpendicular to the basal plane. If the biaxiality is caused by the compression of the crystals perpendicularly to the main axis, the plane of the optic axes in ice, as well as in all optically positive substances, lies in the direction of the pressure; in optically negative crystals it is perpendicular to this direction (see Klocke, 1897, p. 280).

The visual angle of the optic axes of natural ice crystals that have undergone deformation under natural conditions often reaches 10–20°, sometimes it approaches 50°. However, my observations of such ice samples relieved of external loading have shown that the angle of the optic axes in them remains nearly constant over a period of two or even as many as four years. Of course, there must be relaxation of such powerful internal stresses over a period of time as long as this. Furthermore, the diversity of the size of the angles of the optic axes of neighboring crystals and the regular connection between the degree of development of biaxiality and the intensity of the deformation to which the ice was subjected remove all bases for assuming the existence of biaxial polymorphous modifications of ice.

This problem was solved experimentally. It was found that the ice remained monocrystalline during bending with subsequent fairly rapid relaxation and disappearance of biaxiality after the load had been removed (at temperatures within the range $-5°$ to $-12°C$) only when the bends caused a $2V$ no greater than 7–8°. With further deformation, the bent part of a crystal without visible disruptions of continuity breaks down into a number of blocks (units) with more or less similar orientation, thus reaching stable equilibrium which persists even after the load is removed. Furthermore, a number of the newly formed uniaxial crystal blocks, or polygons, coming simultaneously into the field of vision of the microscope, give the same effect as a single optically biaxial, bent crystal. On the Laue diffraction pattern, too, the result of polygonization as well as of blending is manifested in asterism.

Thus, the true optic biaxiality of ice in the temperature interval from 0° to $-12°C$ apparently never exceeds 7–8°; if the angles of the optic axis are larger, we are dealing with pseudo-biaxiality, connected with the strong deformation and disintegration of crystals.

"*Ice flowers.*" An interesting feature of ice, connected with its transparency and low melting point, is its capacity for internal melting due to the absorption of radiant energy, which is analogous to the formation of surficial etch figures in other minerals and in ice itself. Even though tiny inhomogeneous inclusions act as the centers of melting, the behavior of the ice itself in this case is quite characteristic.

After some time, small flat disks of water appear within the irradiated crystal.[4] As melting continues, they grow in the form of flowers with six petals (peculiar "negative crystals") called ice flowers or Tyndall figures, after the man who first described them (see Tyndall, 1858; Schoentjes, 1905; Dobrowolski, 1931, p. 337). A dark disk, a vacuum saturated with water vapor, appears in the center of the growing "flower." This vacuum forms as a result of volume decrease during melting; it appears dark when there is complete internal reflection of the light rays on its boundaries. The appearance of the central vacuum is often accompanied by an audible cracking. The greatly expanding ice flowers attain a diameter of 1.0–1.5 cm; their petals have secondary branching as in star snowflakes, and even the central vacuum may produce six-petaled offshoots (Fig. 9).

---

[4] [For much more complete information, see U. Nakaya, *Properties of single crystals of ice revealed by internal melting*, SIPRE Research Paper No. 13, April, 1956. – D.K.]

FIG. 9.   Expanding "ice flower." (Photograph by H. Schoentjes, 1905.)

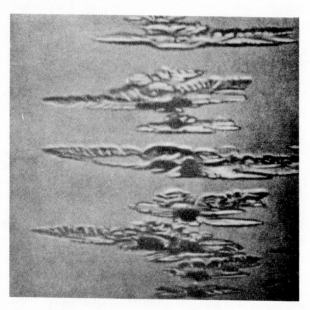

FIG. 10.   "Ice flowers," side view. (Photograph by H. Schoentjes, 1905.)

The flowers are always situated parallel to each other in the basal planes, while the petals are disposed in the direction of the secondary crystallographic axes, as may be seen from the mutually parallel nature of the corresponding petals in all the flowers of one crystal (Figs. 10 and 11). The occurrence of melt figures indicates an anisotropy of the rates of internal melting which progresses along only one of the planes in the crystal, with greater velocity in the specific directions of this plane.

"Forel lines." The so-called "Forel lines"[5] are another manifestation of the anisotropic properties of ice, but this time in the external form

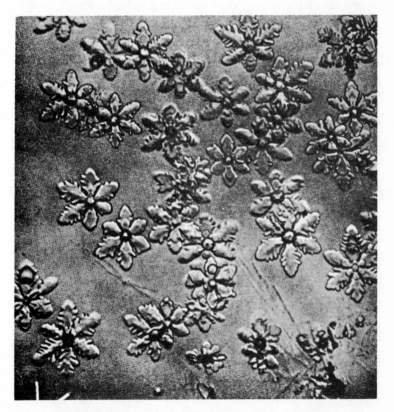

Fig. 11. "Ice flowers" in a single crystal. (Photograph by H. Schoentjes, 1905.)

---

[5] This was the name given by E. Hagenbach-Bischoff (1882) after the name of the investigator who first took their impression in wax. L. Agassiz had sketched "Forel lines" still earlier (1847).

of the crystals. This is a very fine rectilinear ribbing on the surface of ice crystals along the lines of intersection with the basal plane. Slight melting, accompanied by rapid evaporation of the melt water, is a prerequisite for the occurrence of Forel lines. When the melt water runs off along the surface, a deeply etched, meandering and branching system of furrows forms. The force of gravity, not the structure of the crystals, is responsible for the direction of these furrows. It should be mentioned that real "Forel lines" along the basal planes are a relatively rare phenomenon. R. Emden, who made a special study of Forel lines in 1890, denies a connection between these lines and structure, since, according to his observations, they may have any direction with respect to the crystallographic axes and usually are plainly visible even in the absence of evaporation (e.g., in ice caves with an atmospheric humidity of 100%).

Some investigators have assumed that Forel lines are found only in grains of glacier ice and have been inclined to consider them traces of internal gliding along the basal plane, manifested by evaporation. However, as Emden stressed, these lines are observed in ice crystals of any origin. The plate structure and the ribbing caused by it usually show up best as a result of crystallization from water that is rich in soluble impurities, which then arrange themselves at more or less equal intervals in the form of very fine interlayers and lenses along the basal planes of the crystals.

CHAPTER IV

ICE CRYSTAL NUCLEATION

The triple point of vapor, water and ordinary ice and the boiling, melting and sublimation lines that lead from it on the phase diagram correspond, respectively, to the states in which three or two phases of water are in equilibrium. When a substance crosses these boundaries, it becomes unstable and a transition to another aggregate state, stable under the new conditions, becomes possible. However, a phase transition created by thermodynamic conditions of equilibrium is not realized immediately unless the transition is from the solid to the liquid and from the liquid to the gaseous phase, or, in the opposite direction, it is realized only at the boundary of the existing phases. Theoretically, a crystal can be superheated only during the melting process, but experimentally superheating is generally not observed, because a large number of melt centers quickly appears on the surface. Consequently, melting is strictly dependent on a change in the thermodynamic conditions. In this same way, the reverse transition, consisting in the transition from a random to an orderly arrangement of the molecules, is forced by the thermodynamic conditions at the boundary of an established crystal phase and is, therefore, called *forced crystallization*.

The generation of new crystals, i.e., *spontaneous crystallization*, is a much more difficult process. In the absence of established crystals, a melt may exist in a supercooled state, and a solution or vapor may exist in a supersaturated state, without crystallizing. Crystallization from this metastable state never takes place simultaneously in the whole mass, but begins from a few centers, the number of which is negligible compared with the number of molecules in a given volume. This one-way hysteresis of conversion is expressed especially sharply in water.

At the plane of separation of two phases there is always free energy which retards the formation of one phase within the other. For geometric reasons, the specific surface and, consequently, the share of the surface energy in the total energy of the body increases as the volume decreases. Beginning with a size of 2μ and less, the effect of surface tension, which increases pressure within the crystal, is expressed in a noticeable reduction of the melting point or in an

51

increase of the vapor pressure with which the crystal is in equilibrium (Tammann, 1922, p. 209). For a liquid drop, the effect of the surface tension on the vapor pressure is expressed by W. Thomson's equation:

$$\delta = 1n\frac{p_r}{p_\infty} = \frac{2V}{kT} \cdot \frac{\sigma}{r}$$

where δ is supersaturation measured by the logarithm of the ratio of pressures p of the vapor which is in equilibrium with a drop of radius r, and with the plane surface $(r = \infty)$; σ is the specific surface energy or surface tension (for water at 0°C it is 7.71 mg/mm, at −3°C it is 7.84 mg/mm): V is the volume of the molecule; k is the Boltzmann constant (increase of the mean kinetic energy per degree of freedom of a monatomic molecule of gas with a temperature increase of 1°K); T is the temperature in °K.

With respect to water, this equation holds only for drops of radius equal to or greater than 10^{-7} cm, consisting of 133 molecules; if the droplets are smaller, the share of each molecule in the entropy of the drop becomes significant and the latter can no longer be considered as belonging to the liquid phase. The curve showing the entropy of water as a function of volume has a minimum at radius 10^{-7} cm, which corresponds to the transition from a liquid drop to a group of molecules (Rodebush, 1949, p. 269).

A liquid drop of the above dimension or larger will always be unstable: if the vapor is not completely saturated with respect to the drop, the drop will evaporate; however, if the drop is in equilibrium with the vapor, which requires an immense supersaturation with respect to the plane water surface, the drop will grow, since the increase of radius makes the vapor supersaturated with respect to the drop.

This same equation also obtains for a crystal, with the difference that the linear parameter, corresponding to the radius, may increase only in discontinuous stages corresponding to the addition of layers of one unit cell thickness, while the magnitude of the surface tension should be taken as the average for all simple forms of the crystal.

Consequently, the smaller the crystal is, the greater will be its temperature of equilibrium with the melt and the greater its pressure of equilibrium with the vapor. Therefore, there will always be a *critical size* for a given condition of supercooling or supersaturation, and once this size is reached the crystal will grow.

Spontaneous crystallization of a supercooled melt or supersaturated vapor requires the formation of stable embryos (crystalline particles of critical size within the melt or vapor under the given conditions).

However, the thermodynamic conditions of equilibrium alone cannot explain their occurrence; the bases for their occurrence were found in the laws of probability of statistical physics.

According to the kinetic theory of matter, all parameters of state of the system fluctuate at each given point around the mean values corresponding to the maximum entropy. The magnitude of the fluctuations is subject to the Maxwell distribution law; therefore, from time to time the fluctuations can become large at individual points of the system.

The fluctuations may remain within the limits of one aggregate state (homophase fluctuations) or they may be accompanied by the transition of a small volume of the body into another aggregate state (heterophase fluctuations, to use Frenkel's terminology) (see Ia. I. Frenkel', 1939, p. 952).

The probability of transition of part of the initial phase into the embryo of a new, thermodynamically more stable phase is determined by the magnitude of its energy of formation. This energy is expended on overcoming the forces of surface tension, i.e., on creating the free surface energy of the embryo, and, if a change in volume takes place during the transition, on overcoming the resistance of the surrounding medium (N. N. Sirota, 1948, p. 1309). Moreover, during crystallization of ice from water, the second factor is significant only when the process takes place in a confined space, otherwise the resistance of the medium, determined by its elastic properties, can be neglected.

As M. Volmer has shown, the work A of the formation of a volume embryo of a crystal is equivalent to one third of its surface energy:

$$A = \frac{1}{3} F\sigma = \frac{1}{3} \sum F_i \sigma_i$$

where F is the surface area and σ the surface tension. The probability W of the formation of an equilibrium embryo is expressed by the formula

$$W = C \exp \left[-\frac{A}{kT} \right]$$

(C being the constant of the substance), i.e., W is the exponential function of the energy of formation of the embryo, and, beyond a certain limit, increases very quickly with a change in the latter.[1] Thus, if a crystalline embryo is to form, the energy barrier, which

---

[1] For more details see M. Volmer (1939), Ia I. Frenkel' (1945) and M. N. Sirota (1948, p. 1309).

increases quickly with an increase in the size of the equilibrium embryo, must be overcome.

If two phases coexist, an initial stable segment, which can be regarded as a "two-dimensional embryo," is required for the growth of each new crystal layer one unit cell thick.

The probability of formation of a two-dimensional surface embryo is expressed by an analogous formula containing the energy of formation:

$$A_1 = \frac{1}{2} L\chi$$

where L is the perimeter and χ the peripheral energy.

The probabilities of formation of two- and three-dimensional embryos of critical size vary irregularly, depending on the degree of supercooling (supersaturation). Therefore, for each substance directly below the curves of melting and sublimation in the phase diagram there are more or less extensive metastable regions, in which spontaneous crystallization is practically impossible without the influence of foreign matter, and the introduction of established centers causes or, theoretically, substantially accelerates crystallization. With still greater supercooling (supersaturation) the probability of formation of embryos of the critical size sharply increases and spontaneous crystallization ensues, which can no longer be accelerated by seeding.

The general premises of the theory of phase transitions mentioned above apply equally to crystallization from a melt, a solution, and to crystallization from vapor or sublimation.[2] However, there is an essential difference between these processes.

First let us examine the features of the freezing of water.

THE FREEZING OF WATER

As the probability of crystallization during supercooling increases, the viscosity of the melt also increases, which hinders the molecular

---

[2] The term sublimation, like volatilization, indicates essentially the transition from a solid state to a vapor state, and in physics is used in this sense. However, A. Wegener began to apply it in the opposite sense, i.e., as the crystallization from vapor, and this concept has become established in meteorology. For lack of another term, we will use sublimation in the narrow sense to indicate the process which is opposite that of volatilization. In the broader sense, under sublimation we understand the whole process of the transposition of ice through the vapor state, i.e., the volatilization, migration and crystallization of vapor, and by "distillation" we mean the transposition of water through the vapor state (evaporation, migration of water and condensation).

regrouping necessary for crystallization. Substances whose melts become quite viscous during supercooling pass into a solid amorphous state, viz., glass, instead of crystallizing. In less viscous liquids, glass formation is abetted by high cooling rates, due to which crystallization does not occur, despite the appearance of a certain number of crystalline embryos. The crystallization capacity of a substance is defined by the magnitude of the viscosity at the lower boundary of the supercooled metastable state.

We have already mentioned that ice is one of the most typical crystalloids. However, the reason for this (as distinct, e.g., from metals which do not exist in an amorphous state) is not that water is incapable of supercooling but that it has extremely low viscosity. Under normal pressure and at a temperature of 0°C, the viscosity of water is just 17.9 millipoise; at a temperature of −10°C, it is 26 millipoise, while at −20°C, it is as mobile as at a positive temperature.

The relation of temperature to the probability of spontaneous formation of three-dimensional (W) and plane (W') embryos of ice crystals in supercooled water was computed from the Frenkel' formulas[3] by L. G. Kachurin (1951a), on the basis of the values for the specific surface energy which he found for the ice-water interface ($\sigma = 9$ erg/cm^2) and for the constant C ($C = e^{33.1}$cm^{-3}sec^{-1}); see Fig. 12. According to Kachurin's calculation, the metastable region for water occupies the temperature interval between 0° and −55°C.

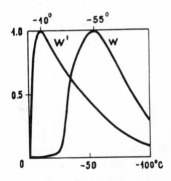

FIG. 12. Temperature relationship of the probability of spontaneous formation of three-dimensional (W) and plane (W') embryos of ice crystals in supercooled water.

---

[3] For more details, see M. Volmer (1939), Ia. I. Frenkel' (1945) and N. M. Sirota (1948, p. 1309).

Experiments show a still greater value for the low temperature interval.

Contrary to the opinion of such investigators as Tammann and Al'tberg, spontaneous crystallization of water cannot take place at very low temperatures unless crystallization nuclei are introduced. It has definitely been established that water does not freeze in considerable volume during supercooling to −33°C (Meyer and Pfaff, 1935). Tiny droplets, which have a smaller probability of introduction of nuclei of crystallization, probably can be supercooled to a considerably lower temperature. Liquid droplets have often been observed in the atmosphere at temperatures as low as −40°C. Weickmann (1949) supercooled tiny drops of water to −50°C, and Rau (1944) supercooled them to −72°C. In Rau's experiments at higher temperatures, crystallization began around the foreign nuclei, first at one point, then at another point of the drop, but after repeated meltings and freezings, these nuclei became ineffective and further supercoolings became possible. Only when −72°C was reached did the crystallization begin at once at many points over the whole drop, independently of the foreign nuclei. Apparently, this temperature is the limit of the supercooled metastable state of water.

Thus, spontaneous volumetric crystallization of water is possible only in the case of very great supercooling. Comparatively slight supercooling is actually sufficient for crystallization in most cases in nature, because of impurities which cause the formation of embryos. When a seed crystal is used (a crystal of a given substance or a substance isomorphous with it) the melt can be supercooled somewhat only during the crystallization process. Experiment has shown that heteromorphous solid bodies also promote the crystallization of water. However, their effectiveness as centers of crystallization differs, therefore the supercooling required for the onset of crystallization may vary.

The role of foreign particles in the formation of ice crystal embryos explains a number of phenomena not explainable from any other point of view. Among these are the lack of influence of the cooling time on the possibility of freezing and the exceptionally small numbers of centers of crystallization. To explain the latter, a number of proposals have been made concerning the effect of special polymeric or anisotropic molecules, crystal fragments, particles with anomalously low molecular velocities, denser packing, regular arrangement, and the like. Actually, the number of centers of crystallization apparently is equivalent to the number of effective foreign nuclei under the given conditions. Therefore, for each sample of water there is a specific negative temperature, above which water cannot freeze and below which it cannot remain unfrozen. According to Dorsey's investigations (1938), great volumes of the dirtiest muddy water had a freezing temperature of $-3.3°C$, while the freezing temperature of the purest water distilled in vacuum from a solution containing chromium was $-21.1°C$. Hence, filtration, centrifugation and insulation of the walls of the vessel by another liquid increase the probability of supercooling.

The mechanism of the effect of heteromorphous foreign nuclei is still not quite clear. The influence of such nuclei is sometimes regarded as a purely mechanical retardation of the thermal motions of the molecules, sometimes as a base for the deposition of molecules, and, finally, sometimes the decisive role is assigned to the sorbed layer on the surface of the particles. Evidently, Dorsey's (1948) hypothesis is in best agreement with the facts; he holds that crystallization of the melt begins in the outer, weakly maintained part of the sorbed layer on convex parts of the surface where the molecules have enough freedom to be mutually oriented by the impacts of the free molecules of the liquid, by vibrations, or by other causes.

Therefore, only segments of the surface within a specific interval of the curve are effective as centers of crystallization. The dispersive suspended particles may be sufficiently effective only at a low temperature, due to the excessive curvature of the surface and the weakness of the adsorption forces, while in large bodies only the rough parts of the surface which have sufficient curvature and are subject to lateral impacts of the free molecules of the liquid are centers of crystallization. The crystal lattice of the ice, originating at the outer boundary of the sorbed layer, expands along the surface of the foreign nucleus, forming a complex embryo capable of further growth, provided it reaches critical size.

SPONTANEOUS SUBLIMATION

The situation is quite different with respect to the spontaneous crystallization of ice from vapor. Ostwald formulated the so-called *step rule*, which states that if a substance can pass from a state that has become unstable into other aggregate states with a different degree of stability, less stable forms which may be replaced later by more stable forms will appear first. According to this rule, supersaturated water vapor at negative temperatures should first condense into drops of supercooled water and then crystallize.

Nevertheless, the *hypothesis of spontaneous sublimation*, formulated by Wegener in 1911 and developed by Findeisen (1938–40), has been widely used in meteorology. At negative temperatures the pressure of vapors that are saturated with respect to ice is lower than the pressure of vapors saturated with respect to water, thus, according to the Wegener-Findeisen theory, water vapor in the presence of nuclei of sublimation will crystallize into ice without condensing into supercooled drops.

It has been proposed that submicroscopic particles of quartz, allegedly isomorphous with ice, constitute the centers of spontaneous crystallization of water vapor in the atmosphere, but no satisfactory answer has been found to the question of how such particles originate. Since it has been established statistically that clouds of water droplets, on an average, supercool to $-12°C$ and then freeze and become ice clouds, it has been asserted that the nuclei of sublimation become effective at a temperature of $-12°C$. This has been called the *sublimation temperature*. Wegener has used the absence of nuclei of sublimation to explain the cases of supercooling of water clouds to $-30°C$ and $-40°C$, observed comparatively rarely, as well as the supersaturation of vapors with respect to ice, which is observed extensively in the atmosphere.

The Wegener-Findeisen hypothesis has only recently been disproved, and evidently many researchers still hold to it. L. Krastanow (1940, 1941) began a re-examination of this hypothesis; he was the first to make a quantitative computation of the effect of foreign nuclei of definite size and surface characteristics on the probability of the formation of atmospheric ice embryos.

The main factor which escapes the adherents of this hypothesis of spontaneous sublimation is the difference in magnitude of the energy barriers during the formation of crystal embryos from vapor and from liquid. Thus far no means have been found for measuring the surface tension of solids; however, according to Volmer, this magnitude can be estimated approximately by the following method. The free surface energy at the crystal-vapor interface should be approximately as many times greater than that at the crystal-liquid interface as the latent heat of sublimation is greater than the heat of fusion. For ice this constitutes as much as an 8 1/2-fold difference. Similarly, the surface energy at the boundary of a foreign solid nucleus of crystallization and vapor should be considerably greater than at its boundary with water. Consequently, the probability of spontaneous crystallization of ice from supercooled drops is greater than spontaneous crystallization directly from vapor. Krastanow concluded that spontaneous sublimation can occur only at very low temperatures and that, as a rule, atmospheric ice crystals form by the freezing of tiny water droplets.

In 1949 Weickmann took a further decisive step in the criticism of the theory of spontaneous sublimation of ice. According to his computations, in the absence of foreign nuclei the line of spontaneous sublimation of ice on the vapor pressure-temperature diagram lies below the line of spontaneous condensation of water droplets in the temperature range 0° to −70°C. Consequently, when water vapors are cooled in air, they will change directly into ice particles only if a great enough supersaturation has been reached below −70°C, which is the "*triple point of spontaneous nucleation*" (see Weickmann, 1949); at higher temperatures the vapor will first condense into water drops and then, when cooled to −70°C, the drops will freeze. Weickmann noted that his triple point of spontaneous nucleation is in good agreement with Rau's experimental data on the temperature of the spontaneous freezing of water (−72°C).

In the presence of sublimation nuclei isomorphous with ice, the point of intersection of the lines of sublimation and condensation is displaced from −70°C toward higher temperatures. This displacement increases as the radius of the particles which act as the centers of crystallization; a radius of 10^{-6} cm has a corresponding temperature of about −15°C, while an infinitely large radius, i.e., a plane surface, has a corresponding temperature of 0°C. Hence, at negative temperatures near zero, only forced sublimation may occur on the surface of sufficiently large crystals of substances isomorphous with the ice, and the smaller the crystal is, the lower the temperature should be.

In analyzing the characteristics of ice structure, Weickmann concluded that this structure is so singular that *substances isomorphous with ice generally do not exist*. In particular, the opinion that quartz or tridymite are isomorphous with ice can be rejected because smooth surfaces of these substances do not have a seeding effect on supercooled water. Water does not freeze any more easily in quartz vessels than in any other vessels, and when it does freeze, only the roughness of the walls is responsible. The creation of a crystal lattice of ice on non-isomorphous solid particles requires the expenditure of additional energy, which decreases the probability of spontaneous sublimation and allows it only at lower temperatures.

Hence, *spontaneous sublimation of ice generally does not occur in the atmosphere* or takes place only at very low, rarely encountered temperatures. During the cooling of water vapors, liquid drops could always condense and then freeze. After water appears, nuclei of condensation begin to act as nuclei of crystallization; therefore, at low temperatures the transitional liquid state is very short-lived, while at temperatures above the limits of the effectiveness of the given particles as centers of freezing, the supercooled liquid drops exist for a long time.

This theoretical deduction was confirmed experimentally by Weickmann, who proved that at a temperature of −40°C in the absence of nuclei of crystallization only condensation of the water drops takes place, while in the presence of nuclei of crystallization, the formation of ice from vapor begins only after saturation has been reached with respect to water, obviously by freezing of the condensed droplets. True, in rare individual cases, ice formation begins in the region of supersaturation with respect to ice, but this is explained by capillary condensation: solid particles with an uneven surface and hygroscopic particles can condense the moisture in the recesses of the surface, beginning at a relative humidity of about 70%.

Solid, liquid and gaseous substances (ozone, e.g., is included among gaseous substances) are the nuclei of condensation of atmospheric water vapor. Of these only the solid particles can serve as nuclei of freezing of the condensed droplets, in which case their effect differs considerably, according to their solubility in water. The degree of effectiveness of the insoluble particles as centers of freezing at a particular negative temperature is determined solely by their size: at optimum size they may be effective beginning at temperatures near 0°C. On the other hand, the widely distributed salt nuclei, which form from sprays of sea water and due to evaporation, become highly concentrated droplets and crystal particles, dissolve and reduce the temperature of the water of crystallization during condensation. The droplets that appear on salt nuclei will freeze, as a result of the insoluble nuclei present there, only after enough water has condensed to decrease the solution concentration sufficiently. Distilled water can be supercooled with ordinary nuclei of freezing, on an average to −10°C to −15°C, while the presence of salts further reduces the temperature of spontaneous freezing as a function of the concentration, just as the temperature of forced freezing of distilled water would decrease from 0°C. As a result, drops in the atmosphere condensed on salt nuclei (primarily NaCl) freeze at temperatures of −30° to −35°C; the occurrence of water clouds at lower temperatures is a rare exception.

Independently of Weickmann and by a somewhat different method, L. G. Kachurin (1951*a* and *b*) concluded that spontaneous sublimation probably does not occur in the atmosphere.[4]

---

[4] Of course, the absence of spontaneous sublimation, i.e., of nucleation directly from water vapor, does not in any way exclude the process of forced sublimation which goes on continuously in the atmosphere, i.e., the growth of already existing ice crystals due to the crystallization of water vapor. The ice crystals formed in this way are quite properly called sublimation crystals.

CHAPTER V

THE GROWTH AND FORM OF ICE CRYSTALS

To a certain extent the growth of a crystal particle which has reached critical size reminds one of the development of a new phase. The first molecule of each new layer of the space lattice at a given crystal face is connected with it on only one side, while the molecules next to the first are connected to the face on two sides, and then on three sides. The more firmly the molecule is bound, the smaller is its free energy and the lower is the supersaturation required for its stable attachment to the space lattice of the crystal. Therefore, if a new layer is to grow on a given crystal face, a new stable segment, a two-dimensional embryo, with the requisite total supersaturation or a corresponding fluctuation must form, and then this layer can grow freely even if the supersaturation is slight.

If the degree of supersaturation or supercooling is small, the rate of formation of two-dimensional embryos as a result of individual fluctuations is small compared to their rate of growth. Then the growth of the whole molecular layer ends before the embryo of the succeeding layer appears, and during growth the crystal maintains regular plane faces. Therefore, the slow growth of crystals is always continuous.

A crystal in equilibrium with its melt or vapor should assume a form corresponding to the free energy minimum in a given volume (Curie principle; see Curie, 1885, p. 145). For a liquid drop this form will be a sphere, and for a crystal, according to Wulff's theorem,[1] it will be a polyhedron somewhat similar to a sphere, with a constant ratio between the distance of the faces from the center and the magnitude of the surface tension of the given faces. Each face occupies a polyhedron segment inversely proportional to the fourth power of the index of the given face, so that an equilibrium form of the crystal should consist of a small number of low-index faces connected by rounded segments (L. D. Landau, 1950, p. 44). However, the difference in the equilibrium saturation or the

---

[1] See G. V. Vul'f (Wulff), (1895).

temperature of the different crystal faces is negligible (for a crystal of several cubic centimeters volume, it is of the order of 10^{-6}),[2] so that the slightest irregularity of the conditions in the surrounding medium disturbs the equilibrium form. A crystal of any form may be in equilibrium with the homogeneous medium, but this equilibrium is unstable and, with frequent fluctuations of temperature or saturation, the form approaches the equilibrium indicated above.

Real crystals, as a rule, have lower symmetry than ideal crystals, owing to the lower symmetry of the medium. However, in the case of rapid growth, the crystal form will differ from the equilibrium form for more than that reason alone. Generally, the growth forms of crystals differ essentially from the equilibrium forms.

A different magnitude of saturation or cooling is required for the growth of faces with different surface tensions. With small degrees of supercooling (supersaturation) there is practically no difference in the rate of growth of the faces, but as the supercooling increases the difference rapidly increases, some of the faces are suppressed, and the crystal, which was approximately isometric at first, departs more and more from the form corresponding to the energy minimum.

As a rule, *when the supersaturation (supercooling) is constant, the rate of growth of a crystal face increases with increasing specific surface energy of the face, i.e. with decreasing reticular density.* Evidently this is explained by the smaller reticular density associated with the smaller distance between the plane nets of the space lattice and, consequently, with a stronger molecular bond in the direction perpendicular to it. Therefore, two-dimensional embryos form most easily on these faces and their growth proceeds more rapidly. It is not difficult to see that in a polyhedron with obtuse angles the more rapidly growing faces (perpendicularly to its surface) will become smaller and disappear, since the growth paths of the edges between them converge (Fig. 13). As a result, the growing crystal is limited by the faces with the smallest rate of growth—the least surface tension—with the greatest reticular density (the law of Bravais).

In ice the reticular density of the basal plane (0001) is considerably greater than that of all other faces; consequently, the rate of growth of the basal plane in the direction of the main axis should be less than at the faces of a prism in the direction of the secondary axes. Hence, during growth there should be a development of plate crystals that are flattened along the main axis and bounded by the basal planes. Actually, *the plate form is the normal form* of freely growing ice crystals. As will be shown below, owing to the asymmetry of the surrounding

---

[2] [Unit not given. – D.K.]

medium, this form may be disrupted even by the formation of needle crystals; however, the growth type in this case remains unchanged, since such needles are extended in the basal plane and not along the main axis.

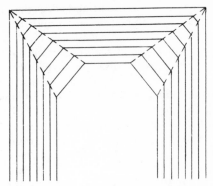

F_{IG}. 13.   Disappearance of rapidly growing crystal faces.

Just the same, the type of growth along secondary axes in the presence of a symmetrical external medium producing a plate form of crystals is characteristic only of the temperature interval from 0° to −15° and −20°C. At lower temperatures this type of growth is supplanted by preferred growth *along the main axis* leading to the formation of *prismatic, columnar crystals*.

A. B. Dobrowolski (1923, pp. 162–173) expressed the opinion, based on the general investigations of F. Bowden in 1818, that admixtures of some unstable gases in the air cause the columnar and needle growth of atmospheric ice crystals. This unfounded proposition does not consider the regular relationship between the crystal form and the temperature; this relationship was known to Dobrowolski through the observations of F. Heim in 1914, but was obscured by the contradictory data of W. Bentley, and only recently has been established more definitely by Weickmann (1949). Furthermore, until now there has been no satisfactory theoretical explanation of the influence of temperature on the type of crystal growth. The situation did not change even after the appearance of Weickmann's work (1949) which attempted to explain plate growth by the migration of molecules from the basal planes onto the prism faces. Weickmann merely states the problem without explaining the causes of this migration of the molecules and growth of the faces, and then proceeds from the erroneous assumption of L. Krastanow (1940) that the conditions for the formation of two-dimensional embryos are more favorable on the basal plane, in contradiction to the law of Bravais.

The surface of a freely-growing crystal is never a surface of equal supersaturation or supercooling but, as a rule, the supersaturation or supercooling is greater at the corners and edges than in the center of the faces. The greater the supersaturation and the more rapid the growth of the crystal, the more substance it will absorb from its surroundings per unit time and the greater will be the gradient of concentration it creates around itself. The same thing occurs with a crystal in a supercooled melt. However, in this case the crystal, instead of exhausting the supply of material in its environs, exhausts the "supply of cold," producing heat of crystallization and reducing the degree of supercooling. Consequently, a region of reduced concentration or reduced supercooling forms around the growing crystal. The rate of growth is determined by the rate of influx of matter in the vapor or the rate of removal of heat of crystallization in the melt, which, in turn, depend on the gradient of concentration or the temperature. It is clear that any projection from the surface of the crystal will occur under conditions more favorable for growth, since the increased gradient maintains a high concentration or supercooling there.

Despite this, the crystal faces can grow, remaining plane owing to the flow of matter along the surface of the crystal. According to Volmer's proposition (1921), confirmed by the work of a number of investigators, a thin film (less than 0.01 mm), which is more concentrated than the surrounding vapor or solution, exists on the surface of the growing crystal. Diffusion, or migration of the molecules, takes place in this layer, balancing the differences in the nourishment of the different parts of the surface. The surface flow is proportional to the influx of matter from the environment and amounts to as much as 7% of the influx. Recently it was established and recorded on movie film that crystal growth is accompanied by the formation of steps which move along the surface, for the most part from the corners toward the center of the faces. The surface layer, which moves along the face towards the step, is absorbed, building up a new layer of the crystal space lattice, while a diffusing layer is recreated on the surface from the rear of the step (Thomson, 1948, p. 409).

Moreover, after the critical supersaturation has been reached, the difference in the rate of nourishment of the projections and of the central parts of the faces can no longer be compensated for by the redistribution of matter along the surface. The edges and the apexes begin to grow more quickly than the faces, and continuous growth yields to *skeletal* growth (Lehmann, 1888). The disappearance of plane crystallographic elements, which are replaced by round surfaces, is characteristic of skeletal growth. The rapidly growing rays that appear in place of the edges lose all traces of crystallographic angles and become paraboloids, which are the more pointed, the greater the supersaturation (Papapetrou, 1935, p. 89).

After the main rays have grown out enough to assure sufficient supersaturation not only at the points but also between the rays, the growth rates begin to become anisotropic, the surface of the rays near the point becomes wavy and, owing to increased nourishment, the crests of the waves develop into lateral rays. In what follows, lateral rays of second and higher orders may form in the same manner, and the simple skeletal growth becomes *dendritic*.

In the central part of the skeletal crystal, during its growth, supersaturation can fall below the critical value. Then the round forms become unstable, the rays which survived the growth process evaporate or become disconnected in the narrow parts at the base and there is a tendency toward increased width with development of plane faces. Thus, single sharp rays or dendrites may grow simultaneously on the periphery of a crystal, while plane elements appear in the center.

Skeletal forms of ice crystals occur both in plate and in columnar types of growth. In the plate type, the rays develop in the direction of the secondary crystallographic axes, forming simple or dendritic stars, typical of snowflakes. When the nourishment from different directions is irregular, asymmetrical skeletal forms with four, three, or two rays develop. Ice needles which extend along one of the secondary axes are an extreme case of asymmetric growth. The skeletal forms which extend along the main axis are hollow prisms

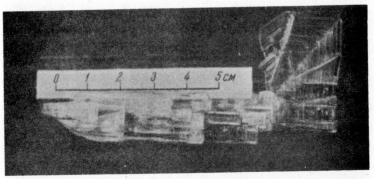

Fig. 14.   Skeletal sublimation ice crystal elongated along the main axis.
(Photograph by N. V. Cherepanov.)

and funnels that form as a result of the growth of the projecting edges alone and not of the whole basal plane (Figs. 14, 15); sometimes they consist of bundles of cylindrical stems oriented along the intersection lines of the faces of the prism and the monohedron and inter-connected by bridges along the edges of the prism. When growth is slower, solid faces form, bearing striations, i.e., lines of growth parallel to the base.

FIG. 15.   Skeletal sublimation ice crystals elongated along the main axis.
(Photograph by N. V. Cherepanov.)

Regularly bounded ice crystals may exist under conditions of equilibrium with the melt and the vapor or under conditions of slow continuous growth. With rapid growth, skeletal and dendritic forms occur, characterized by points, rounded surfaces of rays, and con-cave angles between them, while with melting or sublimation the entire surface of the crystal rounds out and evens out. Owing to the comparatively high reaction rate, the form of the ice crystals is very responsive to external conditions; every change in the degree of saturation or cooling immediately causes a change in the forms that are capable of growing or maintaining themselves.

ICE CRYSTALS IN WATER

The conditions of crystallization of water and water vapor differ substantially. It is difficult to investigate the form of free ice crystals which develop in water, because the supercooling responsible for their formation soon leads to their congelation and usually stops only after the whole mass of water in a given volume has crystallized.

The primary free crystals of ice in water may be skeletal or solid, depending upon circumstances. A rapid removal of generated heat is essential for the formation of skeletal crystals from water, and since this heat may be transferred only to the surrounding medium, a sufficiently strong supercooling of water is required. When water is supercooled to $-12°C$, the so-called linear rate of crystallization of ice from water reaches 5 m/min (Tammann and Büchner, 1935). Under natural conditions, supercooling sufficient for skeletal growth is often noted in the first stage of crystallization in the surface layer of water which releases heat by radiation and as a result of cold air convection. Supercooling soon decreases abruptly in still water owing to the emitted heat of crystallization, but considerable supercooling is maintained in rapidly moving water during the whole process of ice formation. Furthermore, despite supercooling, the crystallization of water always takes place in the temperature interval typified by growth in the direction of the secondary axes.

For the most part, skeletal crystals of ice in water develop near the surface and assume completely different forms, depending on the position of the embryo with respect to the water surface. Long and narrow sharp-pointed needles usually develop during intense super-cooling and rapid growth in the first stage of crystallization on the free surface of the water. In contrast, flat and broad rays with edges notched at an angle of 60° on one or (more rarely) on both sides expand rapidly along the surface from the shores or the walls of the objects which serve as centers of crystallization. These feathery leaf-like or sabre-like rays grow in the direction of the secondary crystallographic axis $[\bar{2}110]$ and provide short embryonic offshoots in the direction of one or both of the other secondary axes $[1\bar{2}10]$ and $[11\bar{2}0]$,[3] with the main axis $[0001]$ perpendicular to the surface of the water. Consequently, the feathery rays correspond to the rays of stellar snowflakes and develop asymmetrically because of the position of the embryos at the edge of the water surface, which leads to rapid growth in one direction only.

Symmetrical hexagonal ice crystals with a vertical main axis are much scarcer at the water surface; they are skeletal only along the edges. In the central part, however, where supercooling is eliminated, the rays always grow together, forming a continuous plate. The primary crystals are from 0.1 mm to several millimeters thick, are completely transparent and often are difficult to distinguish in water. When a small number of embryos appears, crystals may become very large. For example, symmetrical hexagonal crystals up to 1 m in diameter have been observed (Vadilo, 1951), and single rays, growing out from a shore, can reach a size of several meters.

The described crystallographic nature of plane feathery ice rays was established correctly as long ago as 1895 (Mügge, 1895), but

---

[3] [These are $[0001]$, $[0\bar{1}00]$ and $[00\bar{1}0]$ in the original; the change was suggested by Prof. John W. Glen. – D.K.]

F. Klocke's (1879) erroneous opinion that narrow sharp-pointed needles extend in the direction of the main axis long prevailed. Not until 1921 was the opinion expressed that the needles are simply parts of the basal plates, extending linearly along the surface with an edge oriented toward the water surface (Kalb, 1921). Indeed, my optic-crystallographic studies, conducted with the Fedorov universal stage, showed that the optic axis of long ice needles is always perpendicular to the geometric axis and, as a rule, is more or less parallel to the water surface. Evidently, ice needle formation is the result of asymmetrical growth along the line of intersection of the basal plane of the crystal with the thin supercooled layer at the water surface. If the supercooling includes a considerable water layer, the sharp-pointed needles expanding along the surface will continue to grow downward, forming more or less vertical plates, usually with serrate edges, corresponding to plane rays on the surface of the water, but set on edge. Of course, this situation will continue only when the needles grow together at their ends; otherwise, as the needles become plates, they lose equilibrium and, rising, lie flat on the surface of the water.

Evidently, the main crystallographic axis of an ice needle is relatively horizontal simply because only embryos oriented in this fashion grow into needles. If the axis is more inclined, the crystal develops more in the basal plane and before freezing together with other crystals turns flat on the water surface with its main axis vertical.

During needle growth, the magnitude of supercooling decreases quickly and the skeletal growth becomes solid. Then thin ice disks, usually a few millimeters in diameter and lying flat on the water surface, form in the intervals between the needles. Under conditions of slight supercooling, ice disks form during the first stage of crystallization. The disks are crystals that grow in the basal plane, and the equilibrium conditions on the horizontal surface of the water determine the vertical position of their characteristic main axis (Mügge, 1895, 1900). Such disks, described by Al'tberg (1939, pp. 49, 57, and elsewhere), form in slightly supercooled water. With increased supercooling, the disks can change into hexagonal plates and skeletal forms (Bentley, 1907).

When water freezes to a hard surface consisting of a substance that is not isomorphous with ice and when there is no possibility of epitactic growth, plate crystals appear, in most cases with the main axis normal to the surface of freezing.[4]

---

[4] For the growth of ice crystals onto a solid base, see Part II, Chapter IX.

ATMOSPHERIC CRYSTALS

The conditions of atmospheric water-vapor crystallization on existing embryos, i.e., frozen water drops, are more variable than in water. Study of the infinite variety of forms of sublimation crystals of ice began as early as the sixteenth century, when Olaus Magnus, Bishop of Uppsala (1555), published the first sketches of snowflakes. An immense literature containing descriptions and classifications of snow and hoarfrost crystals is now available, but we cannot possibly treat it here.[5] The following is a brief summary of the snowflake classification of Nakaya and Sekido (1943):

I. Needle crystals: simple needles and combination of needles. Rarely encountered.

II. Columnar crystals: simple (pyramids, prisms with a pyramid [bullet] and prisms) and combination (prism with pyramid [bullet] and prism). Rarely encountered.

III. Plane crystals: regular crystals developed in a single plane (simple, dendritic and sector stars, tablets, tablets with angular appendages and stellar crystals with tabularly expanded ends of the branches). Encountered most frequently. Crystals with two nuclei; irregular crystals; stars with a spatial distribution of the branches. Encountered often.

IV. Combination of columnar and plane crystals: prisms with plane crystals; dodecahedral and octodecahedral crystals, combination of prisms, pyramids and plane crystals. Rarely encountered.

V. Columnar crystals with extended side planes. Very rarely encountered.

VI. Granulated [rimed] crystals and graupel: slightly granulated crystals, thick granulated plates, coarse snow.

VII. Irregular snow particles.

Plate snowflakes (with a mean ratio of thickness to diameter of about 1 : 50) are most numerous, comprising around 75% of the total, and of these, dendritic skeletal forms predominate. Snow crystals vary in size from 0.3 to 5 mm.

---

[5] The following works on the classification of snowflakes are most worthy of attention: G. Hellmann (1893), G. Nordenskiöld (1893), I. V. Shukevich (1910), W. A. Bentley and W. J. Humphreys (1931), U. Nakaya and Y. Sekido (1936, 1943), V. I. Arnol'd-Aliab'ev (1939) and A. D. Zamorskii (1951).

The explanation of the conditions of formation of various types of snowflakes was long delayed because these conditions were recorded at the earth's surface during the fall of snowflakes and not at the level of snowflake formation in the atmosphere. Furthermore, the physical conditions are quite different at different heights and one snowfall often consists of snowflakes of many kinds, formed from different clouds and parts of clouds and falling alternately, and in part simultaneously as well. The origin of the various types of snowflakes was not established until snowflakes had been produced artificially, and particularly, not until they had been studied from an airplane at their point of origin in the atmosphere.

U. Nakaya (Nakaya, Toda and Maruyama, 1943) established the values of the absolute supersaturation and rate of growth of the basic forms of snowflakes (Table 1) by producing snow crystals artificially.

TABLE 1

Form of snowflake	Supersaturation mm Hg	Mean rate of growth, mm/h
Needles	—	0.5
Prisms with lateral wings	1.6	0.5
Prisms	1.7	—
Pyramids	2.2	—
Plates	3.5	0.7
Simple stars	4.4	1.3
Dendritic stars	6.6	4.6
Long needles	7.5	—

Snowflakes of the slowly growing forms do not occur at temperatures above −20°C and are abundant at very low temperatures; on the other hand, stars do not form at temperatures below −23°C and reach their maximum development at temperatures of −15°C to −20°C. The rapid rate of growth of long needles and the fact that their fall is observed only at a relatively high temperature (−5°C) affords a basis for assuming that perhaps they do not extend in the direction of the main axis, like columnar crystals, but along one of the secondary axes and that they belong to the asymmetric plate type of crystal.

Nakaya's experiments have proved that all the various forms of snowflakes occur in ordinary air, without any special admixtures, because of differences in temperature, humidity and convection.

The results of airplane investigations (Weickmann, 1949) of the conditions of formation of the different types of snowflakes in the atmosphere are of still greater interest. He found that skeletal growth of ice crystals can occur in different parts of the troposphere, but that the type of skeletal growth differs with the section of the troposphere. In the lower troposphere, where high temperatures (0° to −15°C), high absolute humidities and comparatively low relative supersaturations with respect to ice prevail, plate skeletal forms (stars) develop. Higher up, where the temperature is lower (−30°C and lower), where the absolute humidity is low and the relative supersaturation with respect to ice is high, columnar skeletal forms (hollow prisms) develop. Between these two regions is a zone of continuous crystal growth, where plate forms become prismatic; thick plates and solid prisms are characteristic of this zone. Single crystals of this same type also occur in the upper zone of Cirrostratus clouds where, due to slow ascending motion and cooling, capillary condensation on the most effective nuclei and ice formation can occur even before saturation with respect to water is reached.

Thus, one can make a rough division of the troposphere into the following three zones:

(1) *The lower troposphere* (low supersaturation with respect to ice, high absolute humidity, temperature from 0° to −15°C), *Nimbostratus cloud zone; stars* and *plates*.

(2) *The middle troposphere* (moderate supersaturation with respect to ice, moderate absolute humidity, temperature −15° to −30°C), *Altostratus* and *Altocumulus cloud zone;* solid crystals— *thick plates* and *prisms*.

(3) *The high troposphere* (low absolute humidity, temperature −30°C to −60°C), *Cirrus cloud zone.*

    (a) Cirrostratus clouds (average supersaturation with respect to ice), *single solid crystals—plates* and *prisms*.

    (b) Convective Cirrus clouds (high supersaturation with respect to ice), *hollow prisms*.

A conspicuous fall of ice crystals in the atmosphere begins after the crystals reach a size of about 50μ. When falling, the snowflakes pass through ever-changing temperature and humidity conditions, which are reflected in the form and structure of the snowflakes. The final form of the crystals on reaching the earth is the combined product of all conditions encountered on their path of fall. Snowflakes of different form fall differently; for the most part they do not rotate unless forced to by the air motion. The difference in the conditions of growth or dissolution of the upper and lower sides of the snow-flakes, leading to the development of asymmetric forms, is associated with this.

The irregular growth of atmospheric plate crystals in the direction of the main axis gives them a characteristic structure of three or more layers. Usually the middle layer, which receives less nourishment, grows more slowly than the outer layers which grow along the edges. In the transition from skeletal growth to solid growth in the center of the star, or as the entire star becomes a plate, in the case of decreased supersaturation, the intervals between the rays become grown over; the outer layers grow together, leaving numerous cavities (sometimes up to several hundred in a single snowflake) within the crystal. Cavities form similarly in columnar crystals as well. The primary cavities within the snowflakes are always regular, oval or rod-shaped and, for the most part, are distributed symmetrically. The total volume of the cavities is negligible compared with the volume of ice, so that the snowflake density is close to the specific weight of pure ice, of the order of 0.914–0.9168. The cavities are filled with air having a pressure equal to the atmospheric pressure at the moment they were enclosed.

When supersaturation is intense, new crystals are produced in addition to those that formed earlier, and the embryos, falling more slowly, settle primarily on the lower surface of the descending crystals and fuse with them. This leads to the widespread phenomenon of *"riming" of snowflakes*, i.e., the coating of snowflakes (primarily from one side) with tiny crystal particles of different form growing at an angle to the snowflakes.

Generally, the rapid growth of sublimation crystals in the atmosphere is caused by strong supersaturation with respect to ice, associated with the presence of a multitude of supercooled water droplets in the same space. Clouds which produce snow do not differ in form from most rain clouds, since they too consist primarily of tiny droplets of supercooled water. Very often the supercooled droplets settle on the surface of snowflakes, freezing instantly on contact. This produces the so-called *"granulated" crystals*.

Usually snowflakes grow simultaneously by sublimation of water vapor and by freezing of the precipitating supercooled water droplets. Owing to the rapidity of freezing, these latter form granules or grains on the surface, but in their structural orientation they are inseparable parts of the basic crystal which caused their freezing. According to Nakaya, the average size of the drops freezing to the crystals is 0.03 mm (varying from 0.013–0.045 mm), which coincides with the size of cloud drops.

Upon further intensification of the feeding of the crystal by super-cooled drops, the crystal loses its regular form and becomes a spherical grain of snow hail, white from the numerous air inclusions which remained in the intervals between the drops that had not coagulated completely. If the crystal falls into a part of the cloud with large drops, these drops, owing to their smaller specific surface and, consequently, their slower rate of freezing, fuse with the crystal more completely before crystallization. Under such conditions, a more transparent ice hail or fine hail forms, and the hail granules are from 1 to 5 mm in diameter.

With especially strong supersaturation and rapid condensation, analogous formations reach a considerably larger size, in individual cases up to 15 cm in diameter, due in part to the combination of several primary grains. They reach typical development only in warm weather. Having a great speed of fall, the hailstones are more strongly supercooled and, falling into the zone of positive tempera-tures, continue to grow because of the non-supersaturated water and the vapor which is highly supersaturated with respect to them, until they exhaust their supply of cold. In this last stage of growth, they are covered with a layer of transparent ice of the glazed frost type.

The last member of this series of solid precipitations is *ice rain*, grains of transparent ice which form by the freezing of descending raindrops.

According to the observations of A. D. Zamorskii (1951), half the total amount of solid atmospheric precipitation in Leningrad is formed by the freezing of supercooled water. Since the sublimation ice in the atmosphere also grows (for the most part) by distillation from liquid drops onto crystals in supercooled clouds, the solid atmospheric precipitations originate almost exclusively from super-cooled water.

Each type of ice formation of the free atmosphere, from sub-limation snowflakes to ice rain, has its homologue in precipitation that forms directly on the surface of solid objects. In this case the precipitations that are identical in form and structure differ depend-ing on whether they were formed by supersaturation of the vapors and by supercooling of the water droplets in the air, or by super-cooling of the surface on which the precipitation forms. This latter group, which includes *rime* that forms during radiational cooling and deposits that form after advective warming, ranging from *subli-mation deposit* to the so-called *solid deposit* which forms by freezing of precipitated rain or drizzle, provides only a very small amount of precipitation. In contrast to this group, the formations of the first group, which include various forms of *hoarfrost* and *glazed frost*, may play a very substantial role, and in some mountain regions they are the dominant form of atmospheric precipitation.

This group includes sublimation crystals that develop in the empty spaces among rocks, in the pores of the snow cover, in glacier crevasses, in soil cracks, in friable rocks and native rocks, and in caves. By origin all these are related to hoarfrost.[6] In size they are usually limited to the hollows in which they develop. In cracks, monocrystals reach a diameter of 10 cm, while composite crystals reach a diameter of 30–50 cm; monocrystals up to 60 cm long have been observed in caves.

The sublimation crystals of rime and hoarfrost are as varied as snowflakes and differ from them chiefly by their unilateral restricted growth, due to the influence of the surface on which the sublimation takes place and the neighboring crystals. The sublimation crystals belong to all forms and types of growth, viz., the solid and the skeletal, plate, columnar and needle, and often they form complex irregular aggregates (Figs. 15, 16). We shall not stop here to describe the forms of sublimation crystals, because there is an abundant literature on the subject,[7] but we will merely say that among these crystals, more than among crystals of the free atmosphere, one finds spiral, tubular and funnel-shaped skeletal forms, and the widely distributed threadlike formations, the trichites; among the plate crystals one finds large, completely smooth tablets, similar to window glass.

Plate sublimation crystals grow onto a base primarily by the edge

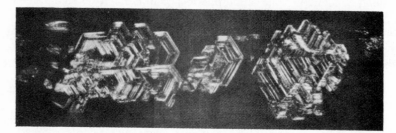

Fig. 16.   Intergrowths of plate crystals of depth hoar taken from glacier crevasses. (Photograph by N. V. Cherepanov.)

---

[6] In Russian literature in recent times the incorrect term "depth rime" has been used extensively to mean the new sublimation formations in the snow layer. This is a translation of Paulcke's term (1934) *der Tiefenreif*. Since these formations are not caused by radiational cooling, they should be called "depth hoar," not "depth rime."

[7] For a systematic survey, see A. B. Dobrowolski (1923, pp. 267–292) and B. P. Veinberg (1940, pp. 328–338).

of the plate, and columnar crystals by the end of the main axis, which provides preferential conditions of growth for those crystals whose greatest growth rate (i.e., whose greatest diameter) is directed toward the source of nourishment; in air they are oriented normal to the surface of accretion.

Cave sublimation crystals, the largest and most accessible for study, have long attracted the attention of investigators.[8] The Kungur ice cave in the Urals is widely known; its ice has been described by V. Ia. Al'tberg and V. F. Troshin (1931) and by M. P. Golovkov (1939). Large solid crystals, which afford the best possibilities for goniometric study, are found under conditions of slow growth in caves and in crevices and crevasses. The largest crystals of this type have been described by N. N. Stulov (1949).

---

[8] Regarding cave ice, see G. A. Maksimovich (1947).

Part II

The Petrology of Ice

General Questions of Ice Petrology

CHAPTER VI

ICE AS A ROCK FORMATION

Ice was considered a rock formation even before petrography became an independent discipline, when rocks were studied merely as geological bodies that play a role in the structure and history of the earth's crust, not as mineral aggregates of a specific composition and structure. Ice was first classified as a rock by G. F. Link,[1] after general attention had been drawn to the discovery of the body of a mammoth in fossil ice ("amidst the blocks of ice") in the Lena delta; some of the remains of this animal were taken to St. Petersburg in 1807 by M. F. Adams. Following Link, the fossil ice in the earth's crust was called rock by A. Chamisso,[2] the naturalist on the Russian *Riurik* expedition, and by K. E. Baer (1838, p. 187). A. F. Middendorf (1862, p. 474), in giving an account of the scientific results of his Siberian journey, wrote: "An essential feature of icy soil is that in it ice becomes a true rock and comprises part of the geognostic rock stratification." E. Tol' (1897) expressed this thought in his term "stony ice," which became widely used to designate underground or fossil ice.[3]

---

[1] The author was unable to obtain Link's work.

[2] *Puteshestvie v Iuzhnyi okean i v Beringov proliv dlia otyskaniia severovostochnogo morskogo prokhoda, predpriniatoe v 1815, 1816, 1817 i 1818 godakh na korable "Riurike" pod nachal'stvom flota leitenanta Kotsebu* (Voyage to the South Seas and Bering Strait for the purpose of finding the Northeast Passage, undertaken in the years 1815–1818 on the ship "Riurik" under the command of Naval Lieutenant Kotsebu), Part III, St. Petersburg, 1823, p. 352. (Arctic Bibliography No. 9192.)

[3] M. M. Ermolaev (1932a) attempted to attach a different meaning to the term "stony ice," using this name to define only those fossil ice masses which are subject to erosion and which develop positive and negative forms of relief.

In this interpretation, inherited from the early stages of development of petrography, ice is considered a rock formation only if it comprises part of the earth's immobile crust, evidently in contrast to the other types of ice, which are not classified as rocks.

As petrography advanced, researchers gradually began to pay heed to other indices that provide a basis for considering ice a rock formation. The well-known petrographer B. Cotta (1858,.p. 81) drew an analogy between ice and lava as products of the hardening of melts. Two years later the Russian philosopher N. G. Chernyshevskii[4] expressed the same opinion. A. Heim (1885) pointed out the similarity between the behavior of glaciers and rock landslides. After completing his work in Greenland, T. Chamberlin (1894–1897, 1904) concluded that glacier movement was of a "solid" non-fluid nature, and classified glaciers as masses of monomineralic crystalline rock. O. Mügge carried the comparison still further (Mügge, 1900), classifying snow and firn masses as sedimentary rocks, and the continental and glacier ice produced from them through recrystallization as crystalline schists.

Later many geologists, petrographers and glaciologists identified the various types of ice as rock formations. The basis for such identification was sometimes an analogy with origin from a melt (A. B. Dobrowolski, E. Blackwelder, F. Iu. Levinson-Lessing, M. P. Golovkov, S. G. Parkhomenko, P. Niggli, P. F. Shvetsov), sometimes the features held in common with sedimentation, metamorphic or weathering processes (P. N. Chirvinskii, P. P. Pilipenko, A. B. Dobrowolski, E. Blackwelder, W. Paulcke, B. Sander, N. I. Tolstikhin, J. Bernal, P. Niggli), and sometimes a similarity between the mechanism of glacier and rock movement (H. Philipp, O. Ampferer, H. Cloos, R. Chamberlin, L. Hawkes, B. Sander, P. Niggli). The various types of ice, according to their origin belong to the basic rock groups, namely, magmatic, sedimentary and metamorphic rocks, in particular tectonites. On the other hand, cases of the gravitational movement of non-ice rocks down slopes or valleys have been compared with the flow of ice ("salt glaciers" in Iran and "rock glaciers" in Canada). Thus, at present, the genetic features of ice, not its mode of occurrence, are considered most important. According to current concepts, any accumulation of ice is a rock, whether it lies

---

[4] "This stone ['water-ice,' Shumskii] differs from those things called 'stones' in everyday speech only in that it melts at a very low temperature, whereas ordinary stones melt only at an extremely high temperature," N. G. Chernyshevskii, "Antropologicheskii printsip v filosofii" (Anthropological principle in philosophy), *Sovremennik*, 80(4), 1860; *Izbrannye Filosofskie Sochineniia*, 3, 1951, p. 194.

between other rocks, above them, or on the surface of water. If the body of ice is not part of what is considered to be the earth's crust, the concept of what constitutes the boundaries of the earth's crust should be expanded, not the concept of ice as a rock formation restricted.

However, one must not overlook certain differences between ice and other rocks, which make glaciology a borderland of the sciences of geological and geographical cycles. Most ice masses (with the exception of underground ice types) are parts of the water cycle, and the spatial distribution of all ice masses conforms to the law of geographic zonality. True, many other rocks have characteristic zonal distribution, but in such cases the relationship to climate is always indirect, through formative agents.

Recognition of ice as a rock expands the scope of processes studied under geology by adding processes which form ice bodies in the atmosphere and the hydrosphere. In this case, water must be examined as an analogue of magma, playing the same role in the formation of surface rocks as magma plays in the formation of rocks deep within the earth's crust. Only then does ice assume all the features required to complete the concept "rock formation," namely: it must play a substantial role in the structure of the earth's crust, it must form facies with constant characteristic structure and composition, it cannot be formed directly from the ambient masses, but is bound to the particular geological process which is also responsible for the structure and mode of occurrence of the given ice body.

The concept of ice as a rock was expressed most completely and systematically by A. B. Dobrowolski (1931) in his petrographic classification of ice.[5] He divides natural ice into the following groups.

I.   Magmatic Ice Rocks

A. Rocks that originate from continuous magma which is not separated into drops.

   (*a*) *Ice cover*, which forms on the surface of relatively calm water.

   (*b*) *The ice of streams*, which forms within more or less rapidly flowing water.

   (*c*) *Bottom ice*, originating at and attached to the bottom of streams.

---

[5] The basic principles of the classification were expressed by A. B. Dobrowolski in his monograph *Historja naturalna lodu* (Natural history of ice), which was published in 1923, but had already been completed in 1916.

B. Rock originating from magma which is separated into drops, *mountain rime* (or solid deposit).

C. Composite rock, i.e., *frozen ground*.

II.　Sedimentary Ice Rocks

Different stages of metamorphism of the snow cover.

(a) *Snow cover:* 1. protected from the wind; 2. exposed to the wind—clastic rock, subject to wind erosion.

(b) *Firn snow.*

(c) *Firn ice.*

(d) *Glacier ice.* In regenerated glaciers—coarse clastic rock.

Among more recent classifications of ice rock formations, those of W. Paulcke and N. I. Tolstikhin should be mentioned.[6] Paulcke's classification (1934), which also includes atmospheric ice crystals, actually differs little from Dobrowolski's in the part that deals with ice rocks. However, Paulcke's artificial and clumsy terminology, which anticipates factual knowledge, his excessive detail in some places and omissions in others, make his classification practically useless.

Tolstikhin's (1936) classification of ice and ice rock formations is quite another matter; he used different principles of classification as his basis. One of the fundamental differences between it and Dobrowolski's classification is that Tolstikhin classifies all forms of ice as sedimentary rock, using the term "sedimentary upward rocks" for Dobrowolski's "magmatic rocks."[7] This was done in order to eliminate magmatic and metamorphic rocks from the classification, because the concept of metamorphism, in his opinion, is not applicable to ice. He divides all ice rock formations into the products of separation from the atmosphere and from water. In each of these groups he distinguishes ice of surface and subsurface origin, and for most of the species he differentiates between contemporary and fossil facies. In the part dealing with the products

---

[6] The other ice classifications are not petrographic classifications, e.g., those of V. I. Vernadskii (1933) and G. Seligman (1936), or else they deal only with certain groups of ice rock formations, e.g., the classifications of E. Leffingwell (1919), M. I. Sumgin (1940), H. Bader (1939) and others.

[7] We will disregard the polymineralic rocks with ice cement, which belong to the study of permafrost, not structural glaciology.

of separation from water, Tolstikhin's classification is considerably more detailed than Dobrowolski's; however, in this instance the division into species is not based on structural-genetic characteristics, but on the form and mode of occurrence of ice bodies, e.g., the ice of rivers, lakes, seas, icings, etc. In the petrology of ice it is very important to establish the true principles of a classification which will summarize all knowledge in the field. Should the ice that originates from the freezing of water be classified as magmatic or sedimentary rock?

In a more recent work, Tolstikhin (1941) subscribes essentially to Dobrowolski's point of view, which had also been expressed independently by O. K. Lange (1925), that water should be regarded as a surface analogue of magma. Natural water in itself is always a mineral solution, rich in volatile components in which, as Lange indicated, H_2O plays the role of the solvent, similar to silicic acid in magma. Crystallization in natural water follows the eutectic system, which in most cases is also true of magma.

In classifying ice formed by the freezing of water as a sedimentary rock, Tolstikhin also points out that the principal difference between such ice and sedimentary rocks is that ice, like magmatic rocks, is produced by the crystallization of the solvent itself, whereas sedimentary rocks are produced by the precipitation of dissolved substances or of mechanical admixtures. Here Tolstikhin's criticism of Dobrowolski's classification rests solely on his objection to the term "magmatic," which Dobrowolski himself admits has its faults.

Undoubtedly, in the terminology it must be emphasized that water is not magma, but, according to the theory of geochemical differentiation, is merely the end product of the fractional crystallization of magma, and ice formation in the thermal sequence is farther removed from the crystallization of magmas than is crystallization from aqueous solutions. Therefore, recognizing that some of the ice types belong to the group of rocks that originate by freezing from a melt, we will not call them "magmatic," but will adopt the quite accurate and genetic term proposed by B. P. Veinberg (1940, p. 16), "congelation ice," i.e., ice formed by freezing. S. V. Kalesnik's term (1939, p. 21) "hydrogenous," in contrast to "atmogenous," is less appropriate from the genetic point of view, since it does not indicate the process of formation, but only the medium from which the ice is separated. Thus, we shall distinguish two types of primary non-metamorphosed ice rocks: *congelation* ice, corresponding to Dobrowolski's group "A" of magmatic rock, and *sedimentary* ice. Included in the latter are the atmospheric sublimation and congelation types of ice[8] (freshly fallen snow, graupel, rime and hoarfrost) precipitated on a solid surface, which are analogous to the chemical sediments of water basins, and the mechanical deposits of ice fragments.

As noted above, Tolstikhin is of the opinion that metamorphism is not applicable to ice, whereby he differs not only from Dobrowolski, but also from a number of well-known petrographers, particularly Niggli (1939).

In petrology the term "metamorphism" is used in various senses. In the broad sense, the term denotes any change, any transformation of a rock formation, while in the narrow sense it denotes a more or less profound change (occurring in the solid state without melting) of the mineralogical, and, for the most part, chemical composition and structure of the rock due to high temperature and pressure or chemical reactions. Actually, it might be objected that metamorphism in the narrow sense cannot be applied to ice, principally because the chemical composition of the ice is too simple for it to experience mineralogical changes. Ice, owing to its specific properties, undergoes profound changes caused by high temperature and pressure at the earth's surface, not deep in the earth's crust. We shall use the term metamorphism in the broad sense, to include not only dislocation metamorphism and recrystallization, but also the changes in the snow cover during winter, corresponding to the diagenesis of other sediments and the processes of infiltration and the remelting of the ice rock by melt water, corresponding to the ultrametamorphism, anatexis and palingenesis of other rocks. From this point of view, the firnified snow cover, glacier ice, and recrystallized congelation ice belong to the group of metamorphic ice rocks.

It is doubtful whether the introduction of an age index (division of ice into contemporary and fossil) is of value in a petrographic classification. Time is only a form of existence of matter and without movement of the matter the concept time has no meaning. To attach meaning to duration in a petrographic classification, one

---

[8] The fact that sedimentary rocks, which are contrasted with congelation ice rocks, form by sedimentation of both sublimation and congelation atmospheric ice, is not a contradiction or a deficiency in terminology, since it corresponds fully to the actual state of affairs and remains, whatever the terminology may be. The apparent contradiction does not exist, because congelation ice in the atmosphere represents particles of the congelation ice mineral, while the products of the freezing of water not separated into drops are congelation rock formations. Sublimation ice is the opposite of the congelation ice mineral, while sedimentary ice, which forms by sedimentation of both sublimation ice crystals and congelation ice crystals, is the opposite of congelation ice rock.

must demonstrate the process of rock transformation which takes place during that time. From the petrographic point of view, fossil glacier ice does not differ from contemporary glacier ice unless there is a difference in composition or texture, but Tolstikhin's classification does not indicate whether such a difference actually exists or what constitutes such a difference.

Similarly, the place of formation and the mode of occurrence of the ice as such cannot serve as the basis of a petrographic classification, because such a classification should be concerned only with differences in composition and texture resulting from a petrogenic process. The geological characteristics in the given case are superficial. This is the only way to avoid a situation in which ice types that are completely identical petrographically must be classified as different types, depending on whether they are found on a river or a lake, in a glacier or an iceberg, and whether they are formed from suprapermafrost waters, or from underground waters outside the permafrost region, etc.

Tolstikhin's classification shows a tendency toward detail not based on the petrographic study of ice; consequently he had to use characteristics that were not petrogenetic.

A genetic classification of the ice rock formations must be based on the study of their formation and transformation processes. Such a study, using accurate physical and structural-petrographic methods, has only just begun. The first steps in this direction were taken almost simultaneously and independently by M. P. Golovkov (1936), M. Perutz (Perutz and Seligman, 1939), H. Bader (1939) and M. Demorest (1941). The methods of structural petrology were practically neglected in the most important previous works (E. Sorge, H. Ahlmann, A. Wegener, H. Philipp and a number of earlier authors).

Before undertaking a survey of the ice formation processes and the composition and structural features attending them, we shall characterize briefly the role of impurities in ice and describe the basic methods of the petrographic study of ice.

CHAPTER VII

IMPURITIES IN ICE

Ice always contains foreign matter which forms inclusions within the ice crystals or between them. In their aggregate state these inclusions may be solid, liquid or gaseous. Atmospheric gases and water-soluble minerals, i.e., salts, are inevitable components of any ice; moreover, under certain conditions ice contains water, and some types of ice have abundant inclusions of water-insoluble minerals and rocks.

All the components of ice form a *mixture* and react to each other only physically, if we ignore chemical erosion of the mineral impurities in the liquid phase. Hence, even during its most profound transformations, ice experiences only structural, not mineralogical changes.

In an ice rock, the rock-forming mineral, ice, plays the main role, even though the actual amount of ice may be very small; for instance, in combination with water the ice may amount to 40%, while in combination with air (in snow) the ice may amount to only fractions of a percent. In such cases, ice forms the rigid skeleton, whose interstices contain other components. Only when the number of inclusions exceeds a certain limit, beyond which the ice skeleton can no longer cohere, does the formation cease to be ice. In this case it converts into a suspension of ice particles in air or in water, e.g., falling snow or snow blown about by the wind, sludge formed during water freezing, and snow gruel during the melting of the snow cover. In mixtures of ice and salt or other mineral particles, the resultant rock formation cannot be called ice, even though there are fewer inclusions than in the above instance, because of the basic change in its physicochemical properties, and though the ice skeleton, which now plays the role of cement, remains intact. This occurs in layers of the hypereutectic, which transforms into efflorescences of salt, penetrated by ice crystals, found on the bottom of salt lakes that are intermittent and subject to freezing, and also in the so-called ice soils and icy rock formations that constitute a transition to frozen rocks.

Thus, if any one of the four secondary components of ice, viz., air, water, salts and other minerals, exceeds the critical limit, a qualitative change is produced, which no longer allows one to view the given system as an ice rock formation but places it within the sphere of one of the allied disciplines, viz., meteorology, hydrology, halurgy or cryopedology.

Ice crystals or parts of ice crystals coming into contact with each other are quite capable of "freezing together," which may be caused by recrystallization, sublimation or regelation, depending on circumstances. Therefore, the fine cracks in ice cannot last long. "Healthy," i.e., unmelted and undisintegrated polycrystalline ice is a rock impermeable for liquids and gases, in contrast to high-temperature rocks which are incapable of recrystallization at the earth's surface and, as a rule, are permeated by a system of fine cracks. In this connection, a genetic classification worked out for intercrystalline inclusions in minerals can be applied to inclusions in polycrystalline ice, even though they may be situated between the crystals.

The following categories of inclusions may be distinguished on the basis of origin, following G. Laemmlein (1929) and N. P. Ermakov (1948, p. 53):

(1) *Primary* or *syngenetic* inclusions which form simultaneously with the ice:

   (*a*) autogenous, which originate from a parent melt or solution (vapor);

   (*b*) xenogenous, which are foreign to the parent melt;

(2) *Secondary* or *epigenetic* inclusions, which appear after the ice has formed:

   (*a*) hypogenous, which are embedded in the cracks or pores of the rocks and are isolated as a result of their regeneration;

   (*b*) hypergenous, which fill the unclosed cracks and pores that communicated with the surface.

GASES

Gaseous inclusions in the ice originate either directly from the atmosphere or from the freezing of water. As a rule, the chemical composition of a gaseous mixture in ice is similar to that of atmospheric air, although in some cases in congelation ice there are also gases of biochemical and chemical origin. The gaseous inclusions of air in ice may belong to any of the enumerated genetic types.

The following are classified as autogenous inclusions:

(1) Air bubbles in congelation ice, which separate from the water and are captured by the ice during freezing, and

(2) Cavities within sublimation ice, formed when the spaces between the rays of the skeletal crystals become covered over.

Xenogenous inclusions form as mechanical impurities (in excess of those contained in the solution) during freezing of water containing gas bubbles. This takes place during the liberation of gases from the bottom of a freezing reservoir or from the lower horizons of freezing soil and during the capture of air bubbles by the descending water of waterfalls or of breaking wave crests.

Hypergenous inclusions consist of air which penetrates into the open cracks and pores of ice. Finally, *hypogenous* inclusions are parts of former pores and cracks isolated from the outside air and from each other.

Primary air inclusions do not play the leading role in sublimation crystals; evidently they never exceed 0.3% of the total volume of the crystals, which corresponds to an ice density of about 0.914 g/cm^3. Congelation ice may contain almost ten times as much autogenous air. The total solubility of the gaseous components of the air in fresh water at 0°C and 1 atm pressure is 29.18 ml/l. If all this air were to remain in the ice when the water froze, 1000 cm^3 of water with dissolved air would transform into 1090.8 cm^3 of ice plus 29.18 cm^3 of air. The air content of such ice would be 2.605% of the total volume and its density would be 0.8936 g/cm^3 instead of 0.9168 g/cm^3 in pure ice. Generally, the autogenous air content of congelation ice is not this large, because of its expulsion by the nascent space lattice of the ice, but in the sections of the ice bodies that were last to freeze in a closed space, the air inclusions may accumulate and considerably exceed the indicated amount.

Only under special conditions of freezing does xenogenous air play a definite role in the ice structure; it is not found in most kinds of natural ice.

In individual cases the amount of hypergenous air in the communicating pores of the snow cover may exceed 99% of the volume, in firn it may reach 56%, while ice in the narrow sense of the word has no pores, and hypergenous inclusions are found only along fracture cracks. After these pores and cracks have been closed by compression or have been stopped up by the newly-forming ice, their remnants constitute hypogenous air inclusions. The amount of inclusions of this type, depending on the way in which the pores are closed, may vary from approximately 1.3% of the volume in ice in which the pores had been stopped up by seeping and freezing melt water, to as much as 12.5–13% in ice in which the pores had been closed by compression and recrystallization without the participation of water.

The data indicate that there is some air in all types of ice, and air plays such an important role in the ice of atmospheric precipitations that it should be considered a second rock-forming component along with the ice itself. The whole process of transformation of the solid atmospheric precipitation in glaciers consists, in large measure, in a change of the quantitative relationship between the ice and the air, first in absorption, then in liberation of the air from the ice.

The physical role of the hypergenous air of open pores differs from that of all the closed air inclusions of the other types in ice. The air that fills the pores in the ice actually does not belong to the ice and since it is in communication with the atmosphere, generally it does not differ from the atmospheric air in composition, except that it is always saturated with water vapor. It has no effect on the water vapor pressure, but it does reduce the diffusion rate of the vapor. The presence of air in water reduces the equilibrium temperature of water and ice from $+0.0099°C$ to $+0.0075°C$ and, owing to pressure on the walls of the pores, to $0°C$. The free air of the pores in the static state does not participate in the transmission of mechanical stresses, but plays an essential role in the rapid, spasmodic settling of snow and firn. Here the role of the air is analogous to that of water in the sudden flow of soils (mudflows), when particles of the solid phase lose cohesion and for a time become suspended in water. With changes in atmospheric pressure and the appearance of a temperature gradient, air transported by the water vapor begins to circulate in the ice pores. The basic role in the process of heat transfer in porous rock is played by the diffusion of the water vapor, which accompanies the sublimation process, not by the thermal conductivity of the ice and not by the circulation of the air.

The air of the bubbles isolated by the ice plays a completely different role. The initial air pressure is equal to the pressure of the ambient medium at the moment the air bubbles are enclosed. In time it may increase owing to plastic deformation of the ice, but in the final analysis it may be lower or higher than the outside pressure, because the ice may encounter different environmental conditions. For example, the pressure of air in snowflakes which are falling from the outer atmosphere is lower than atmospheric pressure, while the air pressure in the lower layers of thick floating ice, the ice of frost cracks, and a large part of the body of a glacier is higher than atmospheric pressure, and some of the excess pressure is retained in the case of melting out onto the surface. After the external load has exceeded the elastic limit of the ice, the air is compressed to the point of pressure equilibrium on the walls of the bubbles from without and within and thus it participates in the transfer of pressure

within the ice. The air bubbles play a negative role in the heat transfer process; having an extremely low coefficient of thermal conductivity, the air plays practically no role in the circulative transfer
of heat and merely reduces the thermal conductivity of the rock.

Air, like all other inclusions, considerably reduces the permeability of ice for radiant energy, even though air is more transparent
than ice. Such an effect is created by reflection and scattering of the
rays on the ice-air interface (air in the form of pores and bubbles),
and this interface expands abruptly with an increase of the air
content. However, while other inclusions intensify radiation
absorption by the ice and lead to more intensive melting, the presence
of air (more exactly, of the ice-air interface) reduces melting
because of increased reflection of the rays, which is manifested
especially strongly in snow.

Each of the enumerated genetic types of air inclusions has its
specific characteristics of form, dimensions, spacing, and, in part,
chemical composition. We shall examine the geometric features of
all the inclusions in connection with the ice formation processes, but
now will give data only on the chemical composition of the gaseous
inclusions.

Few data are available on the gaseous composition of the inclusions in ice and these are contradictory, which probably can be
explained at least in part by the inaccuracy of the earlier analyses
and by the inadequate method of collecting the gas samples, during
which selective dilution of the gases in the melt water occurs.

As mentioned above, the composition of the hypergenous inclusions corresponds to that of the outside air, except that their degree
of saturation by water vapor varies within very narrow limits. It is a
different matter with isolated inclusions.

In gases of xenogenous origin released from soil and especially
from the bottom of reservoirs, gases of biochemical origin may play a
considerable role, namely, methane (CH_4), hydrogen sulfide (H_2S),
heavy hydrocarbons, hydrogen (H_2), and also carbon dioxide (CO_2),
nitrogen (N_2) and oxygen (O_2), which are the products of the
decomposition of organic substances and mineral salts by micro-
organisms.

There may also be biochemical gases among the autogenous gases
in congelation ice that forms from surface runoff, while in the ice of
underground waters there may also be gases of chemical origin
(sulfides, chlorine, sulphur, chlorides, etc.); however, both the
hypogenous and the primary gaseous inclusions in ice are primarily
atmospheric gases.

For the most part the quantitative ratio of the atmospheric gases included in ice is not the same as in normal air, as can be judged from data appearing in the literature. H. and A. Schlagintweit (1850, p. 18) found the oxygen content in the bubbles of glacier ice in the Alps to be 22.7%, i.e., greater than in the atmosphere. O. Christensen (see Steenstrup, 1893, p. 98) found the amount of oxygen in the ice of an iceberg off the coast of Greenland to be 16.8%, i.e., 4% less than in the atmosphere, while A. Hamberg (1895, p. 7) found the oxygen content in the glacier ice of Spitsbergen to be 20.4%. Hamberg established the oxygen content in the air bubbles of Barents Sea ice as 24.0–26.3% (taking $N_2 + O_2$ to be 100%), while B. Bruns (see Zubov, 1945, p. 128) found 15.9–18.3% oxygen and 0–0.6% carbon dioxide.

Evidently these differences are not due solely to inaccuracies in the analyses. At first the chemical composition of the hypogenous inclusions does not differ from that of normal air, but if the air passes through a water-dissolved state and then separates out from the solution during freezing, its composition will change owing to the differences in the solubility of the gases comprising it. At 0°C the solubility of oxygen in fresh water is 48.9 ml/l; of nitrogen, 23.5 ml/l; and of carbon dioxide, 17.1 ml/l. The presence of salts in sea water increases this difference still more, bringing the ratio of the solubility of O_2 to N_2 to almost 3.8 : 1. As a result, the composition of the mixture of gases dissolved in water which is saturated with respect to atmospheric air differs from the composition of the atmospheric air. In atmospheric air the volumetric oxygen content is about 20.95%; nitrogen, argon and the other inert gases, 79.02%; and, on the average, carbon dioxide, 0.03%; while in a mixture of gases dissolved in fresh water at 0°C, the volumetric content is, correspondingly, oxygen, 34.32%; nitrogen and others, 63.96%; carbon dioxide, 1.72% (10.19 ml/l of oxygen dissolve, 18.99 ml/l of nitrogen and the inert gases, and 0.51 ml/l of carbon dioxide).

When the water freezes, the gases dissolved in it separate completely from the solution, forming bubble inclusions with a new quantitative ratio of the gases. Thus, the autogenous air of congelation ice formed from completely aerated, completely fresh water, will be enriched by oxygen to the extent of 13.4%, by carbon dioxide to the extent of 1.7%, and correspondingly deprived of nitrogen and the inert gases.

If ice is further subjected to partial melting, accompanied by migration and removal of water along internal channels, the water will impoverish the remaining air of the isolated inclusions, primarily of carbon dioxide, carrying off in solution a mixture of gases consisting of 47.7% CO_2, 27.2% O_2, and 25.1% N_2 and inert gases. At the instant all the carbon dioxide is dissolved, the inclusions constitute 65.4% N_2 and 34.6% O_2. During further dissolution, the remainder of the gases will be enriched more and more with nitrogen and deprived of oxygen to the point of its complete disappearance. On the other hand, in places where the migrating water freezes, inclusions will occur that are strongly enriched by carbon dioxide and oxygen, which leads to the partial differentiation of the composition of the gases in the different inclusions.

Thus, the metamorphism of atmospheric gases in ice may be presented as in Fig. 17. This whole process may be repeated, accompanied by different conditions of melt-water migration, and gas mixtures of quite different quantitative constituent relationships may result.

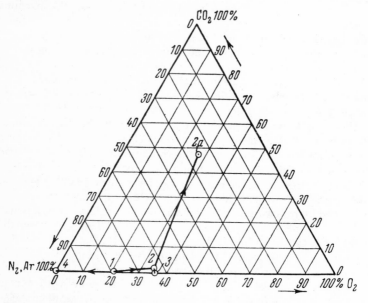

FIG. 17. Scheme of the metamorphism of atmospheric air in ice. 1. atmospheric air; 2. autogenous air of congelation ice; 2a. composition of gases in water saturated with respect to the autogenous air of congelation ice; 3–4. air of melted congelation ice; 1–4. air of melted recrystallization ice.

Nevertheless, in general the enrichment (with respect to atmospheric air) of gaseous inclusions of O_2 and CO_2 indicates that these inclusions are of autogenous origin and that the ice is of congelation origin. A normal O_2 and CO_2 content indicates that the inclusions are hypogenous and that the role of liquid water in the ice formation was negligible and, finally, a low O_2 and CO_2 content indicates secondary melting and the migration of melt water.

WATER

There are three reasons for the appearance of the liquid phase in ice:

(1) the influx of heat or another form of energy which converts into thermal energy;

(2) increased pressure that reduces the melting point of ice; and

(3) a concentration of salts, which also reduces the melting point of part of the substance below the given temperature.

In this chapter we will confine our study to water which owes its existence to the first two causes. It almost always comprises secondary inclusions in ice formations: the hypergenous type in the case of infiltration, and the secondary-autogenous type in the case of local melting.

Ice, having a melting point, may contain any amount of water. In water and in ice not near the melting point, the influx or release of heat causes a temperature change. On the other hand, when the melting point is reached in the ice-water system, any change in the heat content leads to a phase transition of part of the substance, accompanied by a corresponding absorption or emission of latent heat, which keeps the temperature of the system at the melting point.

The atoms of the transitional layer on the boundaries of contiguous crystals are less firmly bound than the internal ones, because they are under the influence of the differently oriented fields of force of the two crystals. In this connection, the melting point of the transitional layer, which is not more than five interatomic distances wide, may be somewhat lower than that of the remaining mass of the substance, whether impurities are present or not. For example, in lead, according to B. Chalmers's experiments, the crystals begin to separate from each other readily at a temperature of 0.14°C below the melting point. Perhaps this does not represent true melting but only a sharp increase of plasticity. In any event, undoubtedly the intermediate layer of atoms is thermodynamically less stable than the internal layers (Seitz, 1943).

Therefore, the melting of ice always begins at the boundaries between the crystals; the main mass of the water contained in the melting ice is also concentrated there. A second, considerably smaller amount of water lies along the basal planes within the crystals, forming "ice flowers." The cohesion between the crystals is disrupted by melt water and the ice becomes permeated by a network of pores, or it disintegrates into grains. In snow and firn, the melt water may fill most of the pores and constitute as much as 60% of the entire volume. When the water content is greater, the contact between the individual crystals becomes weaker and, in part, they float in the water and form an ice gruel.

Such mixtures of water and ice of variable composition form only in the surface layer of the ice, into which the melt water penetrates from above. On the other hand, the water content of a thick impenetrable layer of ice warmed to the melting point remains strictly constant, since the energy required for melting cannot reach that far. Longwave radiation, which exerts a thermal effect, is absorbed by the thin surface layer of ice and even in transparent ice cannot cause melting to a depth of more than 1–2 meters from the surface, and after the boundaries of the crystals have been melted through, the affected layer is still shallower. The direct influx of thermal energy into ice that has reached the melting point almost ceases, owing to the negligible temperature gradient.

The melting point of ice decreases 0.00752°C with a pressure increase of 1 atmosphere. If all of a thick layer of pure ice is at the melting point, the following temperature gradient will be established in it:

$$\frac{dt}{dz} = \frac{dt}{dp} \times \frac{dp}{dz} = \frac{0.00752 \times 0.09168}{1.00332} = 0.000726°/m$$

or 1° per 1377 m. Here t is temperature, p is pressure, z is depth below the surface, 0.09168 kg is the weight of a column of ice 1 m high and 1 cm^2 in cross section, and 1.00332 is the coefficient for conversion of pressure from atmospheres into kg/cm^2.

With such a temperature distribution in the ice, a steady, vanishingly small heat flux, directed downward, is established, with a magnitude of about 11×10^{-8} cal/cm^2/year, and any additional heat influx will be expended on melting the ice surface. Under such conditions, when there is practically no heat exchange in the ice layer and the processes approach the adiabatic, for each melting point there will be a corresponding amount of liquid water v proportional to the pressure. It is defined by a formula derived from the Clapeyron-Clausius equation:

$$v = \frac{T}{L} c \log \frac{273.16}{T}$$

where T is the melting point in °K, L the heat of fusion and c the specific heat capacity.

After substituting pressure for absolute temperature by means of the empirical equation for the curve of melting ($p = -138.5t - 2.1t^2$) for the temperature interval 0° to −1°C, we obtain

$$\nu = 5.41 \times 10^{-5}p \text{ g/cm}^3$$

where p is the pressure in kg/cm² (Hess, 1937).

Thus, under the pressure of an ice layer 750 m thick, the ice at the melting point will contain 3.6 g of liquid water per cubic decimeter, while at a depth of 1500 m it will contain 7.2 g/dm³. The slightest pressure change leads to freezing or to further melting of part of the substance.

SALTS

The purest natural water is a weak, but not infinitely weak solution, in which salt ions surrounded by hydratic shells are evenly distributed. All natural ice contains salts.

Salts are soluble, mostly secondary minerals, the products of the weathering of the minerals of magmatic rocks. The minerals soluble in water are chiefly alkalis (Na, K) and alkaline-earth salts (Ca, Mg) of hydrochloric, sulphuric and carbonic acids.

Salt inclusions in ice may belong to all genetic types; however, the occurrence of secondary inclusions of salts has certain specific features. As a rule, secondary salts in ice are not introduced in pure form, but in mineral inclusions, whose leaching is the most abundant source of salts in sedimentary ice. However, the leaching process always results from partial melting of the ice, usually alternating with freezing; therefore, in a differentiation of secondary mineral inclusions, salts are included in the parent melt and are no longer distinguished from the primary autogenous salt inclusions. The difference between primary and secondary salts in certain cases can be established only by the chemical composition.

The salt composition of ice may vary greatly. As a rule, sedimentary ice contains sodium chloride and other chlorides, nitrous compounds, NH_4, NO_3 and NO_2, and sulfates. Chlorides are crystallization nuclei of atmospheric crystals, and nitrous compounds are captured by them from the air in the process of fall and growth. The average chlorine content of atmospheric ice, according to Buchanan (1887, 1908) is 0.007‰ by weight, while according to L. Keineth and D. Lohner it is from 0.0006‰ to 0.0027‰. The nitrous compound content of snow varies from 0.0007‰ to 0.0074‰ (Veinberg, 1940, p. 312).

The salt content of sedimentary ice increases sharply in the direct proximity of the sea or salt lakes. The composition and quantity of salts in congelation ice varies within very broad limits, depending on the original salinity of the water which served as the source of ice formation, on the composition and amount of mineral particle impurities in the ice and also on the frequency and intensity of its melting.

As a rule, ice containing salts also contains some of the liquid phase. According to Blagden (1788), the freezing point of water, like that of any solvent, decreases in proportion to the weight of the substances dissolved in it. During freezing, the nascent ice lattice tries to drive out the salt ions which concentrate at the boundary of the growing crystal. The water freezes and the remaining solution concentrates, which further reduces the freezing point of the remaining water. When the concentration of salts is very great, a temperature drop no longer results in the freezing of the water, but in the precipitation of salt crystals from the solution because of its reduced solubility.

Consequently, for each temperature of the solution, beginning with the freezing point of pure water, there are two critical equilibrium concentrations of salts: the minimum, below which the excess water in the form of ice crystals separates out from the solution, and the maximum, beyond which the salt excess is separated out in the form of crystals. The curves for both these values, which express the relationship between the critical equilibrium concentrations of the given salt and the temperature, converge at a single point corresponding to the so-called *eutectic temperature* and to a specific concentration of the solution. Under these conditions a further removal of heat leads to precipitation in the form of crystals of both components of the solution, i.e., the solution freezes as a whole, maintaining a constant quantitative relationship of the component parts (Fig. 18) and a *eutectic mixture* of ice and salt crystals results. If the initial concentration of the solution is lower than the eutectic, a *hypoeutectic*, i.e., a mixture of the eutectic with ice, forms after the cooling falls below the eutectic temperature, and if the concentration is higher than the eutectic, a *hypereutectic* is formed, i.e., a mixture of the eutectic and salt.

Thus, salts in ice above the eutectic temperature will appear as liquid brine, which increases in concentration and decreases in amount as it cools. Only after the eutectic temperature is reached does all the brine freeze and the ice no longer contain the liquid phase, having become hypoeutectic.

Some salts, very widely distributed in natural water, have a very low eutectic temperature, e.g., KCl, $-11.1°C$; $NaCl$, $-21.2°C$; NaI, $-30.0°C$; $MgCl_2$, $-33.6°C$; and $CaCl_2$, $-55.0°C$. Therefore, most natural ice, even at the lowest temperatures encountered in ice bodies, contains inclusions of liquid brine; however, the amount of brine depends greatly on the concentration of salts. In sea ice, which has a salt content of about 1.5% and a temperature of −2°C, the

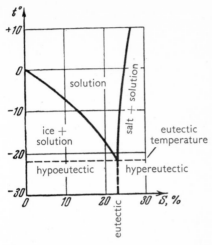

Fig. 18. Graph of the crystallization of an aqueous solution of NaCl.

amount of liquid brine reaches 40% of the weight and at −10°C still exceeds 10%; consequently, young sea ice with a high salt content is very weak and is distinguished by its special dark hue and greasy gloss.

The amount of liquid brine in fresh ice is negligible. For ice containing 0.007‰ Cl, which is characteristic of clean sedimentary ice, the liquid brine produced from NaCl at −0.01°C comprises 7% of the volume, while at −1.0°C it is only 0.07% (Fig. 19). In the temperature interval from −2°C to −21.2°C, there is so little liquid brine in the ice that it cannot be detected experimentally. The amount of brine increases sharply at temperatures near zero; according to the observations of G. Quincke (1905), the inclusions of liquid brine under these conditions become visible under the microscope when the salt content of the ice is between 0.001‰ and 0.0001‰ of the total weight.

In fresh ice formed from atmospheric precipitation or by the slow freezing of water, almost all the brine is concentrated in the form of films and isolated inclusions at the boundaries between the ice crystals. However, as the freezing rate of the water and its salt

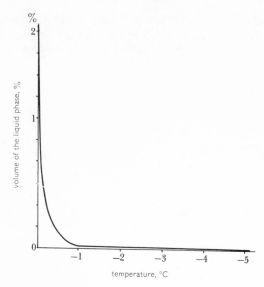

Fig. 19. Relationship between temperature and the liquid phase content of ice with 0.007‰ Cl from NaCl. (After Buchanan, 1908.)

concentration increase, an ever greater amount of brine remains within the crystals. In saline ice, brine forms interlayers in the basal planes of the crystals, dividing the crystals into a series of plates. The more rapid the crystallization and the greater the concentration of the salts, the thicker are the interlayers of brine (up to several millimeters near 0°C) and the thinner, relatively speaking, are the elementary plates of ice separated by them.

In fresh ice, where practically all the salts lie along the intercrystalline boundaries, the thickness of the liquid films is a function of the temperature and the salt content as well as the size of the crystals. Veinberg (1940, p. 501) derived equations for computing the thickness of the brine films between the ice crystals as a function of their size, the salinity of the ice, and the temperature. According to his computations, for Neva ice with 8-mm granules, the thickness of the brine film at −2°C was of the order of 3μ; at −7°C, 1μ; and at −22°C, $1/3\mu$. This approximates the results of E. K. Plyler (1925), who found that the crystal boundaries of fresh ice, which absorb radiant energy more intensely, reach a thickness of 8μ.

Due to the presence of salts, not only saline ice, but also fresh ice, which begins to melt at temperatures somewhat below 0°C, usually has a branching network of fine channels and isolated cells of salt solution that give the ice a whitish appearance (Figs. 20, 21 and 22).

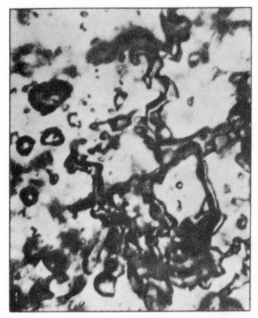

FIG. 20.   Network of channels of salt solution in ice with mineralization of
185 mg/l at the beginning of melting. (Photograph by B. I. Vtiurin.)

If the solution has not escaped from the ice, the network of channels
will again disappear when freezing is renewed, leaving no trace. In
salt ice, part of the brine usually flows downward and is replaced by
outside air, the ice freshens and at the same time becomes permeated
by a system of air pores with a liquid residue.

Thus, any natural ice at a very low temperature is a hypoeutectic,
while at a higher temperature it contains films and channels of
liquid brine. The ice crystals are surrounded and separated by a
solution of salts which solidifies at a temperature lower than that of
the pure ice of the inner part of the crystals. Every crystal is a cell
with walls of liquid salt solution. In this respect, ice is somewhat like
colloidal solutions (e.g., silicic acid, sulphur, albumen, lime), which
harden because of the loss of water, with the difference, however,
that the cell walls harden sooner than the cell content.

Frequently the presence of salts in fresh ice is not taken into consideration at all, but whatever the quantitative relation of the salts
may be, they must be considered in view of the role which salts
play in the processes of crystallization and melting of ice. However,
some researchers went to the other extreme and credited salt with

producing ice flow and other processes which are actually unrelated
to these influences.

An extreme example of exaggeration of the role of salts in ice is
Quincke's concept (1905), which places particular emphasis on the
similarity of ice and colloidal solutions. He held that ice is a frozen
foamy mass with walls of weak salt solution and that a surface tension appears at the boundary of this salt solution and pure water or a

FIG. 21. Surface of lake ice with melted crystal boundaries. (Photograph by
G. G. Laemmlein.)

weaker solution and, consequently, he classified ice as an oily liquid.
Quincke attributes great significance to the tendency of the salt walls
of the chamber crystals to contract, stating that the salt solution
serves as the ice skeleton (*Knochengerüst*). Finally, ignoring the
crystalline nature of ice, Quincke groundlessly identifies ice with
a colloid whose walls and cell content consist of two liquids with
identical components but different concentrations. In his formula-
tion, ice is a fluid gel with foamy walls of a liquid oily saline water-
deficient solution surrounding the foam cells with viscous-liquid,
birefringent, pure or slightly salty water (i.e., ice).

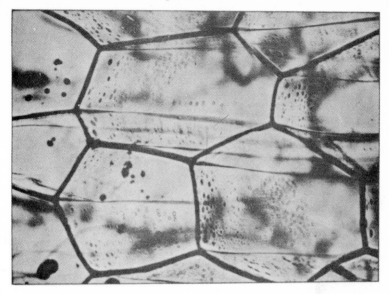

Fig. 22. The melted lake ice shown in Fig. 21. The cut is oblique to the surface. The disk-like melt figures are visible at the boundaries between the columnar crystals. (Photograph by G. G. Laemmlein.)

INSOLUBLE SOLID INCLUSIONS

With few exceptions, any natural ice contains small amounts of insoluble or undissolved fragments of other minerals and rocks, but in most cases they do not play any appreciable role in its structure. Genetically, solid impurities in ice are of the primary xenogenous type of inclusions characteristic of many ground ice types or of the types of secondary inclusions found in sedimentary ice and to a lesser extent in the congelation ice covers of water. Enrichment of only certain layers or parts of layers by mineral impurities is characteristic of sedimentary ice; this is associated with periodicity in the case of accumulation or with secondary enrichment as a result of the partial melting of the ice.

The mechanical composition of the mineral impurities may vary greatly, depending on the agencies responsible for their introduction into the accumulating ice and on their sources: they range from fine dust transported by the wind for great distances and silt present in slowly-moving water to large blocks of rock that fall onto the ice or that are broken off by it. The accumulations of mineral particles on the surface of ice sheets, called cryoconites by A. E. Nordenskiöld

(1886), consist only in small part of cosmic dust, while basically they are products of the weathering of terrestrial rocks and the material of volcanic eruptions.

The role of mineral impurities in ice is quite varied and increases sharply as the number of impurities increases.

As mentioned above, between the surface of the mineral inclusions and the ordinary ice containing them, evidently, there are molecular layers of other polymorphic modifications of ice and "oriented" filmy water. The mineral inclusions themselves are sources of ice salination.

All widely distributed minerals have a considerably larger co-efficient of absorption of radiant energy than does ice; therefore, during radiational heating, tiny mineral particles act as centers of ice melting to an even greater extent than do the salt inclusions.

When present in considerable quantities, the mineral inclusions also exert an influence on the plastic properties of the ice. The presence of fine mineral particles, whose mechanical composition runs from clay and dust to sandy loam, inclusive, somewhat increases the plasticity of ice, while an admixture of sand particles and particles of larger size considerably reduces plasticity. The viscosity of frozen clay is 0.9×10^{12} poise and that of frozen sandy loam is 1.9×10^{12} poise (Tsytovich, 1945), while the viscosity of poly-crystalline ice with regular orientation is 10^{12} to 10^{13} poise.

M. Lagally (1932*b*), using indirect computations, found the viscosity of the "dead" ice (saturated with moraine fragments) of the Pasterze glacier in the Alps to be one third that of pure ice. However, the propriety of employing viscous flow formulas in the given case is very doubtful, since the initial data indicate the prevalence of sliding motion along the internal shearing planes. The author's observations of the behavior of the ice layers that contain sand particles in parts of glaciers which have experienced deformation by folding indicate that they are considerably less plastic than pure ice; they are always "competent" layers and, because of their rigidity, melt in places under excess pressure.

The reduction of plasticity in the latter case is quite understandable, since non-ice rocks are not plastic at low temperatures and pressures. The opposite behavior of ice in the case of an admixture of finely dispersed inclusions evidently is explained by the presence of liquid, loosely bound water and the melting of ice at numerous points of contact with particles that have a great surface curvature and that, consequently, create a very high specific pressure (Tsytovich and Sumgin, 1937, p. 31).

CHAPTER VIII

METHODS OF PETROGRAPHIC ICE STUDY

The study of ice as a rock is distinct from the study of the physical properties of ice as a mineral, because the ends pursued are completely different. In a geologico-petrographic study, the physical constants of pure ice crystals are considered known and are used as the initial data for solving the special problems, viz., the laws governing the mode of occurrence, the composition and the structure of the ice bodies considered as polycrystalline ice aggregates with an admixture of other material, and as the result of the distinct geological process responsible for their formation. Here we must include the determination of certain physical properties as additional means of characterizing structure. However, petrographic study does not completely replace physical study; rather, it supplements it or, to be more exact, it should serve as the foundation upon which the study of the physical properties of natural ice is built.

At the same time, the petrographic study of ice differs essentially from that of other rock formations. The differences are due basically to the specific physical properties of ice and to its simple mineralogical composition. Usually, when collections of stone samples are studied, the chief petrographic problems are the identification of mineral types by their physicochemical properties, mainly by their optic constants, and the classification of rock on this basis. This problem does not arise in the case of ice, because it has only one modification, Ice I, which can easily be identified visually. The problem of determining the chemico-mineralogical and phase composition of an ice rock formation arises only in connection with the presence of impurities and the possibility that part of the ice will change into the liquid phase. However, the main thing here is the determination of the total content of the gases, water, salts, and insoluble impurities and the characteristics of their distribution in ice, i.e., questions connected with the study of structure. Classification of the impurities by their chemical or mineralogical composition is of secondary importance. The investigator's attention may be drawn mainly to the study of the structural characteristics of the ice, rather than to its

103

material composition, an approach ordinarily adopted only in special petrotectonic studies.

The study of natural ice as a rock comprises two stages: (1) field studies, and (2) laboratory studies.

Field studies are carried out primarily by geological methods and the main problem is to determine the mode of occurrence of the ice rock formations. In field studies, the rocks are distinguished by their structural features, with visual macroscopic descriptions and elementary determinations of the composition and structure; later these features are defined more accurately in the laboratory by petrographic methods.

Laboratory investigation aims at studying first the structure and second, the material composition of the ice rocks.

By the *texture* of a rock we mean the peculiarities of its structure, based on the dimensions, relative amount, form and orientation of its component parts.

The following elements enter into the concept of the texture of a monomineralic ice rock:

(1) the external form and size of the crystals;[1]

(2) the spatial relationships of the crystals;

(3) their relationship to the inclusions;

(4) the relationship of the crystallographic orientation to the external form of the crystals; and

(5) the relation of the crystallographic orientation to the bedding elements or the regularity of texture.

In petrography, the structure of a rock is distinguished from its texture in that structure defines the spatial disposition, essentially the spatial differentiation of the component parts and the extent to which the rock fills space. In particular, structure treats of such factors as stratification, schistosity, cleavage, porosity and jointing. As a rule, the component parts of the rock are of different

---

[1] There are special terms for defining crystals with irregular boundaries that do not coincide with the complex of faces inherent to the given crystal class, i.e., faces that form part of the polycrystalline aggregate. In physics and metallurgy these are called *crystallites;* however, this term is inappropriate, because in geology it is used to define the embryonic crystals of volcanic glass which have a weak effect on polarized light and which as yet do not provide a basis for defining a mineral species. The geological term "granule" is not always applicable either, because it usually includes an isometric index (of approximately identical dimensions in all directions).

mineralogical composition. For ice, use of the term *structure* to indicate the spatial disposition of crystals is artificial, because in the absence of impurities the ice rock, to external appearances, is uniform without signs of structure. Ice structure is created only by the type of distribution of its inclusions.

The structural trend of investigation is closely related to the study of the material composition through the relationship between crystals and their inclusions as a textural element and through structure. Investigations, carried out by various methods, are mutually supplementary.

The material composition is usually studied by determining the impurity content of the ice, by classifying the impurities according to their aggregate state and also (mainly for determination of the origin of the initial material) by performing chemical, mineralogical and granulometric analyses of the impurities.

The specific physical properties of ice require the use of a special method, which is in part inappropriate, and in part unnecessary when working with other rocks. The method is based mainly on the low melting point and low sublimation point of ice, which cause its great instability and also its transparency and its weakness. Below is a short survey of the special methods used in the petrographic study of ice and which differ somewhat from those for other rocks. Where there is no such difference, we have limited ourselves to indicating a program of study with the recommendation that the reader consult standard handbooks for a description of the method to be used. In arranging our material, we have held basically to the sequence in which it is most convenient to carry out the research.

STUDY OF THE MODES OF OCCURRENCE

By mode of occurrence we mean (1) the type of bedding of the given rock formation, i.e., stratified, veined, lenticular, etc.; (2) the size of the bodies formed by the rock; and when there is some regularity of form, also (3) the bed positions, i.e., the direction of strike, the dip and the angles of incidence of the surfaces and internal planes of the given body; and, finally, (4) the relationship to other rocks and the local forms of relief.

The enumerated types of study in no way differ from the study of the mode of occurrence of the other rocks, because ice is not an exception in this respect. In particular, moving glacier ice is often subject to folding, is divided by cracks, faults and series of overthrusts, and assumes a complex tectonic structure, inferior only in size to the structures in the regions of intense tectogenesis within the earth's crust. In studying such areas, the main difficulty lies in distinguishing the initial structural elements among the metamorphic neogenes.

In many cases ice rocks form more rapidly than do other rocks, hence, *direct study of the processes of ice formation under natural conditions* is of great interest and also presents splendid opportunities for petrological experimentation. A direct study of this type can be made if stationary or repeated observations can be made. Observations which relate directly to the study of the mode of occurrence include observations of the rate of growth of ice under different conditions, the processes of deposition of the snow cover, the settling of snow and firn, and the development of unconformities in ice.

The last two types of observations can be made not only visually or with measuring apparatus in the walls of pits, crevasses or cliffs, but also with automatic recorders, which make a continuous record of the rate of deformation and which permit study of the relationship between the deformation process and time, pressure, temperature, structural changes and other factors. In particular, from knowledge of the subsidence of the layer one can establish the role played by compression in the change of density of the rock and the extent to which this change is due to the migration of material.

MACROSCOPIC DESCRIPTION OF STRUCTURE

Macroscopic descriptions are made in the field and later, in more detail, in the laboratory from samples delivered there. All characteristics of the rock which can be observed with the naked eye or with a magnifying glass and without special processing or use of polarized light are described and, when possible, measured, sketched and photographed. These include, chiefly, the characteristics of form, size, and distribution of inclusions: air pores, bubbles, cavities, solid impurities, channels and cells containing liquid, and also the structural inhomogeneities created by them: stratification, porosity, columnarity, inclusions of solid ice amid snow and firn, etc. If there are formations consisting of even partially separated large crystals, their form, size and mutual disposition are described. The average size of the crystals is determined by comparison with standards or tables.[2]

---

[2] See, for example, the table for determining grain size under field conditions constructed by the Hydrogeological Section of the National Geological Institute of the USSR (Pustovalov, 1940, Part II, Fig. 1).

DETERMINATION OF THE HARDNESS AND AIR PERMEABILITY OF POROUS ICE FORMATIONS. GRANULOMETRIC ANALYSIS OF SUCH FORMATIONS

Hardness and permeability to air are the most important physical properties of the porous ice formations, i.e., snow and firn.

Hardness, i.e., the capacity of a body to resist the penetration of another body without experiencing residual deformations, is a constant of the mineral, ice, which depends on temperature alone. However, if the air inclusions are numerous, hardness becomes a petrographic characteristic; specifically, for porous ice formations, the relation of hardness to density determines the strength of the bonds between the crystals (which, of course, is also a function of temperature). Certain other mechanical properties could also provide analogous characteristics, but hardness has the advantage that it can be determined easily under field conditions.

It is most convenient to determine hardness by the indentation of a cone, because in this case the result does not depend on the load applied. If we label hardness H, the force applied to the cone P, the depth of penetration of the cone h, and the apex angle of the cone 2α, we get the following expression:

$$H = \frac{P}{\pi h^2 \tan^2 \alpha}$$

The works of I. V. Kragel'skii (1945) and R. Haefeli (1939, p. 143) give descriptions of hardness gauges and probes, and discuss the theories of determining snow hardness. For petrographic study, it is convenient to employ small models of the hardness gauges which permit individual characterizations of the thin layers of a rock, and probes which permit study of hardness distribution in the vertical profile of the snow cover without disturbing the snow. If hardness gauges are not available, hardness can be determined on a relative scale. Of the scales designed for this purpose, Sorge's (Sorge, 1935), with some modifications, can be recommended. According to it, ice hardness is rated 10. For practical purposes, the first five ratings should be used for snow and firn:

(1) A finger can be forced into the snow easily; a man in hard footwear leaves a shallow trail;

(2) A sharpened pencil can be forced in easily; a man walking on the snow leaves no trail;

(3) A pencil can be forced in only with difficulty;

(4) A pencil cannot be forced in; a knife blade can be forced in easily;

(5) A knife blade can be forced in only with difficulty.

Permeability to air is a characteristic of porous ice that is more difficult to determine, but one which is very important. The coefficient of permeability to air K is the mean laminar velocity of the flow of air through the ice (at $t = 0°C$), with a pressure gradient of 1 cm water column per 1 cm path. A description of the apparatus and method of determining the permeability of snow to air is given in Bader's work (1939, p. 31).

Permeability to air is an indirect quantitative characteristic of the absolute dimensions, meandering and branching of the communicating pores. The air permeability also characterizes the potential permeability of the rock for both water (with the temperature of both phases equal to the melting point) and for water vapor, thus defining the possibility of migration of the material and, consequently, the intensity of the metamorphic processes connected with it. Moreover, the different combinations of ice crystal size, porosity (the ratio of the pores to the total volume of the rock) and permeability to air are evidently not accidental, but the regular consequences of previous stages of ice rock formation. From investigations of permeability to air and porosity, Bader has worked out a structural classification of snow (see Fig. 77 and accompanying text), but this relationship has not yet been studied with respect to firn.

The size distribution of crystal fractions is also one of the characteristics which can be determined only for porous ice rocks. As a rule the methods of *granulometric analysis*, applicable to other friable rocks, are not applicable to ice. This method cannot be used for monolithic ice because such ice cannot be separated into individual crystals without partial peripheral melting of the crystals, while in the case of snow, the complex skeletal form of the crystals prevents it. Granulometric analysis, after separation into individual grains, can only be employed for the intermediate stages, viz., in the case of old snow with rounded crystals and firn which is not too dense. A rubber pestle is used to crush the specimen; dry ice which maintains a temperature of $-78.5°C$ is added to the mortar for cooling. However, all this does not eliminate the possibility that the more durable intergrowths will be preserved or, with stronger applications, that the monocrystals will be fractured. Bader (1939, p. 38) carried out his analysis mechanically or manually using sieves (strainers) and adding dry ice; however, it was found that crystals were abraded by this method. Analysis by precipitation in kerosene with automatic recording of the weight of the precipitating grain yields better results; this was the method used by de Quervain (1948). However, even if conditions are optimum for the above methods, direct measurements on slides provides more accurate data on crystal sizes, although the method is considerably more cumbersome.

CRYSTALLOGRAPHIC RESEARCH

Crystallographic research provides the basis for the whole petrographic study of ice because, properly speaking, modes of occurrence are determined by geological, not petrographic methods, and other methods are required only for the study of impurities in ice.

The aim of crystallographic research is to establish the dimensions, form and spatial relationships of ice crystals in the ice, and of the orientation of the crystallographic axes with respect to the external form of the crystals, the bed positions, the direction of ice movement, and the like. Ice is unstable and difficult to preserve; thus, as a rule, crystallographic study is carried out in field laboratories and, in part, in the field itself. Further, crystallographic study of the porous species must be made as quickly as possible after extraction. This is the specific feature of work with ice as opposed to the study of samples, which is usually done after field work has been completed. The need for equipping the field laboratory with the means for maintaining a constant negative temperature and good lighting creates a number of difficulties, only partially alleviated by the ease of mechanical processing and the transparency of ice, thanks to which sections of the required thickness can be prepared manually.

The methods of crystallographic ice study are rather diverse. First, there is a difference between the study of porous and monolithic ice. In porous ice, the form, size and spatial relationships of the crystals can be studied in part in reflected light, in the undisturbed state, and in a state in which the ice is broken down into the individual crystals or their intergrowths. However, to determine crystallographic orientation, both porous species (with the exception of new snow) and compact ice should be studied by optical crystallographic methods.

In a normal, unmelted state, the crystals of monolithic ice are invisible. There are three principal types of methods of studying them. The first is based on selective, primarily radiational, melting of ice, the second on the application of polarized light, and the third on the application of x-rays. The second method, the optical crystallographic, not only permits study of the configuration of the crystals and the spatial orientation of the main crystallographic axes, but also establishes the presence of internal stresses in the space lattice of crystals, expressed in the optic anomalies. X-ray methods permit an accurate study of the space lattice of the crystals, including of course, the spatial orientation of the crystals, but they give no idea of the geometric contours of the crystals; however, these methods can be applied petrographically (i.e., to study the crystal aggregate) except in the case of fine-grained specimens, which are rare among natural ice types. Furthermore, x-ray studies require complex equipment and special training, and thus we will not discuss them here.[3]

In most cases, crystallographic research is carried out on rock specimens taken from their place of deposition, hence a few words must be said about the technique of selecting samples. In contrast to samples prepared for material composition analyses, samples for crystallographic study must be *oriented*, i.e., the position of each sample in space must be known. For this purpose, the samples must have regular form or be bounded on at least one side by a plane with a specified strike and dip in natural bedding. When there is danger of melting, it is best to cut out a regular parallelepiped, mark one of its directions with an arrow (an incision), and freeze a label indicating orientation onto each face.

An ice saw or a pick, a chisel, a mallet and a hatchet are required for extracting the ice samples, while a saw and a spade or a metal box-sonde corresponding to the size of the sample are required for extracting snow and soft firn samples. After four lateral saw cuts have been made, the ice around the sample is picked away from two or three sides and the last, the back face of the sample, is sawed out from the cleared space. The technique used to pack the sample depends on the distance and the means of transportation; in any event, for brittle porous species one needs a sturdy crating, appropriate to the size of the samples.

Because of the difficulty of preserving the ice for a long time and the inconvenience of working at low temperatures, photography or some other method of accurate portrayal of structure becomes important both for establishing the form and spatial relationships and for measuring the dimensions of the ice crystals. Photographs of the preparations, on the basis of which part of the measurements and descriptions are made subsequently, must be included in a complete program of crystallographic research. For detailed study, a positive print of the photograph of the preparation must be made, the number

---

[3] There is an extensive literature devoted to the x-ray method; one of the most complete works is the handbook by A. I. Kitaigorodskii, *Rentgenostrukturnyi analiz* (X-ray structural analysis), Moscow, 1950.

of each crystal must be marked on it and all further measurements and descriptions must be listed separately for each crystal.

Study of Porous Ice Formations in Reflected Light

The form of snow and firn crystals may be studied from their surface in ordinary reflected light by examining the natural surface or the surface of fracture of a small sample. The form of these crystals can also be studied after the specimen has been broken up into individual crystals. Furthermore, polished slides can be prepared, i.e., preparations with one plane surface on which the cross sections of the crystals can be seen. By preparing a series of equally spaced slices in successive sections and by photographing them, one may obtain a picture of the spatial arrangement of the ice skeleton and of the pores that permeate it. Weak porous ice can be cut into sections by filling in the pores with a liquid and freezing it. We will say more about this when describing the technique of preparing sections. De Quervain (1948) recommends that the surface of the slice be colored with a dark typographic dye which is then spread around with a bit of chamois soaked in alcohol; next the dye is wiped off the ice and the ice stands out against the dark background of the remaining filler (ethylorate).[4]

Inasmuch as porous ice formations are always comparatively fine-grained, a microscope, or at least a strong magnifying glass, must be used to study them. Photographing is done with a photographic adapter fitted onto the microscope or with a camera having a double extension with a diaphragming objective and a short focal length; the camera should have a ground-glass screen for focusing. When taking photographs one must determine the scale of the image. The preparation should be placed on a black background, best of all on short-napped velvet.

Another method is also used for recording the form of the ice skeleton of the snow cover and firn as well as individual snowflakes, viz., the method of taking impressions on film. This will be described in the next section.

Study of Ice Texture by Methods of Partial Melting

Melting of ice always begins at the crystal boundaries and in individual centers within the crystals, because the crystal boundaries are thermodynamically less stable than other regions and

---

[4] [Ethylorate: a term which does not appear in any of the Russian reference works available to the translator and which is unknown to American chemists; perhaps it is ethylene dichloride. – D.K.]

because the inclusions, which reduce the melting point and strongly absorb radiant energy, are unevenly distributed along the crystal boundaries. Therefore, melting, as it were, "reveals," i.e., makes visible, the ice texture. The design of the crystal contours appears on the surface of the melting ice in the form of a network of furrows that are narrow at first and then broaden. Tyndall figures appear inside fairly large crystals; some of these formations may even emerge onto the surface, forming fine surface striations that are uniformly oriented in each crystal. Thus, both the outlines of the crystals and the orientation of their basal planes become evident in the melting ice. With intense melting of coarse crystalline ice, when "petals" appear on the "ice flowers," the orientation may be established more fully. The structure shows up best during melting due to radiant energy, when the melting is abetted by the intensified absorption of rays by the inclusions, but the same effect may also be observed in the case of melting caused by conductive heat transfer due only to the lower melting point around the inclusions containing salt.

The method of partial melting is simple and convenient in that it can be used in the field, even without taking the ice from its place of exposure. When the weather is favorable, the melt pattern of the grains and embryonic Tyndall figures often appear as a result of natural processes and may be observed on an ice surface or in ice cliffs (see Figs. 21 and 22). Texture can be displayed artificially by smoothing the ice surface with a plane and then melting it with a blowtorch (Ahlmann and Droessler, 1949) or by rubbing it with a clump of blotting paper (Seligman, 1949), or better still by exposing it to a powerful lamp. Longer exposure to a powerful light source or passage of a high-voltage alternating current through ice may cause it to disintegrate completely into individual crystals, but in that case the crystals must necessarily melt somewhat around the edges. Usually, the form, dimensions and orientation of the crystals are studied in plane cross section.

The rubbing method has long been used to fix the contours of crystals in natural size (Deeley, 1910). Soft paper is placed on the melted surface of ice and is shaded with a soft pencil. The crystal boundaries remain as white bands on the dark background, while the air bubbles remain as little white spots (Fig. 23). If the surface of the ice is moist, it should be dried first with blotting paper.

Other methods of establishing crystal outlines were used before the shading method, viz., the taking of wax impressions from the melted surface of ice (Schlagintweit, 1854) or the taking of gypsum casts (Lohmann, 1895). Finally, in recent times a method of making

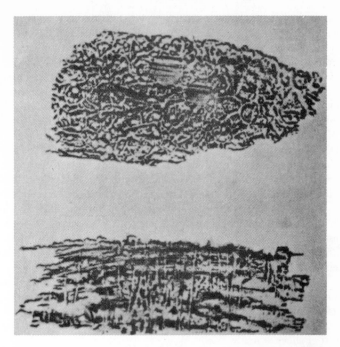

Fig. 23. Sketch of the ice texture made by the rubbing method (actual size).

replicas of a colored ice surface on paper has come into use (Selig-man, 1949; Ahlmann and Droessler, 1949). A water-insoluble powdered dye mixed with clay is used for coloring. If the surface has melted but little, the dye is rubbed forcibly into the furrows between the crystals, which show up as dark lines on the replica. If there has been too much melting, the opposite method is used, i.e., the dye is smeared over the surface in an even layer and then the crystal boundaries on the replica remain as white streaks amidst the colored surface.

Even better results are obtained in the laboratory by using contact photographs of stained ice plates.[5] The polished surface of a plate of ice is melted by irradiation with a powerful lamp having a reflector, in a moderately warm room, and next the plate is colored, with either powdered lead oxide, some other water-soluble dye, or soot. The dye is rubbed into the furrows on the crystal boundaries and into the Tyndall figures that come to the surface. After freezing has occurred,

---

[5] The author was the first to use this method (1947).

a sheet of photographic paper is pressed onto the stained surface of the ice; a light source is placed on the opposite side and the necessary exposure is made. If there are no large mineral inclusions, the light source should be moved back and forth; then only the details of the surface next to the paper will be printed. If there are large opaque inclusions, the light source should be kept stationary and then the inclusions in the whole mass of the ice will be depicted on the photograph.

Next, a positive is printed from the negative by the same contact method, and if the ice is coarse-crystalline and Tyndall figures have melted in it, the orientation of these formations is measured and marked on the photographs, as is done when the attitude of beds is indicated on geological maps. Their strike is immediately evident on the photograph, and the dip is measured as follows. The flattened end of a metal rod is carefully inserted into the plane of the melt figure and the angle between it and the surface of the ice is measured with a protractor. If the formations do not emerge onto the surface, their orientation can be measured by sighting. The photograph, Fig. 24, with the orientation of the basal planes sketched in, gives a complete picture of the texture of the samples for a given plane. For detailed investigations, three mutually perpendicular slices are made in the most characteristic direction, or a series of equally spaced parallel slices is made.

The outlines of ice crystals and even the presence of mosaic texture within monocrystals may also be observed without melting the ice, simply by subjecting an ice sample with a polished surface to conditions under which it will experience sublimation or, conversely, to conditions under which water vapor will sublime on its surface. In the first instance the ice must be heated above the temperature of the ambient air, which is more or less saturated with water vapor; in the second instance it must be cooled below the temperature of the air. Both the etching of the surface and the sublimation of the fine ice crystals on it display tiny differences in the crystallographic orientation of the neighboring parts of the surface when examined at a specific viewing angle in reflected light. The sublimation method, which is analogous to the "dew method" employed in crystallography, was evidently first employed by D. Mawson (1916) on Shackleton's Antarctic Expedition of 1907–1909.

P. S. Vadilo (1939, 1951) used the same method, supplemented by goniometric measurement of the angles between the faces of sublimed subindividuals on neighboring crystals. By measuring the deflection angles of the surface up to positions where the reflection of light from the surface in a given direction is most intense, one may

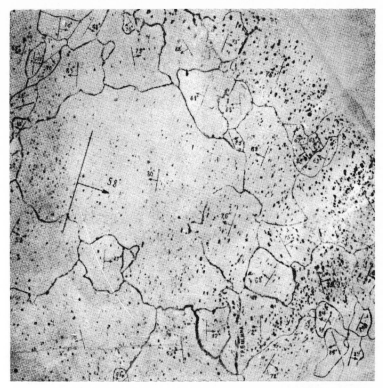

Fig. 24. Contact photograph of ice textures. Curves—crystal boundaries; dark lines—Tyndall figures; dark spots—air bubbles; the small indications of bedding refer to the basal planes of the crystals; the large indications, to the stratification of the ice. 0.6 actual size. (Photograph by N. V. Cherepanov.)

determine the crystallographic symbols of the ice crystal faces. On the other hand, V. Schaefer (1942*a*, *b*, and other works) obtained microrelief replicas on film by using an etched ice surface. The replica method has been used in metallography since 1906, then in mineralography, where originally it was based on the chemical reaction of the metals or minerals of a polished section. In contrast to this, Schaefer employed a cold solution of pitch on which he obtained mechanical replicas that gave the most minute details of the surface relief. In this way, he recorded the form of snowflakes in the vertical cross section of the snow cover, of metals, and of glacier ice in polished slides. For snowflakes, he employed a 1–2% solution of polyvinyl alcohol and dichloride of ethylene; for glacier ice, a 3%

solution; for the snow cover, a 3–5% solution. When this method is used the snowflakes are placed on a drop of solution, or a piece of cold glass covered with a thin film of solution is exposed to falling snow. In studying the cross section of the snow cover, window glass with a film of solution is pressed for a while against a vertical wall of snow. In the process, the solvent and the snow particles that adhere to it vaporize, and the replica is then ready.

The procedure for obtaining replicas of an etched surface of ice is analogous to that practised in metallography. The ice is covered with a layer of solution and some time after the solvent has evaporated, the film is removed with tweezers and spread out on the glass with the replica side up. The film can be put onto the glass more conveniently if it is placed on a water surface containing a small amount of dissolved gelatin and the glass lifted to come into contact with the floating film; the gelatin prevents the film from separating from the glass after drying. The replicas of the relief of an etched surface obtained in this way can be studied under ordinary light and electron microscopes. Schaefer recommends replicas on a film containing dye for studying ice under a light microscope.

Optical Crystallographic Methods of Studying Ice Structure

When the optical crystallographic method is employed on thin slices or sections of ice, a polarizing microscope or polaroids are used.[6]

Polaroids are two transparent plates with a thin gelatinous film containing a mass of uniformly oriented submicroscopic crystals of iodine and quinine sulfate compounds. One of these, serving as the polarizer, is placed between the light source and the preparation; the second, the analyzer, is placed between the preparation and the eye, with the plane of polarization perpendicular to the first. Polaroids are very useful for simple optical crystallographic investigation in the field and have an advantage over a microscope in that they provide a large field of vision, since actually they can be made in any size. Thus, polaroids must be used in the laboratory, too, along with

---

[6] We assume that the reader is familiar with the fundamentals of optical crystallography. The following handbooks on optical crystallography are recommended: D. S. Beliankin, *Kristallooptika* (Optical crystallography), Moscow, 1949; V. N. Lodochnikov, *Osnovy kristallooptiki* (Principles of optical crystallography), Moscow, 1947; V. I. Luchitskii, *Petrografiia* (Petrography), Vol. I, Moscow, 1949; V. B. Tatarskii, *Kristallooptika i immersionnyi metod opredeleniia veshchestva* (Optical crystallography and the immersion method of defining matter), Leningrad, 1949.

a polarizing microscope, for studying and photographing the structure of rocks that have medium and large crystals.

The simplest kind of polariscope, made, for example, from photographic negatives (Vadilo, 1951), can be substituted for the polaroids. There is no need to use polaroids for studying porous ice types.

Sections of ice to be studied with polaroids may be prepared at a positive temperature by hand-grinding a piece of ice on two sides using a sheet of metal, in which case thermal reaction plays the main role. At a negative temperature, the ice is ground with sheets of emery paper, first coarse, then fine grits, and finally is polished with soft writing paper. The sections must always be oriented, i.e., one must know exactly the spatial position of the section in natural bedding. The dimensions of the section depend largely on the size of the grains. A section more than 1 mm thick may be prepared in sizes 5 × 5 cm and larger; a thinner section should be smaller in area.

The proper thickness of the section is determined by the following considerations. The diameter of the crystals is the upper limit of thickness, and the upper limit of large crystals is 3–4 mm, at which one gets very pale interference coloration of higher orders. A thick section allows study of a considerable number of inclusions, but the crystal boundaries oblique to the line of sight appear as a broad fringe of interference colors. More distinct crystal profiles are obtained in thin sections (0.1–0.2 mm), but such sections are smaller, their preparation is more difficult, takes longer, and their crystals show up in low interference colors that are harder to distinguish. The best sections are 0.4–0.8 mm thick, in which the crystals with cross section parallel to the optic axis have bright second-order colors.

If the work is done at positive temperatures, as is often the case in the field, the section is placed on glass between polaroids and is described as quickly as possible. At negative temperatures, the ground side of the sample is frozen to a glass slide, for which purpose the glass is first warmed in one's hand until the ice shows signs of melting; then the other side is ground. At higher temperatures, it is better to place the slide in a wooden frame so that it will not be warmed by contact with the hand. If a section is to be preserved for any length of time, a cover glass should be frozen to it from above, and the lateral spaces between the pieces of glass filled with vaseline.

Each crystal of the slide between the polarized plates has its own interference color; thus, the crystal outlines become visible, and the orientation of the optic axes of the crystals with respect to the plane of the section can be determined by the intensity of the interference colors (more about this later).

To photograph the texture, the polaroid plates, the preparation, the double convex lens which serves as a condenser, and the camera are attached in line with the light source on the same axis, which makes it possible to move each part separately for purposes of focusing.

Considerably more accurate data on the orientation of crystals can be obtained with a *polarizing microscope*. Further, the polarizing microscope can be used to study optic anomalies and its high magnification makes it indispensable for studying fine crystal formations and fine inclusions in ice.

The techniques of *preparing sections* of ice for study under the microscope and with polaroids differ only in that all microscopic work must be carried out more painstakingly, since the preparations are used for detailed investigation. Special care must be taken that the section does not melt too much while being frozen to the slides, since this may cause secondary crystal particles to appear, and care must be taken that air bubbles do not form between the glass and the ice.

The sections should be oriented accurately, for which purpose a regular block is first sawed out of the ice, and an arrow direction indicator is then placed on one of its faces in the plane of the future section before attachment to the microscopic slide. After the block has been frozen to the slide, the slide itself acts as the direction indicator; the slide is always numbered on a particular side. After attachment to the slide, the block can be sawed off instead of being ground. H. Bader (1939) used a bench saw, on which he could saw off plates 0.3–0.5 mm thick.

Preparation of sections of snow and firn presents special difficulties, but Bader (1939) has worked out a method for it. The porous ice is not strong enough to endure grinding, and therefore the pores should first be filled with a hard substance. For this purpose the specimen is drenched with a liquid which is then allowed to freeze. The liquid should have a melting point of $0°C$, be capable of being supercooled to $-5°$ to $-10°C$, have low viscosity, moisten ice, be insoluble in water, be non-volatile, freeze without changing volume and yield a strong fine-grained aggregate as hard as ice, which will have good cohesion with ice and which can be distinguished easily from ice under the microscope. A tetrabromethane (acetylene tetrabromide) and ethylene dichloride best satisfy these requirements.

A small oriented block of the rock to be studied, with a weight attached to keep it from floating, is placed in a beaker. A supercooled liquid is poured into the beaker along the side so that the level of the liquid will rise slowly and force all the air out of the pores.

Friable snow with a density less than 0.2 g/cm^3 cannot survive immersion and is destroyed by the forces of surface tension, capillary suction and hydrostatic pressure, so that sections cannot be prepared from it. After pouring has been completed, the contents of the beaker are frozen and removed after being warmed with the hand, and oriented sections are cut out of the block in the usual manner. After the section has been prepared, and before a glass cover is applied, the filler may be melted by a drop of vaseline or paraffin oil (de Quervain, 1948). This eliminates the scattered light coming from it, which prevents one from working with crossed Nicols and which obscures the details of the bonds between the crystals.

A full presentation of the structure of a given segment of the specimen is provided by study of three mutually perpendicular slices. The directions of the slices are chosen in accordance with the mode of occurrence of the rock and the deformations it undergoes. The following symbols introduced by B. Sander (1930, p. 57) for structural directions have been adopted in petrology:

a: direction of the completed motion and dip of the layers;

b: direction of the fold and strike axes of the layers perpendicular to a; and

c: the normal to the plane ab, the direction of rock pressure.

Further, for ice, c often coincides with the direction of the heat flux which exerts an influence on the formation of growth structures.

As a rule, the sections are cut out in planes ab, bc, and ac. The form, size, spatial relationships of the crystals, optic anomalies and relationship of the ice crystals to the inclusions are studied in all three mutually perpendicular slices. The crystallographic orientation can be measured accurately in only one of the sections; in the remaining sections only approximate control estimates can be made, based on the height of the interference colors or the sign of the principal section of the elongated crystals.

A section is studied under the microscope according to the following plan:

1. The section is examined without the analyzer and under crossed Nicols; the general character of the form, dimensions, spatial relationships of the crystals and their relations to the inclusions are examined.

2. The section is photographed in polarized light with an analyzer. A polaroid arrangement is used in photographing the entire section, while individual interesting details are examined under a microscope using different magnifications. Color photography gives the best results (see Figs. 37 and 38); without it, neighboring crystals with close orientation may blend on the photograph. To avoid this,

sets of two photographs showing different positions of the section with respect to the planes of oscillation of the polarizers should be made or the photographs should be retouched. In an extreme case, a sketch may be made with a drawing set. All crystals are numbered on a positive print of the section.

3. The dimensions of the crystals are measured. If the photograph still does not show the outline of all the grains, because of their close crystallographic orientation, and the fine-grained structure of the species does not allow accurate sketching, it may be necessary to measure the crystal sizes directly under the microscope. Then the length and width of the crystals are measured by a linear ocular micrometer, while the area is measured by a reticular ocular micrometer. The section is moved back and forth on a track.

4. The axiality is determined and the angle of optic axes of the biaxial crystals is measured conoscopically for crystals with cross sections more or less close to the perpendicular cross sections of the optic axis (or the acute bisectrix). Whether or not a crystal belongs to the optically uniaxial or biaxial type is determined by the character of the conoscopic figure. In uniaxial crystals, the conoscopic figure is a cross, while in oblique cross sections, the isogyres, passing through the center of the field of vision, coincide with the cross hairs of the ocular. In biaxial crystals, when the microscope stage is rotated, the cross breaks down into the two branches of a hyperbola. To determine the angle of the optic axes $2V$, one must know the Mallard constant K for the given optic system and use an ocular micrometer to measure the maximum distance $2D$ between the apexes of the branches of the hyperbolas that are the traces of the optic axes at the moment the stage is turned $45°$ from the position of the cross. The Mallard constant is measured by an apertometer or by measuring D for some mineral with an accurately known angle of the optic axes.

When ice crystals are measured in the air, the sine of half the angle of the optic axes may be assumed equal to

$$\sin V = \frac{KD}{n_m} = \frac{KD}{1.31}$$

In case of biaxiality, indicating that the ice has undergone elastic deformations, the angles are measured for the optic axes of all biaxial crystals having measurable orientation.

5. The sign of elongation and the nature of the extinction are determined. In sections not studied on the universal stage, the sign of the principal section of the elongated crystals is determined by using

a gypsum plate or a quartz wedge. Positive elongation of the ice indicates elongation of the crystal along the main axis and, consequently, the columnar type of growth, while negative elongation indicates flattening along the main axis and, thus, the plate type of crystal.

The character of the extinction can also be determined for the rarely encountered crystals of regular form. In the non-transmitting sections perpendicular to the optic axis, the type of the face is immediately evident from the symmetry of the profile. Parallel extinction is observed with respect to the faces of a monohedron or a pinacoid in any position, and also of a prism perpendicular to the plane of the section. Symmetrical extinction is peculiar to the face of a pyramid which is perpendicular to the plane of the section, and oblique extinction is peculiar to the inclined faces of the prism and pyramid.

When the Fedorov universal stage is used, the relationship between the crystallographic axes and the external form of the crystal, and also the character of the faces, are revealed from direct measurements.

6. The orientation of the optic axes of the crystals may be determined by different methods with varying degrees of accuracy. The simplest and roughest method is the division of the crystals in the section into categories according to the height of their interference colors (e.g., low, medium and high coloration). If a count is made of a large number of crystals of each category, especially in the three mutually perpendicular slices, it becomes possible to form an approximate picture of the predominant orientation of the optic axes.

A more accurate, but also merely statistical method of determining the prevalence of one or another orientation is the method of determining the azimuths of the traces of the optic axes of crystals in three mutually perpendicular slices (de Quervain, 1948). For each crystal, that azimuth of the extinction position is measured which, when turned 45°, is inversely parallel to the gypsum plate or the quartz wedge (with the n_p axis longitudinal). With random orientation, each 15° angular sector should have an average of approximately 4.17% of the azimuths of all the optic axes. A regular tendency towards the prevalence of certain azimuths indicates ordered structure.

The orientation of the optic axis of every crystal can be determined more accurately by supplementing the measurement of the azimuth of the main cross section with the value of the angular distance of the trace of the optic axis from the center of the field of vision.[7] For this purpose, first the direction in which the optic axis is inclined in the plane of the main cross section is determined conoscopically (keeping in mind that when a Bertrand lens has been included, the conoscopic figure will be rotated 180°). If the trace of the optic axis appears in the field of vision of the microscope, the angular distance from the center is determined conoscopically by Mallard's formula. Otherwise, the angle of inclination of the optic axis is determined by measuring the thickness of the section and the difference in the paths assumed by the ordinary and extraordinary rays in the crystal.

To measure the thickness of the microscopic section d under sufficiently strong magnification, repeated measurement is made (with a micrometer screw) of the displacement d_1 of the draw tube between the positions where the upper and lower surfaces of the ice in the section are brought into focus; this can be determined from the dust particles or bubbles between the ice and the glass slides: $d = 1.311\ d_1$. The difference of the paths Δ is measured by the compensation method with an ordinary or a graduated quartz wedge (accuracy from $\pm$ 10 to 40 mμ) and more accurately using a Berek or Babinet compensator. The angle of inclination of the optic axis ϕ is computed by the formula

$$\sin \phi \, \frac{n_e}{n_e'} \sqrt{\frac{n_e'^2 - n_0^2}{n_e^2 - n_0^2}}$$

where $n_e' = n_0 + \dfrac{\Delta}{d}$.[8] Bader (1939, p. 54) constructed a nomogram of the relationship, for ice, between the difference in the ray paths and the thickness of a microscopic section, making it possible to find the angle of inclination of the optic axis graphically (Fig. 25).

The method described is very cumbersome and cannot assure an accuracy above $\pm 5°$. Under all circumstances, preference should be given to E. S. Fedorov's universal stage method.[9] When the universal stage method is used in textural investigations, systematic study must be made of the whole area of the section with its orientation

---

[7] This method was applied to ice by H. Bader (1939) and M. Perutz (Perutz and Seligman, 1939).

[8] $n_e = 1.3120$; $n_0 = 1.3106$.

[9] For literature on the E. S. Fedorov method, see E. A. Kuznetsov, *Kratkii kurs metoda Fedorova v petrografii* (Short course on the Fedorov method in petrography), 1949; A. K. Podnogin, *Mikroskopicheskoe issledovanie porodoobrazuiushchikh mineralov po metodu E. S. Fedorova* (Microscopic study of rock-forming minerals using the E. S. Fedorov method), 1937; V. V. Nikitin, *Universal'nyi metod Fedorova* (The Fedorov universal method), lithograph edition, St. Petersburg, 1911–1915.

preserved. A Schmidt carriage is used to move the section back and
forth along the stand. To get enough crystals of coarse-grained ice,
one must study several identically oriented sections. However, this
can be avoided by employing either a large theodolite microscope
(Drescher, 1932, p. 167), which allows study of sections up to 25 cm²
in area, or by employing a universal stage with polaroids.

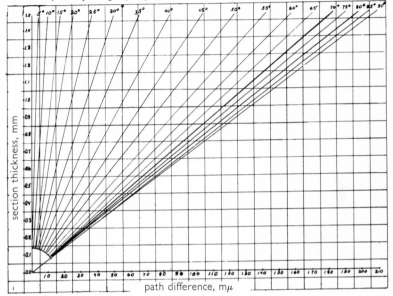

Fig. 25. Relationship of the difference in path of ordinary and extraordinary
rays to the thickness of the microscopic section of ice. (After H. Bader, 1939.)

There are no glass hemispheres with an index of refraction as low
as that of ice, so a correction factor must be introduced into the
values of the angles measured on the universal stage, computed by
the formula

$$\sin \beta = \frac{n}{1.311} \sin \alpha$$

where β is the true angle, α the measured angle and n the index of
refraction of the glass of the hemisphere.

For ice, instead of the ordinary graphic determination of the
corrections based on the Fedorov diagram, it is more convenient to
use the table of true angles computed by the formula given above
(see Table 2).

TABLE 2

Translation of the angles α, measured on the Fedorov stage, into true angles β in the ice-glass system with $n = 1.516$.

α	0	0.1	0.2	0.3	0.4	0.5	0.6	0.7	0.8	0.9
0	0.0	0.1	0.2	0.35	0.5	0.6	0.7	0.8	0.9	1.0
1	1.2	1.3	1.4	1.5	1.6	1.7	1.85	2.0	2.1	2.2
2	2.3	2.4	2.5	2.7	2.8	2.9	3.0	3.1	3.2	3.35
3	3.5	3.6	3.7	3.8	3.9	4.0	4.2	4.3	4.4	4.5
4	4.6	4.7	4.8	5.0	5.1	5.2	5.3	5.4	5.5	5.7
5	5.8	5.9	6.0	6.1	6.2	6.4	6.5	6.6	6.7	6.8
6	6.9	7.0	7.2	7.3	7.4	7.5	7.6	7.7	7.9	8.0
7	8.1	8.2	8.3	8.4	8.5	8.7	8.8	8.9	9.0	9.1
8	9.2	9.4	9.5	9.6	9.7	9.8	9.9	10.1	10.2	10.3
9	10.4	10.5	10.6	10.7	10.9	11.0	11.1	11.2	11.3	11.4
10	11.6	11.7	11.8	11.9	12.0	12.1	12.2	12.4	12.5	12.6
11	12.7	12.8	12.9	13.1	13.2	13.3	13.4	13.5	13.6	13.8
12	13.9	14.0	14.1	14.2	14.3	14.4	14.6	14.7	14.8	14.9
13	15.0	15.1	15.3	15.4	15.5	15.6	15.7	15.8	15.9	16.1
14	16.2	16.3	16.4	16.5	16.6	16.8	16.9	17.0	17.1	17.2
15	17.3	17.5	17.6	17.7	17.8	17.9	18.0	18.1	18.3	18.4
16	18.5	18.6	18.7	18.8	19.0	19.1	19.2	19.3	19.4	19.5
17	19.6	19.8	19.9	20.0	20.1	20.2	20.3	20.5	20.6	20.7
18	20.8	20.9	21.0	21.1	21.3	21.4	21.5	21.6	21.7	21.8
19	22.0	22.1	22.2	22.3	22.4	22.5	22.7	22.8	22.9	23.0
20	23.1	23.2	23.3	23.5	23.6	23.7	23.8	23.9	24.0	24.2
21	24.3	24.4	24.5	24.6	24.7	24.8	25.0	25.1	25.2	25.3
22	25.4	25.5	25.7	25.8	25.9	26.0	26.1	26.2	26.3	26.5
23	26.6	26.7	26.8	26.9	27.0	27.2	27.3	27.4	27.5	27.6
24	27.7	27.9	28.0	28.1	28.2	28.3	28.4	28.5	28.7	28.8
25	28.9	29.0	29.1	29.2	29.4	29.5	29.6	29.7	29.8	29.9
26	30.1	30.2	30.3	30.4	30.5	30.6	30.7	30.9	31.0	31.1
27	31.2	31.3	31.4	31.6	31.7	31.8	31.9	32.0	32.1	32.2
28	32.4	32.5	32.6	32.7	32.8	32.9	33.1	33.2	33.3	33.4
29	33.5	33.6	33.7	33.9	34.0	34.1	34.2	34.3	34.4	34.6
30	34.7	34.8	34.9	35.0	35.1	35.3	35.4	35.5	35.6	35.7
31	35.8	35.9	36.1	36.2	36.3	36.4	36.5	36.6	36.8	36.9
32	37.0	37.1	37.2	37.3	37.4	37.6	37.7	37.8	37.9	38.0
33	38.1	38.3	38.4	38.5	38.6	38.7	38.8	39.0	39.1	39.2
34	39.3	39.4	39.5	39.6	39.8	39.9	40.0	40.1	40.2	40.3
35	40.5	40.6	40.7	40.8	40.9	41.0	41.1	41.3	41.4	41.5
36	41.6	41.7	41.8	42.0	42.1	42.2	42.3	42.4	42.5	42.7
37	42.8	42.9	43.0	43.1	43.2	43.3	43.5	43.6	43.7	43.8
38	43.9	44.0	44.2	44.3	44.4	44.5	44.6	44.7	44.8	45.0
39	45.1	45.2	45.3	45.4	45.5	45.7	45.8	45.9	46.0	46.1
40	46.2	46.4	46.5	46.6	46.7	46.8	46.9	47.0	47.2	47.3
41	47.4	47.5	47.6	47.7	47.9	48.0	48.1	48.2	48.3	48.4

α	0	0.1	0.2	0.3	0.4	0.5	0.6	0.7	0.8	0.9
42	48.5	48.7	48.8	48.9	49.0	49.1	49.2	49.4	49.5	49.6
43	49.7	49.8	49.9	50.0	50.2	50.3	50.4	50.5	50.6	50.7
44	50.9	51.0	51.1	51.2	51.3	51.4	51.6	51.7	51.8	51.9
45	52.0	52.1	52.2	52.4	52.5	52.6	52.7	52.8	52.9	53.1
46	53.2	53.3	53.4	53.5	53.6	53.7	53.9	54.0	54.1	54.2
47	54.3	54.4	54.6	54.7	54.8	54.9	55.0	55.1	55.3	55.4
48	55.5	55.6	55.7	55.8	55.9	56.1	56.2	56.3	56.4	56.5
49	56.6	56.8	56.9	57.0	57.1	57.2	57.3	57.4	57.6	57.7
50	57.8	57.9	58.0	58.1	58.3	58.4	58.5	58.6	58.7	58.8

Measurement of the orientation of the optic axes of uniaxial crystals on the universal stage is considerably less complicated than measurement of biaxial crystals, thus simplifying the work considerably.[10] In this case, only three axes need be used: N, I and H, not counting the axis of the microscope stage, A (Fig. 26).

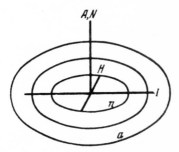

Fɪɢ. 26.   Sketch of the axes of the Fedorov stage in the initial position.

The orientation of the optic axis of a uniaxial crystal on the universal stage may be determined by two means:

(a) By arrangement of the optic axis of the crystal parallel to the axis of the microscope, *the polar position*, which requires (1) that the section be rotated from the initial position around axis N until the crystal is extinguished, and the extinction continued during rotation around axis I (it is assumed that the extinction is not maintained at 90° to the given position); (2) that the

---

[10] On the universal stage, crystals with the angle between their optic axes up to 30° are practically indistinguishable from uniaxial crystals.

stage be rotated 45° around axis *A;* and (3) that rotation around axis *I* be continued until extinction. In this position the optic axis of the crystal is parallel to the axis of the microscope, which may be verified by rotation around axis *A;* having assured ourselves that darkness was maintained, we can note the readings along the *N* and *I* axes.

(*b*) If extinction is not attained by rotation around axis *I*, the optic axis of the crystal will be inclined more than 50–60° to the axis of the microscope; then the orientation of the crystal will be determined by arrangement of the plane of the indicatrix, which is perpendicular to the optic axis of the crystal, parallel to the axis of the microscope—the *equatorial position.* For this purpose, (4) the stage is rotated into the first position with zero readings along the *I* and *A* axes; (5) the stage is rotated 90° around the *N* axis to the next position of extinction; (6) the stage is rotated 30–35° around axis *I*; (7) the stage is rotated around the *H* axis to extinction and returned to the zero position on the *I* axis. Now the optic axis of the crystal is parallel to the *I* axis. When the observer is convinced that the extinction was not maintained during rotation around the *A* axis, he notes the readings along the *N* and *H* axes.

The described procedure is employed in the ordinary case of an inclined position of the optic axis. There are special cases of positions where, during the first operation, the crystal remains dark at all times (optic axis parallel or nearly parallel to the axis of the microscope) or when both extinctions are maintained during rotation around the *I* axis (optic axis coincides or nearly coincides with the plane of the section).

In the first case it is difficult to determine whether the extinction is complete or partial. To determine the orientation accurately, (1) the stand is rotated several degrees around the *I* axis, (2) it is rotated around the *H* axis to find the true position of extinction, and the reading is taken along the *H* axis, (3) the stand is rotated several degrees around the *H* axis, and (4) it is rotated around the *I* axis, revealing the true position of extinction and the reading is taken along the *I* axis.

In the second case, we must determine in which of two possible positions the optic axis lies. In one of the positions of extinction the stage is rotated by an arbitrary angle around axis *I*, and then around axis *H*. If the extinction is maintained, the optic axis coincides with the *H* axis; if, however, light comes through, the optic axis coincides with the *I* axis; in both cases the reading is taken along the *N* axis.

There is still another, a third, indirect method of determining the orientation of the optic axis as the pole of a circular section of the optic indicatrix. This is the method whereby two or, better, three main cross sections (first operation, of type *a*) are determined for different arbitrary positions along the *H* axis. Then the position of the optic axis is obtained graphically on a Wulff or Schmidt net at the point of intersection of the main cross sections found.

7. Measurement of the orientation of the faces of the rarely encountered, regularly bounded crystals, and of the fracture planes and the like on the universal stage, is made as follows:

(1) by rotation around the *N* axis, the face is set parallel to the vertical cross hair of the ocular;

(2) by rotation around the *H* axis, a position is reached whereby the face appears as the narrowest and most sharply defined line; in this position the face is parallel to the axis of the microscope and the *H* axis of the stage; after verifying the accuracy of the arrangement by turning the micrometer screw of the draw tube (the face should not be moved), we take our reading along the *N* and *H* axes.

Processing Optical Crystallographic Data

To give an objective quantitative definition of the structure of an ice formation on the basis of optical crystallographic data, all measurement results must be processed statistically.

Crystal sizes. If the size of the crystal has not been measured directly under the microscope or determined by granulometric analysis, it is measured by photographs, contact prints, etc., with a scale used for comparison. There are various methods of measuring size, with varying degrees of accuracy. The simplest method consists in measuring the largest and smallest axes of the plane cross section of the crystal; the approximate area cross section is found by multiplying the values.

Better results are obtained by comparing each crystal with a series of standard areas, viz., circles, squares or rectangles (depending on the dominant crystal shape), plotted on tracing paper. The standard areas are selected such that the ratio between the neighboring larger and smaller standards remains constant. For example, Seligman (1949) used a series of circles with diameters 0.25, 0.4, 0.6, 1.0, 1.6, 2.5, 4.0, 6.3 and 10.0 cm. Each crystal is classified according to the standard size nearest it in area. Measurement gives the number of granules of each size, which is then converted into percentages of the total area cross section of the investigated sample. Planimetric measurement of each crystal is the most accurate method.

The greatest source of error in determining crystal size is the following: a plane cross section of a polycrystalline aggregate can never pass through the largest cross section of all the crystals. The fine crystal particles observed in polished slides are usually angular cross sections of larger crystals and therefore the average size is undervalued. To avoid this source of error, a method of computing the true crystal sizes has been worked out in metallography on the basis of the data for the plane cross section (Johnson, 1946, p. 87).

The crystals are divided into groups with n numbers on the basis of the sizes of the plane cross sections, each with an average area of $S = 2^{1-n} cm^2$, in which case all grains having the area

$$2^{1-(n-1/2)} < S \leq 2^{1-(n+1/2)}$$

are assigned to a given group.

The equivalent linear dimensions of the crystals of each group are assumed to be $l = \sqrt{S}$ cm. For example, crystals of the first group $(n = 1)$ have an average area cross section of 1 cm² (from 0.71 to 1.41 cm²) and a diameter of $l = 1$ cm; crystals of the second group have $S = 0.5$ cm² and $l = 0.7$ cm; crystals of the zero group have $S = 2$ cm² and $l = 1.44$ cm; crystals of the minus third group have $S = 16$ cm² and $l = 4$ cm; etc.

The crystals measured by planimeter or by comparison with standard areas are separated into the indicated groups and the percentage of the total area of the sample (slide) occupied by crystals of each group is reckoned.

Mathematical analysis, based on experimental data, has shown that in an aggregate of crystals of any (including variable) form but of uniform volume (e.g., corresponding to the first group), 72.8% of the area of the cut will be occupied by cross sections of crystals of the first group, 20.3% by cross sections of the second group, 5.1% by cross sections of the third group, 1.3% by the fourth, 0.4% by the fifth and 0.1% by the sixth and subsequent groups. If the crystals of the first group occupy a portion f of the volume of the sample, they will comprise plane sections of the first group over an area 72.8f% of the total area of the cut, etc. Thus, if the percentage of the area occupied by the largest sections is measured, the percentage of the volume occupied by the grains of this group can be found by dividing by 0.728. Then the portions of the total area occupied by the smaller cross sections of the crystals of this group are computed and subtracted from those measured in the slide. Next, the volume of the sample which is occupied by the grains of the next (smaller) group can be found, etc. The computation is considerably simplified by using Johnson's table and the standard shapes.

The accumulation curve of distribution of the total volume of the crystals of different sizes (Fig. 27) is plotted on the basis of the percentages of area, with processing done by the Johnson method, i.e., according to the percentages of the volume occupied by the crystals of each group in the sample, and also on the basis of the data from the granulometric analysis. The mean linear size of the crystals of the sample in the given cut corresponds to the ordinate point on the

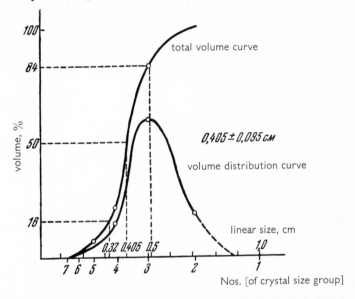

FIG. 27. Curve of distribution of crystals of different linear dimensions in the total volume of a rock.

accumulation curve that represents 50% of the volume. Half the difference of the sizes, corresponding to 16 and 84% of the volume, respectively, is taken as the mean deviation. The extreme crystal sizes are taken from the planimetric data. Thus, the quantitative character of the crystal sizes, according to the data from one cut, consists of (1) the average linear dimension of the crystals in the given cut, (2) the average absolute and relative (in percentages of the average size) deviations from it, (3) the greatest absolute and relative deviations from the mean size and (4) the curve of distribution of the crystal sizes or the histograms.

If we need know only the average and extreme crystal sizes, we can limit ourselves to planimetric measurement or other means of determining the area cross sections of the largest and smallest crystals and the total area cross section of all the crystals in the slide, from which values we can then compute the average area cross section of one crystal. Comparison of the results thus obtained with the data obtained from processing by the Johnson method shows that for ice, the first method gives an average crystal diameter that is, on the average, 20% too small. Therefore, in determining sizes by the method described, we must introduce a correction factor of 1.25 for the average diameter of the crystals, or 1.5625 for the average area cross section of the crystals.

Having obtained the areas of three mutually perpendicular cross sections ab, ac and bc, from three slides, we compute the linear dimensions of the crystals in the three structural directions by the formulas

$$a = \sqrt{\frac{ab \times ac}{bc}} \; ; \quad b = \sqrt{\frac{ab \times bc}{ac}} \; ; \quad c = \sqrt{\frac{ac \times bc}{ab}}$$

and the volume by the formula

$$V = abc = \sqrt{ab \times ac \times bc}$$

The ratio of the linear dimensions in the three structural directions characterizes the typical form of the crystals.

Computation of the coefficient of irregularity of the crystal boundaries and the area of the crystal surfaces. Another quantitative characteristic of crystal form, obtained from photographs or from contact prints of the plane cross section of a rock sample, is the average length of the boundaries of a single crystal having an area equal to unity. This is the so-called coefficient of irregularity of the grain boundaries C, computed from the formula (Bain, 1941, p. 199):

$$C = \frac{L}{\sqrt{N}}$$

where L is the length of contact of the grains per cubic centimeter and N is the number of grains per cubic centimeter.

To determine the coefficient of irregularity on an impression, a rectangle of maximum size is outlined, in which the number of crystals is computed with consideration of the visually estimable portion of the crystals included within the boundaries of the rectangle; the total length of the inner boundaries between the crystals is measured by a curvometer.

For rectangular crystals with rectilinear boundaries, $C = 2$; for a

circle $C = 1.18$. Regular hexagons, corresponding to a cross section
of euhedral crystals in the basal planes give $C = 1.86$. Thus, to a
certain extent, the coefficient of irregularity can characterize the
state of idiomorphism or allotriomorphism of the texture; the values
$C < 1.86$ are associated with the prevalence of rounded crystals, the
$C > 1.86$–2.00 values with notched, irregular crystals. This is of
genetic importance in ice as well as in other rocks.

The area s of contact of the crystal boundaries per unit volume of
the rock may be determined approximately by the formula

$$s = L^{3/2}$$

The value S of the crystal surfaces per unit volume of the rock is
twice as large:

$$S = 2 L^{3/2}$$

This value is essential for computing the thickness of the liquid
film between the ice crystals, with salinity and temperature known.

Orientation of the optic axes of the crystals. The results of measurements
of the optic-axes orientation are depicted graphically by the Schmidt
method (Schmidt, 1925, p. 392) as a diagram of the density distribution of traces of the optic axes on the surface of a sphere. The point
of intersection of the optic axis of each crystal with the surface of the
sphere is plotted on a Schmidt net, which depicts the inner surface
of a hemisphere in equiareal projection. The standard net is 20 cm
in diameter and consists of a system of meridians and parallels
drawn every 2° (Fig. 28). The equiareal projection was chosen because it permits a statistical count of the number of points per unit
plane surface without distorting the result in comparison with a
spherical surface.

To plot the point, the tracing paper placed on the Schmidt net is
turned until the initial zero reading coincides with the reading along
the periphery of the net corresponding to the reading on the N axis.
On the net, the readings along the I axis of the universal stage correspond to latitude, those along the H axis, to longitude. If the determination is made by adjustment to the polar position, the reading on
the net is made from the center; if the adjustment is to the equatorial
position, the reading is made from the periphery. All operations are
so performed that the point of intersection of the optic axis with
the surface of the lower hemisphere is plotted.

After all axes have been plotted, a diagram of densities is constructed by calculating the number of points, in turn, on each segment of surface where a segment is equal to 1 % of the total surface

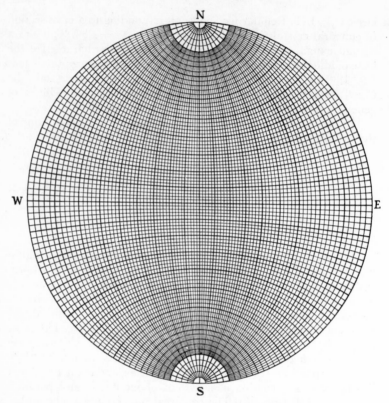

FIG. 28.   The Schmidt net

of the hemisphere.[11] Points of equal density are joined by isolines. An isoline, corresponding to 1%, forms the boundary of areas of higher and lower densities of the disposition of axes. If there is no dominant crystallographic orientation, the entire surface of the diagram will be a space with more or less equal (approximately 1%) density of disposition of axes, but if there is a clearly defined uniform orientation, a part of the surface will have very high density, while the remaining surface will not have any traces of axes whatsoever.

The density diagrams may be all-inclusive, based on all crystals, or partial, based on crystals selected for a particular feature (e.g.,

---

[11] For a description of the practical methods of constructing a density diagram, see E. A. Kuznetsov's book *Kratkii kurs metoda Fedorova v petrografii* (Short course in the Fedorov method in petrography), 1949, and for more details, see J. C. Haff (1938).

diagrams constructed separately for large and small crystals, for special crystal shapes, etc.). Of course, whenever a diagram is constructed, enough crystals must be used to provide sound statistics. In the case of a clearly defined dominant orientation in segments of high density, this requirement is satisfied by merely a few dozen points, while in segments of minimum density, the distribution is random, even when the total number of crystals is considerably larger. Therefore, only the general nature of the distribution is important, not the individual details.

For a comparison of the crystallographic orientation in different slides, the projection of the diagram must be turned to 90° or some other angle. This can be done easily in a graphic manner by moving the characteristic points of each isoline the appropriate number of degrees on the Schmidt net along the parallel. The diagram is turned beforehand so that the required direction of turn of the projection will coincide with the equator of the net. If the periphery of the net is intersected during the turning, the remaining angle is read in the same direction along the parallel from a point situated at 180° on the periphery of the net (Fig. 29).[12]

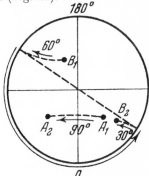

FIG. 29.   Turning the projection 90°.

Quantitative definition of the development of optic anomalies. Optic anomalies, appearing in the wavy extinction and in the biaxiality of crystals undergoing bending, may be characterized quantitatively by the size of the largest and the average angles of the optic axes. The average angle of the optic axes is taken as the arithmetic mean of all the crystals and the uniaxial crystal is considered a particular

---

[12] The most important new method of studying structure is B. Sander's (1950) analysis of the distribution of axes, which demonstrates the spatial distribution of variously oriented crystals in a rock.

case of a biaxial crystal with the angle $2V = 0°$. A comparison of the average and the maximum angles of the optic axes of crystals of different orientation, size, and shape, yields interesting data.

INVESTIGATION OF IMPURITIES

The presence of impurities in ice suggests the following requirements for making a petrographic study of ice:
   (1) study of the size, form and nature of distribution of inclusions in the ice rock, and
   (2) investigation of the material composition and the quantity of the impurities.

The nature of the distribution of inclusions with respect to the ice crystals is an important textural index and in crystallographic investigation is studied both macroscopically and microscopically. In studying the slides, the macroscopic description of the inclusions is supplemented and given in more detail, and the characteristic forms of the air bubbles, pores, brine cells and mineral particles are photographed.

When the crystallographic investigation of the ice is finished, the slide may be used for mineralogical analysis of the inclusions. For this purpose, the cover glass is removed and the ice is sublimed at a negative temperature, with slight heating by the rays of a lamp. Then, diffuse brine bands remain on the glass slide, forming a pattern corresponding to the outlines of the crystal. When dried out, tiny crystal particles of salt separate out. Their composition may be determined by the external form, by the presence of birefringence and by the temperature of dissociation and vaporization during heating (Tammann, 1929). A more complete analysis of the dry remnant of the sections, including determination of the water-insoluble minerals, can be made by the immersion method (Tatarskii, 1949).

In studying the material composition of inclusions, the total content of gases, salts, insoluble minerals and the liquid phase are of prime importance for characterizing the ice. The determination of their total content is examined in the next section. A complete investigation of inclusions also includes chemical, mineralogical and granulometric analyses.

Quantitative Analysis of the Impurities

Determining the density of ice. The specific gravity of pure ice ρ_0 at 0°C and normal pressure is 0.9168 g/cm^3 and in most cases the dependence of the specific weight on temperature and pressure can be neglected. Any departure of the density of ice from this value indicates the presence of impurities. When the impurity is air, the specific gravity of the ice drops below normal; when the impurity is liquid water, salt and insoluble mineral inclusions, it is above normal. Fresh ice, with rare exceptions, has a density of less than 0.9168 g/cm³, because the main constituent of its impurities is air.

The density of ice δ is determined by weighing a known volume of ice. The greatest difficulty comes in measuring the volume, which also limits the accuracy of determining the density. A sample of soft snow and firn is taken with a densitometer, a metal cylinder or a rectangular vessel with sharp edges, whose volume and weight are known accurately. Regular cubes or parallelepipeds are cut out of hard firn and ice and their volume is computed from measurements of all the sides. In the case of ice without liquid water and open air pores, much more accurate results are obtained by weighing a specific volume hydrostatically in liquid; this method will be described below.

If we call the weight of the sample m_{samp} and the volume V_{samp}, we get

$$\delta = \frac{m_{\text{samp}}}{V_{\text{samp}}} \tag{1}$$

Determining the liquid phase content. In fresh ice the amount of liquid phase at negative temperatures is so small that the results of direct measurements will fall within the limits of error of the existing methods. In fresh ice the liquid phase content may be computed from data on the salinity of the ice, while in ice under high pressure, the water content may be computed on the basis of known pressure and temperature data. Direct determinations of the liquid water content are made with respect to porous ice rocks permeated with water and at a temperature of 0°C.

The calorimetric methods are the most widely used methods of determining the liquid water content of ice, based on measurement of the amount of heat expended on melting the sample.[13] The amount of liquid water is judged from the difference between the total weight of the sample and the amount of ice, determined by the quantity of the absorbed heat of fusion.

There are also non-calorimetric methods whereby the amount of

---

[13] Descriptions of the calorimetric methods are given by M. M. Popov (1934) and Ostwald-Luther-Drucker (1935). Calorimetric experiments with wet snow under field conditions are reported by P. P. Kuz'min (1947), M. I. Gurevich (1949), and J. G. Halliday (1950a and b).

liquid water is determined by measuring the temperature reduction caused by the addition of a solution of caustic soda to the sample, or by measurement of the decrease in concentration of the solution after this addition (Bader, 1948).

All such methods have one fundamental disadvantage: they provide only for measurement of samples extracted from their natural mode of occurrence, which often leads to a loss of part of the water, especially if the amount of water exceeds the capillary water-retention capacity of the ice.

Electrometer methods are used to determine the water content of ice in its natural mode of occurrence. One such method is based on measurement of the conductivity of ice (Ostwald-Luther-Drucker, 1935), another on measurement of its electrostatic capacitance.[14] In the first case the apparatus consists of a current source, metal electrodes immersed in the ice rock to be studied, and an ohm-meter. However, the electric conductivity of ice depends not only on its water content but also on the extent of its mineralization; therefore, the results of conductivity measurements should be checked by other methods. This method is more suitable for determining the salinity of melt water.

The second method, based on consideration of the dielectric properties of the rock, consists of high-frequency measurements of the capacitor capacitance, where the investigated ice acts as the dielectric between the condenser plates which are immersed in it. However, the capacitor capacitance varies greatly with the configuration of the volume occupied by water and air in the pores of the ice; therefore, the measurement result depends not only on the amount of water, but also on the structure of the ice. This method is suitable only for the initial stages of snow melt when the moisture content does not exceed 10–12% (Gurevich, 1949), because after the initial stages, the structure changes, in that the pores become considerably larger.

The *mineralization (salinity) of ice* is determined in samples of melt water and therefore does not represent anything specific. The total mineralization can be established if chemical analysis of the substances dissolved in the melt water is included in the investigations. Otherwise, it can be determined electrometrically or (less accurately) from the dry residue.

To study the distribution of salts in the ice, besides what may be revealed under the microscope in the dry residue of the sections, a

---

[14] A method proposed for soils by B. P. Aleksandrov in 1935 and applied to snow by V. A. Rymsha (1948).

series of individual samples of melt water must be taken from the successive melt stages of an irradiated piece of ice (Renaud, 1949). Since melting takes place primarily at the crystal boundaries, the first samples will contain the surface layer, while the central parts of the ice crystals will be contained in the succeeding samples. If the whole mass of the specimen is divided into ten equal samples, the first will contain the surface layer of the crystal, whose thickness will be 0.035 of the diameter of the crystals, and the last will contain the central part, whose thickness will be 0.465 of the diameter of the crystals.

The *amount of solid inclusions* is determined by weighing the sediment or the residue filtered off after the sample has melted.

Porosity of the ice. The porosity of the ice usually means the volume of the air-filled cavities, expressed as a percentage of the total volume of the ice. For dry fresh ice without mineral inclusions, the porosity can be determined from data on ice density δ, which is associated with porosity n as follows:

$$n = \frac{\rho_0 - \delta}{\rho_0} \, 100\% \qquad (2)$$

and

$$\delta = \rho_0 \left(1 - \frac{n}{100} \right) \qquad (3)$$

($\rho_0 = 0.9168$ g/cm^3 is the specific gravity of pure ice).

In the presence of a considerable quantity of non-gaseous impurities, the density δ_{ice} of the system ice + air must be used to compute the porosity instead of the usual density δ of the ice. This may be found by the formula:

$$\delta_{ice} = \frac{m_{samp} - (m_{min} + m_{liq})}{V_{samp} - (V_{min} + V_{liq})} \qquad (4)$$

(m_{min} and m_{liq} are the weights of the mineral impurities and of liquid water, respectively, while V_{min} and V_{liq} are the corresponding volumes, whereby the dissolved salts are calculated by their weight in the m_{min}, not by their volume). In this case, the total salinity and liquid-phase content of the ice must be determined, and also the amount of mineral inclusions and their specific gravity, particularly in the given sample, since usually the mineral impurity content changes from one section of the ice to another. Consequently, the dry residue of the sample must be weighed and its specific gravity determined (by mineralogical analysis or soil analysis methods).

The methods described give only the total volume of the open pores and the enclosed air bubbles; however, the physical role of the two is completely different, and they must be differentiated when establishing the character of the ice. Accordingly, the volume of the communicating pores *s*, or specifically, the *porosity*, must be distinguished from the *volume* of the enclosed air bubbles *q*, which, by analogy, may be called the *vesicularity*.

The porosity and vesicularity values can be determined separately by measuring the ice density in two ways: (1) by the method described above which gives the density δ, with account taken of the volume of all the air inclusions, and (2) by hydrostatic weighing which gives the specific gravity ρ minus the volume of the open pores.

For hydrostatic weighing one must use a wetting non-volatile liquid, but one which will dissolve the ice as little as possible, which is lighter than the ice and which has a freezing temperature lower than that of water. Kerosene fulfills all these requirements quite well. The density of the kerosene at the temperature at which the ice is weighed in it must be determined accurately, for which purpose the method of hydrostatic weighing of any object (e.g., glass) in air, in water, and in kerosene, may be used.

Calling the results of these three weighings $m_{obj\ a}$, $m_{obj\ w}$, and $m_{obj\ k}$, respectively,[15] and the specific gravity of kerosene ρ_k, in agreement with Archimedes' principle we get

$$\rho_k = \frac{m_{obj\ a} - m_{obj\ k}}{m_{obj\ a} - m_{obj\ w}} \tag{5}$$

or, more exactly, with consideration of the loss of weight in air and the change in density of water with temperature,

$$\rho_k = \frac{\rho_w(m_{obj\ a} - m_{obj\ k}) + \rho_a(m_{obj\ k} - m_{obj\ w})}{m_{obj\ a} - m_{obj\ w}} \tag{5'}$$

Here ρ_w and ρ_a are the specific gravity of water and air; for water the specific gravity is taken from prepared tables, for air it is derived from the formula

$$\rho_a = \frac{0.0004648\ B}{273.16 + t}$$

where *B* is atmospheric pressure in mm Hg and *t* is the temperature in °C.

---

[15] [Here obj, a, w and k stand for object, air, water and kerosene, respectively. – D.K.]

An appropriate correction is made for the change in volume of the body due to the difference in temperatures during the weighing in water and in kerosene. The linear relation of the density of a given amount of kerosene to the temperature (in the range of negative temperatures where the ice is weighed in kerosene) is established by a series of weighings.

Next the ice sample is immersed in cold kerosene and a vacuum is created so that the kerosene will penetrate into all the pores, after which the sample is weighed on a dilatometer. Knowing the weight of the sample in air $m_{\text{samp a}}$ and in kerosene $m_{\text{samp k}}$, the specific gravity of ice without pores is computed by the formula

$$\rho = \frac{\rho_k m_{\text{samp a}}}{m_{\text{samp a}} - m_{\text{samp k}}} \qquad (6)$$

or, more exactly,

$$\rho = \frac{\rho_k m_{\text{samp a}} - \rho_a m_{\text{samp k}}}{m_{\text{samp a}} - m_{\text{samp k}}} \qquad (6')$$

If the amount of nongaseous impurities is considerable, the impurities must be taken into consideration. First the weight and volume of the system ice + air are computed successively by subtracting the weight and volume of the mineral inclusions from the totals.

Knowing the total density δ and the density without the open pores ρ, it is not difficult to compute the relative volume of the sample occupied by pure ice l, by the open pores s and by the enclosed bubbles q:

$$l = \frac{\delta}{\rho_0} 1000\%_0 \qquad (7)$$

$$s = \frac{\rho - \delta}{\rho} 1000\%_0 \qquad (8)$$

$$q = \frac{\delta(\rho_0 - \rho)}{\rho_0 \rho} 1000\%_0 \qquad (9)$$

We must keep in mind that some of the enclosed bubbles are dissected by the boundaries of the sample; consequently, the volume of the bubbles is always somewhat undervalued, while the volume of the open pores is somewhat overvalued. Since it is impossible to avoid this, we must resort to conventional characteristics with a certain constant degree of distortion when preparing all samples of identical size (e.g., $15 \times 15 \times 15$ cm), with the exception of those weighed in a densitometer.

If observations are made of the settling of the layers, in addition to quantitative analyses of the ice, that is, if two sets of values are available, h_1 (layer thickness), δ_1, ρ_1, and h_2, δ_2, ρ_2 for the two moments of time, the total result of measurement of the amount of ice, pores and air bubbles over a certain period of time can be established as well as the role of the processes of compression and migration[16] of the substance in the changes of the density and quantity of ice:

$$\Delta\delta_{comp} = \frac{h_2 - h_2}{h_2}\, \delta_1 \qquad (10)$$

and

$$\Delta\delta_{migr} = \delta_2 - \frac{h_1}{h_2}\, \delta_1 \qquad (11)$$

$$\Delta l_{comp} = \frac{\Delta\delta_{comp}}{\rho_0} \qquad (12)$$

and

$$\Delta l_{migr} = \frac{\Delta\delta_{migr}}{\rho_0} \qquad (13)$$

where $\Delta\delta_{comp}$ and Δl_{comp} are the changes in the density and relative volume of the ice due to compression, while $\Delta\delta_{migr}$ and Δl_{migr} are the corresponding changes due to migration of the substance. It is impossible to establish the relative role of the compression and migration of the substance that occur simultaneously with the changes of the other magnitudes (ρ, s, q), if the ice contains both open pores and enclosed bubbles.

Determination of the pressure of the air enclosed in the ice. If the amount of air contained in the enclosed bubbles is measured together with the volume of the enclosed bubbles, the ratio of the two volumes will give the value of the pressure of the air in the ice. Determinations of the pressure of air in ice, based on this principle, were first made by J. Koch and A. Wegener in 1913 at the Storström Glacier in Greenland (Koch and Wegener, 1930, pp. 302–308). The Koch-Wegener method was employed subsequently in the Alps, in Greenland and on Spitsbergen by other investigators; however, because of its low accuracy (for dense ice the errors reach an order of 35–50%), determinations of this very important characteristic of ice could not be used in practical ice study. In 1947, Shumskii developed a method by which pressure could be determined within an accuracy of $\pm\, 0.5\%$ in pure ice and $\pm\, 3\%$ in ice with mineral impurities, and

---

[16] [Hereafter abbreviated "comp" and "migr" in the formulas. – D.K.]

thus it became possible to determine air pressure in the enclosed bubbles of snow and firn.

There is still another method of determining the pressure of air in ice, based on the same principle and proposed by Bader (1950), but we have not described it here because it is considerably less accurate than the method outlined below.

To determine the pressure of enclosed air, the sample is first weighed in air and in kerosene, by which density is established with an accuracy up to the fourth or fifth decimal place. Then the sample is placed in a hermetically sealed vessel, with a burette, filled to the top with cold kerosene (see Figs. 30a and b). To regulate pressure, the vessel is connected with another, an open vessel,

Fig. 30a.   Instrument for determining the pressure of the air included in the ice.

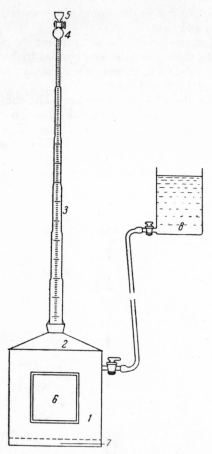

Fig. 30b. Instrument for determining the pressure of the air included in the ice. 1. metal cube 20 × 20 × 20 cm, open upward; 2. metal cover in the form of a tetrahedral pyramid on bolts with a gasket of benzene-resistant rubber; 3. burette; 4. bulb; 5. funnel; 6. window; 7. salt; 8. communicating vessel with kerosene, capacity 1–2 liters.

through a hose. The burette consists of several sections with diameters increasing downward, by which the greatest volume is attained at a given height without sacrificing the preassigned accuracy of volume measurement.

The ice in the vessel is melted and the air from the bubbles is collected in the burette. To reduce the dissolution of air in the melt water to a minimum at the moment of melting, a layer of table salt is poured onto the bottom of the vessel. In cases where the ice contains mineral impurities which must be weighed, salt should not be added, because this would increase the weight of the dry residue. In such cases the amount of dissolved air V_p may be considered separately and on an average is equal to

$$V_p = \frac{m_{\text{samp}}}{0.914} - \frac{m_{\text{samp}}}{\rho_0} \tag{14}$$

After the ice has melted and the temperature in the vessel has become equal to that of the outside air, simultaneous readings are made of the volume of air in the burette V cm^3, the temperature $t°$C, the atmospheric pressure B in mm Hg, and the difference in the levels of the kerosene h_{mm} in the burette and in the open communicating vessel. The volume of the air liberated from the ice is reduced to the temperature of ice under natural conditions t_0 and to normal atmospheric pressure by means of the formula

$$V_0 = \frac{B - h\dfrac{\rho_k}{\rho_{Hg}}}{760} \times \frac{273.16 + t_0}{273.16 + t} V \tag{15}$$

where $\rho_{Hg} = 13.595$ g/cm^3 is the density of mercury and ρ_k is the density of kerosene.

The air pressure in the ice p is computed by the formula

$$p = \frac{V_0 \rho_0 \rho_k}{m_{\text{samp a}}(\rho_0 - \rho_k) - m_{\text{samp k}}\rho_0} \tag{16}$$

or, more exactly,

$$p = \frac{V_0 \rho_0 (\rho_k - \rho_a)}{m_{\text{samp a}}(\rho_0 - \rho_k) - m_{\text{samp k}}(\rho_0 + \rho_a)} \tag{16'}$$

where ρ_a is the specific gravity of the air at the time the sample is weighed in air.

If ice contains mineral impurities, their weight and volume are subtracted from the weight and volume of the sample. The volume of the sample V_{samp} is calculated on the basis of the formula

$$V_{\text{samp}} = \frac{m_{\text{samp}} - m_{\text{samp k}}}{\rho_k} \tag{17}$$

The initial air pressure in the isolated bubbles inside the ice is equal to the pressure of the external medium (water, air) at the time the bubbles are enclosed. The air pressure of bubbles in ice which formed beneath the surface of water is higher than in atmospheric ice, while the air pressure in snowflakes that grew in the upper layers of the atmosphere is lower than that in the bubbles. If, afterwards, the ice is subjected to external pressure exceeding its elastic limit and the pressure of the air included in it, it experiences plastic compressive deformation almost to the point where the external pressure enters into equilibrium with the air pressure in the bubbles. This process is irreversible, since its work is expended basically on overcoming the internal friction of the ice and not on compressing the air. If the ice does not melt in the process and the amount of air in the bubbles does not change, the following relationship will exist between the specific gravity of the ice ρ (without consideration of the pores) and the air pressure in the bubbles p:

$$\frac{\rho_0 - \rho_2}{\rho_0 - \rho_1} \times \frac{\rho_1}{\rho_2} = \frac{p_1}{p_2} \qquad (18)$$

This relationship makes it possible to compute the specific gravity of the ice at any previous pressure, particularly for the case of sedimentary ice at the stage of formation where the open pores become enclosed bubbles and the air pressure is equal to the atmospheric pressure ($p_1 = 1$):

$$\rho_1 = \frac{\rho_0 p_2}{\rho_0 p_2 + \rho_2 - \rho_2 p_2} \qquad (18')$$

In the case of undeformed congelation ice, the air pressure in the bubbles (p in atmospheres) is an indication of the freezing point ($t = -0.00752\ p$).

Chemical, Mineralogical and Granulometric Analyses of Impurities

Chemical, mineralogical and granulometric analyses of impurities indicate chiefly the origin of the initial ice-forming materials. Such analyses are conducted on samples of air, melt water and the dry residue of ice and are not specific in any way. Chemical analysis is applied to melt water samples (to determine their salt composition[17]) and to ice samples (to determine the gas content of the enclosed air).

To get samples of air, ice is melted in water under a bell jar topped by an inverted bottle or special flask completely filled with water

---

[17] For a currently accepted method of taking samples and of field chemical analysis of water, see V. A. Priklonskii and F. F. Laptev (1949).

and attached to the bell jar by a rubber hose. To avoid selective dilution of the gases in the water, a layer of table salt is poured onto the bottom of the vessel used for melting the ice. As the ice melts, the air from the bubbles rises and fills the bottle or flask. When the bottle is nearly full of gas, it is closed with a boiled cork stopper and quickly smeared with Mendeleev cement or sealing wax. The bottle is kept neck down and the water remaining in it serves as a water seal. If the gas is collected in a flask, the flask is soldered shut after being filled with gas.

All the enumerated analyses may be carried out in a field laboratory or after return from field work.

In addition to the above types of analysis of the material composition, *microbiological* analysis is of considerable interest, especially *pollen analysis* of ice, which is another means of analyzing structure (seasonal stratification), conditions of formation and age of the ice (Vareschi, 1935, and others; Gorodkov, 1948). We have not treated microbiological analyses here, since they do not fall within the framework of petrographic methods of investigation.

Congelation Ice

CHAPTER IX

CONGELATION ICE FORMATION

INTRODUCTORY REMARKS

By congelation ice, we mean the types of ice which result from the freezing of water and which are the low temperature surface equivalents of magmatic rocks.

Atmospheric congelation ice consists of individual ice grains (graupel, hail, ice rain) which may give rise to sedimentary ice rocks after falling to the earth. In this section, we shall examine only that congelation ice which forms solid bodies of ice, i.e., congelation ice rocks. This occurs when water which is not separated into droplets freezes, as in the atmosphere or in the pores of other rocks, i.e., the water of both surface and underground reservoirs and streams. Special conditions are required for congelation ice rocks to form by the freezing of water which fills the pores of friable sedimentary rock. We shall use the narrow, petrographic interpretation of the term *ice formation*, i.e., the formation of a solid ice rock, instead of the broader, mineralogical or physical interpretation, i.e. the crystallization of water or water vapor.

Different structural types of congelation ice appear under different conditions of ice formation, but thus far little study has been devoted to them. The *growth* structures and textures, which distinguish congelation ice from sedimentary and metamorphic ice, form under the influence of the following factors:

(1) the magnitude and the direction of the temperature gradient and the radiation intensity in the water;

(2) the number and efficiency of the nuclei of crystallization;

(3) the anisotropy of the rates of growth and the anisotropy of the thermal conductivity of the ice crystals;

(4) the orienting effect and the form of surface from which crystallization begins;

(5) the movement of the freezing water;

(6) the number and nature of impurities in the water which do not act as nuclei of crystallization.

The relative role of each of these factors determines the nature of the incipient structure and texture of growth.

When external conditions remain constant, the process of congelation ice formation passes through several stages, during which the various textures form. The diversity of the external conditions of ice formation is manifested in part by the hypertrophy of a particular stage of the process and in part by the introduction of new features. First, we shall examine the full cycle of congelation ice formation processes during the omnidirectional freezing of a limited amount of water and then we shall treat the characteristics of the variety of growth textures that appear under special conditions.

The omnidirectional freezing of a limited amount of water consists of three more or less distinct stages:

(1) the nucleation and growth of isolated ice crystals, up to and including their intergrowth and the formation of a closed front of crystallization, i.e., the stage during which the primary layer of ice forms, or the protocrystallization stage;[1]

(2) mutually restricted growth of ice crystals normal to the surface of the crystallization front, the orthotropic crystallization stage;

(3) crystallization of the closed central nucleus, the residual stage.

THE FORMATION OF THE PRIMARY LAYER OF ICE

The first stage of congelation ice formation, the formation of the primary layer of ice from free crystals, occurs differently at the free upper surface of water, on the solid surface of walls and on the bottom of a water container.

---

[1] The term "protocrystallization" is an adequate definition of the first stage of the crystallization process, i.e., the appearance of crystal embryos and the beginning of their growth (before they come into contact with each other and form a more or less solid aggregate), as distinct from the subsequent stages of development of the crystal aggregate. On the other hand, the term "spontaneous crystallization" may cause misunderstanding, because sometimes it is not applied to all nucleation of new crystals (as opposed to crystallization forced by existing crystals of a given substance), but only to nucleation which occurs in the absence of particles of substances anisomorphous with the given substance (or rough spots on the walls of the enclosing vessel) which may act as foreign nuclei of crystallization. The concept "protocrystallization," as we shall use it, includes all nucleation and initial stages of crystal growth, both at the boundary of the metastable state and the nucleation stimulated by foreign nuclei of crystallization during weaker supercooling or supersaturation.

The processes of the *freezing of the free upper water surface* have been studied most thoroughly. These processes occur extensively in the lower boundary zone of the cryosphere and thus are of the greatest practical importance. However, hydrologists have been interested primarily in the thermal and caloric aspects of the freezing processes and their studies have produced a quantitative theory of these phenomena and forecasts of ice formation. Far too little study has been devoted to the structure of newly forming ice as a function of the conditions of freezing.

The structure and texture of the primary layer of ice result from the above described processes of nucleation and growth of free ice crystals at a supercooled water surface.

Other conditions being equal, crystal size is a function of the rate of heat transfer from the water surface. If the cooling rate is slow, few embryos appear, their rate of growth is great, and a small number of large crystals appears, but when the supercooling increases rapidly, a myriad of minute crystals forms and the rate of appearance of the embryos and the rate of crystal growth are of the same order of magnitude.

The flow of water exerts a very great influence on the ice formation process and, according to O. Devik, "static" and "dynamic" ice formation may be differentiated in this case. Water movement has a twofold effect on texture: a direct mechanical effect manifested in the position of the free crystals and their intergrowths at the moment of freezing and an indirect effect manifested in the duration and degree of supercooling, which can be greatly facilitated by rapid motion.

The degree of supercooling determines the growth type of the primary crystals (solid or skeletal), their form (needle or disk) and their crystallographic orientation on the water surface in a state of equilibrium.

The available data seem to indicate that in a typical case the primary ice layer forms as follows on the surface of still or slowly moving water. First, supercooling is comparatively intense[2] and skeletal platy crystals grow on the water surface. The embryos, whose main axes are oriented more or less horizontally, grow rapidly along the basal plane in the thin supercooled surface layer, becoming long sharp ice needles that freeze together at the ends and form an irregular lattice on the water surface. The other crystals, which were more obliquely oriented at their moment of origin (and thus

---

[2] For example, Devik (1942) measured supercooling of more than 1° on the surface of a reservoir under natural conditions.

could grow laterally to a certain extent as well as longitudinally within the supercooled layer), turn flat on the water surface before fusing with the other crystals so that their main axes are vertical and they become stellate or tabular. The supercooling decreases rapidly during the growth of skeletal crystals and continuous growth begins, during which the needles, expanding very slowly, become long, flat parallelepipeds, but the crystals which have vertical axes in the cells of the lattice formed by the needles and which are more favorably oriented for horizontal growth become round disks which cement the aggregate into a continuous thin ice crust.[3]

Ice which forms in this manner has granular or crystalline granular texture. The crystals are comparatively small, of the order of 1–10 mm (fine-grained and medium-grained texture); in general they are anhedral, i.e., without regular faces, but in cross section most of them are elongated perpendicular to the main axis, which indicates that they are tabular.

Thus, the ice texture ranges from *allotriomorphic-granular* to *hypidiomorphic-granular* with *tabular crystals*. At first glance the crystallographic orientation of the grains appears to be random, but precise measurement shows that it is strictly regular, although peculiar. The optic axes of some of the crystals (usually the majority) are oriented in various directions in the horizontal plane, forming a *zonal* arrangement on the Schmidt net. The optic axes of the rest of the

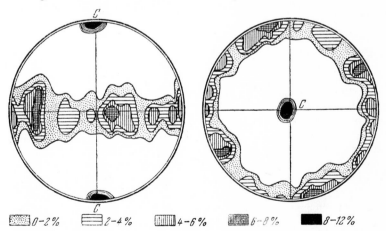

$\boxed{0-2\%}$ $\boxed{2-4\%}$ $\boxed{4-6\%}$ $\boxed{6-8\%}$ $\boxed{8-12\%}$

FIG. 31. Stereogram of the crystallographic orientation of a primary layer of congelation ice on a calm water surface. 52 crystals. Standard case. C—vertical direction.

[3] M. P. Golovkov (1936) observed a similar phenomenon.

crystals are oriented vertically (Fig. 31). The case in which the main axes of all the crystals are oriented horizontally is an exception.

Apparently, the case in which there is insufficient supercooling for needle growth is less common. Here ice formation begins immediately after the formation of the disk-shaped crystals, which develop partly into stellate skeletal forms oriented flat on the water surface. W. Bentley (1907) made a detailed study of the growth of tabular crystals up to the formation of a continuous, thin layer of ice as transparent as glass. An allotriomorphic-granular, strictly ordered texture with uniform vertical orientation of the optic axes appears under these conditions (Fig. 32).

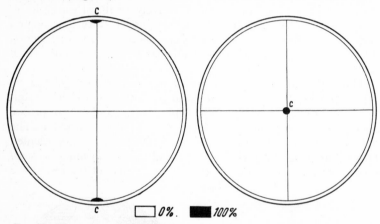

FIG. 32.   Stereogram of the crystallographic orientation of a primary layer of congelation ice on a calm water surface (very slow freezing).

If the first stage of ice formation occurs during a snowfall or blowing snow, the snowflakes which fall into the water will act as the centers of crystallization. They will float flat on the surface of the water until they become too numerous to do so. Consequently, if the snowfall consists exclusively of plate crystals, the only texture to occur should be one with vertically oriented optic axes.[4] The optic axes of columnar snowflakes should be oriented horizontally, while the texture depicted in Fig. 31 should appear during a mixed snowfall.

The ice formation process is different in a quite rapidly flowing medium or in a medium mixed by agitation, which is usually associated with considerable and steady supercooling of a thick

[4] G. Quincke (1905) assumed this to be the reason why the main crystal axes are oriented perpendicular to the surface in the case of lake ice.

layer of water. According to the observations of A. Hamberg (1915), under these conditions a myriad of randomly oriented tabular skeletal crystals will grow throughout the supercooled layer. These crystals will fuse into porous, spongy masses with disordered crystallographic orientation of the component parts. The agitation often drives them together into round clusters on the water surface, forming the so-called *pancake ice*. Then the water in the interstices between the primary crystals freezes out, joining the crystals and thus forming a primary layer which is much thicker than in the case of slight supercooling. This primary layer has hypidiomorphic-granular tabular or allotriomorphic-granular texture and random orientation of the main axes. Drygalski (1897, pp. 485, 504) observed similar formations in stream beds and stressed their similarity to glacier ice. Sludge ice crystals, which act as material for the formation of the primary ice layer, often have acicular, not tabular habit, but under the conditions described this affects only the form of the grains and does not alter their tabular type of growth and disordered crystallographic orientation.

During rapid growth and fusion of sludge-ice crystals, some of the escaping autogenous air and relatively concentrated salt solution is captured by the ice and forms blobs of gaseous and in part liquid inclusions. Furthermore, when agitation occurs, xenogenous atmospheric air in the form of minute bubbles often enters the water. Owing to the abundance of inclusions, the ice becomes cloudy, opaque and whitish. To a certain extent, an abundant snowfall during the freezing of a water surface produces a similar effect. Snowflakes, falling into the water in great numbers, form a water-permeated freezing gruel with disordered orientation of the crystals, known as snow water or snow slush.

Thus, when a calm surface freezes, a completely transparent, very thin ice "glass" forms with tabular grains or with grains elongated in the horizontal plane and with ordered crystallographic orientation. However, when rapidly flowing water freezes, the thick layer of primary ice which forms is cloudy and whitish because of the autogenous and xenogenous inclusions and the random orientation of the geometric and crystallographic axes of the grains. Between these extreme types of the primary ice layer, there are gradual transitions of thickness, structure and texture.

The freezing of water on the solid surface of walls and on the bottom of a reservoir. The primary layer of ice forms quite differently on the solid surface of walls and on the bottom of a freezing reservoir. Here we shall emphasize freezing from below and from the sides rather than on the bottom ice of streams and reservoirs, which forms during the supercooling of the whole body of water because of the upward flow of heat.[5]

Bottom ice, which grows like rime, in the form of bushy growths of tabular, and in part dendritic, crystals, does not form enduring ice rock. Although bottom ice is of great practical importance because it changes the regime of rivers and disrupts the normal operation of hydrotechnical installations, its role in the process of congelation ice formation does not differ in principle from the previously examined role of underwater ice crystals, whose fusion leads to the formation of the primary layer of ice on the water surface. In this respect, the only special feature of bottom ice is that it floats up from the bottom in fairly large concretions, rather than as individual crystals. These concretions are somewhat denser than those of ordinary sludge ice and contain silt and other mineral inclusions. Of course, bottom ice could conceivably be buried *in situ* by alluvium and preserved in a layer of frozen rock. Unfortunately, the described finds of buried bottom ice (by I. A. Lopatin [1876] on the right bank of the lower Yenisei in 1866 and by V. Stefansson on the banks of the Colville River in 1910) are too equivocal and do not provide an adequate picture of either the bedding conditions or the texture of the ice.

Less attention has been paid to the formation of ice on the walls or the bottom of reservoirs in the case of freezing from the sides and from below, since this phenomenon is observed only in regions where frozen rocks develop. Here, we must distinguish between two completely different processes. If the wall or the bottom of a reservoir consists of ice, the first stage of congelation ice formation may not occur at all; forced crystallization, leading to *conformal growth of each exposed crystal*, begins upon the slightest supercooling of the surface. Consequently, the process begins immediately after the stage of oriented closed crystal growth. In this case, the texture of the newly forming layer, at least in the beginning, will not differ in the slightest from that of the ice base; only the number, form and arrangement of the inclusions can differ if the ice of the base formed under different conditions.

Crystals of the given substance and also crystals of substances isomorphous with it can act as seeds for conformal crystallization of the melt or solution that comes into contact with these crystals. Royer (1928, p. 7) also reported a special type of regular, oriented

---

[5] Although the conditions and fundamentals of the processes of bottom ice formation have not been completely established as yet, it is clear that removal of heat through the soil (F. I. Bydin's hypothesis) cannot explain this complex phenomenon.

growth of different crystals, the so-called *epitaxy*, caused, as in the previous cases, by the interaction between the space lattice of a growing crystal and that of a crystal of the base. However, even in this case the textures of the two substances must have something in common, viz., the so-called second-order isomorphism. Epitactic accretion is possible only if a space lattice plane whose geometry is sufficiently close to that of one of the lattice planes of the growing crystal appears at the crystal/base interface and if the substitutional structural units of the two crystals are homogeneous (e.g., ions of the same sign) and if the bonds between them are identical in nature. Such structurally similar space lattice planes actually act as a *seed* that induces crystallization of the growing crystal, whose orientation is determined by the position of the substratum.

It has not been proven that epitaxy phenomena actually exist in ice. The interpretation of a reported case of oriented growth of ice on a fresh cleavage surface of mica (Nakaya, Toda and Maruyama, 1938) as epitactic (Weickmann, 1949, p. 10) was not based on textural data and perhaps can be explained by the passive orienting influence of the base. In any event, ice structure is unique, thus it is difficult to imagine that epitactic ice growth could be widespread. Generally speaking, no substance is completely isomorphous with ice. Therefore, we can say that only a substratum composed of ice can exert an orienting influence (based on the interaction of crystal lattices) on ice.

However, even the ice base does not always induce forced crystallization with conformal accretion; when the surface is contaminated and when it cools rapidly, protocrystallization develops as it does on the surface of any other substance, i.e., by the nucleation and growth of new crystals. In this case, usually the rough spots on the surface act as the centers of crystallization. The density of packing of the incipient crystals and, consequently, their size and form (in cross section parallel to the base) after they have combined into a continuous layer depend on the abundance and the efficiency of these centers of crystallization and their rate of cooling. The crystals of such a layer often have ordered orientation, but clearly not because of the influence of the crystal lattice of the base. In contrast to the *active* seeding effect of the crystal lattice of the substratum, the orienting effect of the surface of the base on the independently nucleating crystals can be called *passive* (after D. P. Grigor'ev, 1947, p. 25), since in this case the role of the base amounts, essentially, to that of changing the external conditions of existence of the crystals.

Although the general crystallographic problem of the passive

orienting influence of the base on growing crystals has been discussed for more than a century,[6] no generally accepted solution has
yet been found. Relatively speaking, the theory of selection of crystal
embryos in the first stage of crystallization is the most widely accepted
explanation, but opinions differ as to the selection factors. The
selection theory first appeared in connection with the study of the
polar crystals of grape sugar, when it was established that they grew
onto the base primarily with their most soluble face. This formed
the basis for the *principle of greatest resistance to solution,* which states
that because of fluctuations of the degree of saturation only the
embryos which conceal their most soluble side in the base will
survive and grow during primary nucleation, while the others either
will not form at all or will dissolve rapidly (Becke, 1889, p. 494).
Later this principle, which had been developed mainly to explain
the laws of crystal fusion, was extended to non-polar substances as
the principle of minimum surface, namely: those crystals will survive
which are best protected because a large portion of their surface is
concealed from the mother liquor by contact with the base or by
twinning (Mügge, 1903, p. 455).

However, more abundant factual data soon demanded a principle diametrically opposed to the principle of greatest resistance to
solution, namely, the *principle of the greatest rate of growth* and, correspondingly, of the *greatest free specific surface* during growth. It was
shown that this applies to solutions that are highly supersaturated
during the formation of embryos, where there is no possibility of
temporary incomplete saturation, and that the principle of greatest
resistance to solution applies under the opposite, less frequently encountered conditions (Johnsen, 1907, p. 326; Holzner, 1927, p. 199).

Properly speaking, the principle of greatest rate of growth was
formulated earlier by Trouton, not, however, in connection with the
magnitude of the free surface of crystals, but in connection with the
differences of thermal conductivity in different crystallographic
directions. According to this hypothesis, during the crystallization
of a melt, those embryos develop whose *axis of greatest thermal conductivity* lies *in the direction of heat transfer* (Trouton, 1898, 1900).
Trouton also used it to explain the orientation of the main ice crystal
axes normal to the surface of freezing in the ice cover of reservoirs,
under the assumption that the thermal conductivity of ice is slightly
greater along the main axis than in the other direction.

In contrast to these variants of the selection theory, which assumes
disordered primary orientation of the crystal embryos, opinions were

---

[6] To my knowledge, since 1835.

expressed that crystals can nucleate only while in a specific position. Some authors considered the orienting factor to be the thermal flux, which allegedly acts directly on the liquid particles during crystallization (*thermotropy* hypothesis) (Mallet, 1845, p. 592; Rinne, 1926, p. 71), while Kalb held the orienting factor to be the surface energy of the crystal (Kalb, 1920, p. 286). According to the Kalb hypothesis, derived from the principle of minimum surface energy, for the most part the crystal faces with the greatest surface tension are the ones which grow to the base, and since the surface tension causes the greatest rate of growth normal to the given face, the crystal tends to arrange itself in such a way that its greatest diameter is normal to the surface of the base (Kalb, 1920, pp. 66 and 69).

Finally, the opinion was expressed that a crystal should grow onto the base primarily by the face with the greatest area, because of gravity (especially on vertical surfaces) and the force of adhesion (Holzner, 1927). Obviously, this presumes that the crystalline embryos, which originally were randomly oriented, shift into the indicated position.

When these various and mutually contradictory hypotheses are compared with the facts, clearly they do not provide a satisfactory explanation for the orientational features of ice crystals that grow onto a solid base. Bertin (1878) established that the main axes of ice crystals are oriented normal to the surface of the base. His conclusion was based on experiments in which water was frozen in wooden vessels with one glass wall inclined at angles of 45° and 90° to the horizon. Subsequently, Klocke (1879) and Sherzer (1907) confirmed "Bertin's law" for congelation ice. However, Quincke (1905), who experimented with the freezing of water in vessels, observed disordered orientation for the most part, while Kalb (1921) observed ordered orientation, but with the main axes parallel to the base.

The author's observations made in the field and laboratory confirm the existence of all three types of growth, i.e., main axis normal to the base, random orientation and main axis parallel to the base, in both congelation and sublimation ice. Not having considered the possibility that all three types could exist, previous investigators raised one of the growth types to a general law and then could not explain it. For example, Dobrowolski (1923, p. 350) relied on Bertin's law alone, while Kalb (1921, p. 212) used only his own law of growth of the greatest diameter normal to the base for plate crystals, which is exactly the opposite of Bertin's law.

During the freezing of ice onto a solid base, the crystals nucleate on the irregularities of the surface of the base and become attached to it from the very beginning; therefore, the crystals cannot turn their largest face toward the base under the influence of gravity or adhesion, as observed on a free water surface. The thermotropy hypothesis is an improbable explanation of ordered crystallographic orientation from the standpoint of the kinetic theory of phase conversions and is definitely refuted by the occurrence of different orientations (including random), especially under conditions where there can be no additional extraneous influences (the influence of the base, etc., for example, during very rapid freezing of water that has been cooled with liquid nitrogen). The Kalb hypothesis is inconsistent with the facts of tabular crystal accretion according to Bertin's law. Selection can result from differences in the rate of growth caused by anisotropic heat conduction. Probably such selection actually does take place in the second stage of ice formation, when heat is lost through the ice (see below). However, such selection is impossible in the first stage, since crystal nucleation occurs after quite considerable supercooling has been attained, in connection with which each crystal releases the heat of crystallization in all directions into the ambient supercooled medium. At first glance, the selection theory holds up better if the principles of greatest resistance to destruction are combined with the principle of greatest rate of growth. Obviously, the first requires accretion according to Bertin's law, while the second requires that the main axis be parallel to the surface of the base. However, the conditions under which the various types of accretion occur do not correspond to the conditions required by the theory.

The basic shortcoming of previous investigations was that they did not consider the difference in the conditions under which a particular type of accretion occurred. This was connected with the tendency to accept one of the possible types of crystal growth as a general law. My experiments along these lines have revealed the following features:

(1) The orderliness of the crystallographic orientation of ice which has grown onto a solid heteromorphic base is never strict, consequently the so-called laws of accretion are merely statistical.

(2) Ice crystals grow primarily with their main axes normal to the base (Bertin's law) when the heat transfer is in that direction and the supercooling in the protocrystallization stage is limited to the fairly thin layer of water adjacent to the base. The more rapid the cooling, and, consequently, the thinner the supercooled layer is at the moment of crystal nucleation, the more uniform the orientation will be.

(3) Random orientation is observed when the supercooling of a substantial layer of water is approximately uniform. This is observed during very slow cooling or when heat is transferred at an oblique angle to the surface of the base, i.e., when there is a fairly large temperature gradient parallel to the surface in the substratum itself and when the cooling spreads not only from the base, but through the water parallel to the base.

(4) Crystals grow primarily with their main axis parallel to the base (according to Kalb's law) in the case of inverse temperature stratification, when supercooling increases with distance from the surface of the base toward the center of the water layer and the base does not act as a cold source, but merely provides centers of crystal nucleation; this is relatively rare for accretion of congelation ice, but it is possible and occurred more than once during the experiments (Fig. 33).

All this pertains to congelation ice, whose crystals are always tabular under conditions of free growth. The few available data indicate that the reverse is true of columnar sublimation crystals at low temperatures and that growth according to Kalb's law is most common for sublimation crystals. This is associated with the inverse stratification of the degree of saturation of the air with water vapor, which is especially characteristic of hoarfrost formation during a wind.

These data indicate that the mechanism of the passive orienting influence of the base on growing crystals can be presented as follows. The statistical nature of the laws of growth indicate that ordered orientation is the result of selection and of the preferential development of only the more favorably oriented crystals. In the main, those crystals develop whose direction of greatest rate of growth does not go beyond the limits of the supercooled layer of water (or the supersaturated layer of solution, vapor). The thinner this layer is, the greater will be the passive orienting influence of the base and *vice versa*, up to the point where the base will have no passive orienting influence whatsoever, when a considerable layer of water is supercooled uniformly. The tabular crystals, which grow most rapidly along the basal plane during cooling from the base, grow primarily according to Bertin's law, with the plates parallel to the base (since otherwise a plate, upon reaching the limit of supercooling, would curtail growth). When the cooling is in the opposite direction, the crystals will grow primarily according to Kalb's law, i.e., by the edges of the basal platelets. The laws are analogous but not as clearly defined for the columnar crystals, which have smaller anisotropic rates of growth (in the first case discussed above, they

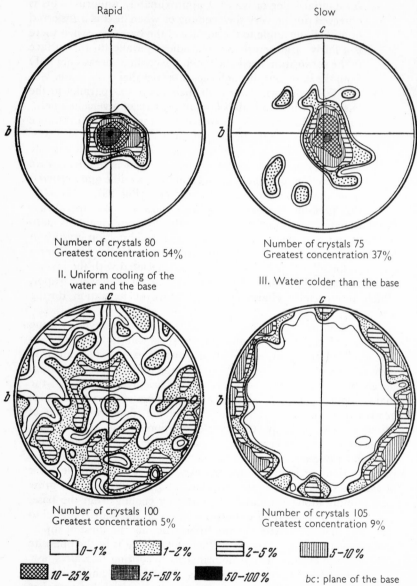

FIG. 33. Stereograms of the crystallographic orientation of three types of growth of a primary layer of congelation ice into a solid heteromorphic base.

grow primarily with their main axes parallel to the base, in the second case, normal to the base). Departures from uniform orientation are also amplified by irregularities of the surface of the base.

Thus, four main types of primary congelation ice layers may be distinguished on the basis of crystallographic orientation.

(1) The main axes are oriented primarily normal to the surface of freezing (*linear orientation*). This occurs during slow freezing of a calm water surface and during freezing onto a smooth solid surface under conditions of intense heat transfer normal to this surface.

(2) The main axes are predominantly parallel to the surface of freezing (*zonal orientation*). This occurs during freezing onto a solid smooth base under conditions of inverse temperature stratification (supercooling within the water is greater than at the base).

(3) The main axes are in part normal to the surface of freezing and in part parallel to it (*linear-zonal orientation*). This is the ordinary case of the freezing of a calm water surface.

(4) *Random crystallographic orientation.* This occurs during the freezing of rapidly flowing water and during freezing onto a smooth solid base with uniform supercooling of a considerable layer of water (with heat transfer oblique to the surface of the base or with very slow cooling).

Some of the crystals of the primary layer of congelation ice are anhedral; however, most of them are subhedral tabular crystals. Thus, the texture of the primary layer of congelation ice varies between allotriomorphic-granular and hypidiomorphic-granular tabular crystals with linear, zonal, linear-zonal or random orientation.

ORTHOTROPIC CRYSTALLIZATION

The second stage of congelation ice formation is the main stage, which provides the main mass of congelation ice. It differs from the first stage in that:

(1) the forced growth of crystals is strictly normal to the surface of the crystallization front, because neighboring crystals prevent growth in any other direction;

(2) the supercooling of the water, which emanates only from the growing ice crystals, because the heat lost through these crystals is slight, slowly leads to the crystallization of the water. As a rule, this is crystallization forced by the already existing crystals (without nucleation of new crystals).

Geometric selection. The first of these characteristics, i.e., the regular oriented growth leading to the appearance of parallel-fibrous or prismatic-granular texture, was called *orthotropy* or *orthotaxy*[7] by F. Rinne (1926, p. 71). Rinne considered the previously mentioned *thermotropy*, i.e., oriented crystal growth caused by the direct orienting influence of a heat flux, to be a special case of orthotropy. Here, Rinne did not distinguish between crystallographic orientation, on the one hand, and the direction of growth and the external form of the crystals, on the other; in orienting the space lattice of the crystals, the heat flux, as it were, dictates the direction of crystal growth and the geometric features specified by the orthotropy concept.

We have already mentioned the error involved in one aspect of the Rinne hypothesis, involving the effect of the heat flux on the crystallographic orientation. Another aspect of the hypothesis was disproved by A. V. Shubnikov and G. G. Laemmlein (1927), who showed, by a simple experiment, that orthotropic crystal growth is due strictly to geometry, i.e., to the mutual restriction of the crystals, and that the direction of the heat flux does not play any role in the process.

However, in most cases the orthotropic mutually restricted growth of crystals also exerts an influence on the crystallographic orientation of the incipient polycrystalline aggregate. The occurrence of linear orientation of the main axes in the direction of freezing in congelation ice crystals (in the ice cover of reservoirs) was established as long ago as 1817 (see Brewster, 1818) and has subsequently been confirmed by an immense number of observations. For a long time it was believed that this orientation appeared in the protocrystallization stage in the primary layer. However, at the close of the nineteenth century data became available which indicated the possibility of the secondary development of ordered orientation in cases where the primary ice layer did not have ordered orientation. Drygalski (1897, p. 411), who first noted this phenomenon, attempted to explain it by the orienting effect of pressure which appeared after a continuous layer of ice had formed on the water surface. This hypothesis, which contains logical errors in addition to its other shortcomings, was soon disproved experimentally (Mügge, 1900) and is of no interest.

It was not until 1915 that a new attempt was made to solve the problem of the secondary development of uniform orientation, which

---

[7] The concepts orthotropy (orthotaxy) and thermotropy (thermotaxy) were borrowed from biology, where they specify growth features of living organisms, in particular those caused by some external influences (e.g., the heliotropy of plants).

was distinctly observed in river ice (Hamberg, 1915). As we shall show later, this attempt can scarcely be called successful either, but it is interesting in that it was based on the concept of selection in the growth process of more favorably oriented and thus faster growing crystals.

The principle of selection in a growing crystal aggregate was formulated more clearly in 1923 on the basis of the study of crystal growth in hollow tubes (Gross and Möller, 1923, p. 375), and then was developed into an orderly theory, which was eventually refined in the works of G. G. Laemmlein (1945) and A. N. Kolmogorov (1949). In contrast to selection during the nucleation of crystals, the selection in a growing aggregate is *geometric*. It is based on the *anisotropy of the rates of crystal growth* and is demonstrated by the fact that the only crystals that survive in a growing aggregate are those whose directions of greatest growth coincide with the direction of orthotropic crystallization or depart from it only slightly; in the process of growth the remaining crystals are forced out by the more favorably oriented neighboring crystals.

The mechanism of geometric selection is as follows. During mutually restricted growth, the growing faces of each crystal border on the melt, while the crystal is restricted laterally by the neighboring crystals. The crystal boundaries in the growth structure are formed by the paths of the edges that separate the growing faces of these crystals. When the rate of growth of two neighboring faces is equal, the path of the edge between them passes along the angular symmetry of these faces, i.e., along the plane that bisects the angle between them. However, if the rate of growth of the neighboring faces differs, the angle between them is cut by the path of the edge such that the sines of the resultant angles are related as the rates of growth of the corresponding faces. Thus, the path of the edge will deviate from the angular symmetry toward the face with the smallest rate of growth and subsequently this face will become smaller. If the paths of the edges that limit a given crystal face converge during growth, the face will disappear and, *vice versa*, if the paths of the edges diverge, the given face will become larger. However, if a crystal in the structure is limited by faces which disappear during the growth process, the entire crystal will also disappear, having been overgrown by neighboring crystals.

Consequently, crystals which grow more slowly due to less favorable orientation will eventually be supplanted by more rapidly growing crystals.

This process is depicted schematically in Fig. 34, which shows a cross section of part of a growth structure, consisting of three crystals

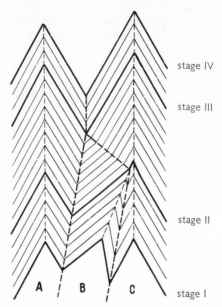

stage IV

stage III

stage II

A   B   C   stage I

FIG. 34. Diagram of the geometric selection process during the growth of a crystal aggregate. (After O. Schmidegg, 1928.)

(O. Schmidegg, 1928, p. 1). Crystals A and C are normal to the plane of the crystallization front and crystal B is inclined to it. In the first stage of growth, the apexes of all three crystals advance uniformly. The growth paths of the apexes of B and C and the interface B/C converge. The apex which first converges with the B/C interface should disappear in the second stage of growth. This is the apex of the more inclined crystal B, which should traverse a longer path. In the third stage, the B/C interface tilts strongly to the left and quickly converges with the A/B interface, consequently B disappears rapidly and is overgrown by its neighbors. Next, crystals A and B grow in parallel, without crowding each other and, together with other crystals, form a parallel-columnar structure.

The geometric selection mechanism depicted here also occurs during the growth of an ice crystal aggregate. The surface of the growing edges of ice crystals is also uneven but is of a different form, viz., it consists of basal planes and prism faces that form a number of steps, usually 0.4–0.6 mm high. Often a fine scalloping can be observed on the edges of the plates at an angle of 60° to the periphery. These are rudiments of skeletal growth along one of the secondary axes. The irregularities become considerably larger when the main axes are strongly tilted in the direction of growth. The ice surface at the ice/water interface does not become smooth during the freezing process, but only as a result of melting.

In the case analyzed above, the base from which the crystals grew had a planar surface. When the surface is irregular, with convexities and concavities that are wider than the crystals of the primary layer, at first beamlike and fanlike radiolitic formations will appear and later, beyond the zone of direct influence of the surface form, they will become a parallel aggregate.

When the initial orientation of the crystals is random, the rate of geometric selection will be a function of the size of the crystal cross sections at the moment mutually restricted growth begins and of the difference in the rates of growth in different directions. Of course, the lifetime of an unfavorably oriented crystal will increase as the size of its cross section. If one takes the average diameter of a crystal at the beginning of restricted growth as the unit of distance, the rate of geometric selection will depend on another factor. If the rate of crystal growth is identical in all directions, there will be no selection and a parallel-fibrous aggregate will form, in which the number of fibers will be equal to the original number of crystals.

The fastest selection will occur when growth proceeds in one crystallographic direction, in the form of needles randomly oriented in the primary layer (Laemmlein, 1945).

Experimenting with thymol crystals, Laemmlein established the curve of decrease of the number of crystals in an aggregate grown in a thin layer between two slides as a function of distance from the origin of growth. Initially, the decrease was so rapid that at a distance of two diameters only 50% of the crystals remained, and at a distance of 10 diameters, only 20% of the original number remained. As the less favorably oriented crystals are wedged out, the rate of selection decreases and the number of grains approaches the minimum more and more slowly.

A. N. Kolmogorov (1949) formulated the law of selection mathematically. The decrease in the number of crystals n per unit area cross section with increasing distance from the origin of restricted growth x is defined by the equation

$$n = \frac{c\sqrt{N}}{x}$$

where N is the number of crystal embryos at the beginning of restricted growth and c is a constant which depends on the magnitude of the anisotropy of the rates of crystal growth.

As the number of crystals decreases during growth of the aggregate, the crystallographic orientation becomes orderly. At first, the ordering of the growth structure increases rapidly, next it gradually reaches a maximum value characteristic of the given structure and then varies but little. If the number of crystals and the degree of ordering of the growth structure were dictated solely by the process of geometric selection, the development of the aggregate would be limited to a monocrystal with its axis of greatest rate of growth in the direction of growth (with $x = \infty$ and $n = 0$, which corresponds to the part of the crystal with an infinitely large cross section), but actually the number of crystals in the aggregate will be determined by the fraction of the total number of crystals which at first had an orientation quite close to the direction of growth.

Thus, in a growing crystal aggregate the axes of greatest rate of crystal growth will coincide with the direction of growth, owing to geometric selection. Freely growing ice crystals at temperatures above $-15°$ to $-20°$ will grow most rapidly in the basal plane and particularly in the directions of the secondary axes, which also decides their tabular form. Furthermore, it has definitely been established that the main axes of crystals in the ice cover of water and in other products of orthotropic crystallization of ice are oriented in the direction of growth. An obvious contradiction appears, which Hamberg, who made the first attempt to formulate a theory of geometric selection for ice, tried to resolve.

Hamberg assigned the main role in the selection process to the smaller surface tension of the basal planes of ice crystals, because of which they are more stable (less soluble). At first the basal planes grow slowly and develop tabular crystals which form irregular intergrowths. However, after supercooling has been eliminated, the advancing, obliquely oriented thin platelets, since they are farther from the cold source, release the heat of crystallization more slowly than do crystals whose basal planes are parallel to the surface of freezing. All further crystallization is concentrated on crystals which grew more slowly during the first stage, while the advancing platelets melt, since their narrow edges are less stable than the basal planes.

The error of Hamberg's reasoning is obvious. Actually, if the advancing crystals were in a less favorable position than the retarded crystals during restricted growth because of the greater distance from the cold source, the advantage of the crystals which grew more slowly could lead only to some equalization of the crystallization front, for if they were to advance they, too, would be in a less favorable position.

Consequently, other conditions being equal, crystals which grow more rapidly in a given direction will be just far enough ahead of the other crystals that their advantageous orientation will be compensated by their less favorable position as the advance guard of the growing crystals. Thus, they will be victorious in the geometric selection process, since they can grow laterally. The smaller surface tension of the basal planes of the crystals gives the advantage of greater stability, but it is unimportant except that it prevents the crystals and embryos from melting and, simultaneously, involves a lesser rate of growth than at the other faces. Thus, if other factors do not exert an influence, the crystals whose basal planes are parallel to the surface of freezing (or whose main axes lie in the direction of growth) will not grow as quickly as the rest and will not survive. However, just the opposite actually happens. The only explanation for the orientation of ice crystals in an aggregate whereby the main axes are in the direction of growth is that *the rate of growth is greater along the main axis.*

Thus, it must be recognized that the direction of greatest rate of growth of ice crystals changes 90° in passing from the free growth of discrete ice crystals to mutually restricted growth in an aggregate, i.e., the direction changes from the basal plane to the main axis. What is the reason for this change?

Evidently, the only possible cause is the somewhat greater thermal conductivity along the main axis. In adopting this explanation, we are returning to Trouton's viewpoint, but we apply the anisotropy of thermal conductivity to the stage of restricted growth of the crystal aggregate, not to the stage of protocrystallization. Some authors have objected to Trouton's hypothesis (Dobrowolski, 1923, p. 351; Veinberg, 1940, p. 162, and others) on the grounds that if anisotropic thermal conductivity actually does occur in ice, it is too weak to change the relationship between the rates of growth of the faces of a prism and a monohedron, where the rate of growth of the faces of a prism exceeds that of a monohedron. However, these authors forget that this difference is proportional to the degree of supercooling, even when the supercooling is insignificant and one of the most important differences between the second and first stages of ice formation is this slight supercooling of the water.

Another essential difference in the stage of orthotropic crystallization, noted by Hamberg, is that in the case of restricted growth, heat is removed through the growing crystals and not into the ambient supercooled melt, as in the case of free growth. Thus, the receding, not the advancing parts of the surface are in a more favorable position and skeletal growth becomes impossible. All this leads us to think that the greater rate of ice crystal growth in the direction of the main axis in a closed aggregate is due to the greater thermal conductivity of the crystals in that direction.

The change of direction of the greatest rate of growth due to differences in thermal conductivity is a special feature of ice, since in most other minerals the textural tendency in the granular aggregate is subordinate to the anisotropy of the rates of growth of freely growing crystals, i.e., the difference in the rates of growth in the various crystallographic directions in crystals which grow as a closed front is the same as in freely growing crystals (Schmidegg, 1928). According to Shubnikov and Laemmlein (1927), in this last case the ordering of crystallographic orientation in the process of mutually restricted growth has nothing to do with the direction of heat loss. However, if the direction of the greatest rate of growth in a granular aggregate changes in comparison to that of a freely growing crystal owing to anisotropic thermal conductivity, as in the case of ice, the connection between the direction of heat loss and the direction of dominant crystallographic orientation is causal, not merely a superficial coincidence. Therefore, we can speak of *thermotropic* crystal growth in this case, keeping in mind only that the direction of the heat flux has an indirect orienting effect on the crystals, through the change in the direction of the greatest rate of growth and the process of geometric selection, *not* a direct effect, as Rinne conceived it.

In congelation ice, the geometric selection varies with the character of the primary layer. The more the angles of deflection of the main axes of the crystals of the primary layer deviate from a direction normal to the surface of freezing, the more rapid will be the geometric selection.

In the widespread case of the freezing of a calm water surface, when the main axes of most of the crystals are horizontally oriented and only a few crystals are vertically oriented, the entire selection process usually ends at a distance of 50–100 mean diameters of the crystals of the primary layer from the surface. Over this distance, all crystals with a horizontal axis wedge out, while the few remaining crystals with a vertical axis show a corresponding increase in diameter (Fig. 35). Characteristically, no intermediate oblique orientations appear in the layer in which geometric selection rearranges the texture from a predominantly horizontal to an exclusively vertical orientation. If the stages of this process were represented by a series of stereograms, the type of texture shown in Fig. 31 would become the type shown in Fig. 32, owing to constant reduction of the relative number of horizontal axes and the corresponding increase in the number of vertical axes.

Geometric selection certainly does not take place in two opposite orientations of the main crystal axes of the primary layer; it occurs either normal to the surface of freezing or parallel to it. Evidently parallel orientation occurred in the famous case of the freezing of Lake St. Moritz in Engadine, when vertical columnar crystals 30 cm long and 1 cm and less in diameter formed and had approximately horizontal optic axes (McConnel and Kidd, 1888).

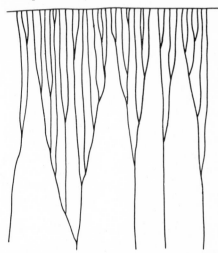

Fig. 35.   Diagram of ice texture in the zone of geometric selection.

However, geometric selection is not the only factor involved in the formation of a growth texture, since the ordering effect of geometric selection by its very mechanism is associated only with forced crystallization, i.e., with the growth of already existing crystals.

The prevalence of forced crystallization, due to the heat loss through already existing ice crystals and the slight supercooling of water associated with it, comprises the second distinctive feature of this stage of ice formation. However, *spontaneous crystallization* (on foreign nuclei) must also play some role here along with forced crystallization. Not only do the previously existing crystals grow, but new crystals appear and become members of the growing aggregate, disturbing its regularity.

The relationship between the roles of forced and spontaneous crystallization depends on the presence of effective nuclei of crystallization and on the rate of cooling, i.e., on the magnitude of the temperature gradient. As the temperature gradient increases at the crystallization front, the supercooling which it can support in the crystal melt increases and the rate of forced crystallization also increases, but this means that nucleation and the growth of new crystals will play an increasingly important role. During rapid growth, perhaps ejection of embryos by growing crystals occurs [described by Shubnikov (1935) for salol] in addition to nucleation. In any case, when freezing is very rapid, the aggregate grows considerably by incorporation of new, randomly oriented crystals, each of which then begins to participate in the mutually restricted, orthotropic growth and in the processes of geometric selection. Therefore, the texture becomes finer-grained and to a certain extent loses its parallel-fibrous structure and orderly crystallographic orientation. The impurity content of the ice, which increases considerably with increasing crystallization, also plays some role in these changes.

Thus, two opposite tendencies compete in the formation of growth textures:

(1) forced orthotropic crystallization with geometric selection and ordering of the texture competes with

(2) random protocrystallization, which disrupts the regularity of the form and the crystallographic orientation of the grains.

Slow cooling and a pure melt favor the first tendency, while rapid freezing and contamination by impurities promote the second tendency.

Actually, under natural conditions, protocrystallization rarely plays a large enough role in the second stage of ice formation to change the nature of the growth texture substantially. The heat transfer process always takes time. A considerable mass may freeze quickly only if a large temperature gradient is established suddenly (e.g., when water is discharged onto the earth's surface during intense cold), especially during the crystallization of supercooled water released rapidly from under pressure.

If random protocrystallization prevails during very rapid congelation, essentially the processes of the first stage of congelation ice formation will be re-established under slightly different conditions.

Under conditions of very slow freezing in the second stage of congelation ice formation, a completely transparent, parallel-columnar aggregate without autogenous inclusions develops. In the zone next to the primary layer, where the texture is rearranged by geometric selection, some of the crystals are constricted and wedged out and some expand in the direction of growth and their crystallographic orientation may not be systematically related to the external form. However, after geometric selection has been completed, the ice will consist of large, very long crystals, in which the geometric and main crystallographic axes will coincide and be parallel in the direction of growth (Fig. 36). The aggregate does not fuse into a monocrystal simply because the secondary axes have different orientation. In petrography, this texture is called *prismatic-granular* or *panidiomorphic-granular*. Of course, total idiomorphism (euhedralism) is never attained under natural conditions, because the relationship between the rates of growth and also the direction of the faces of neighboring crystals vary because of continuous minor changes, while the cross sections of the crystals rarely become regular (see Figs. 22, 37 and 38).[8]

Fig. 36. Prismatic-granular texture of congelation ice. (Photograph by V. P. Sedov and P. F. Shvetsov.)

---

[8] In cross section, the appearance and wedging out of some of the crystals still does not mean that they were actually nucleated and crowded out during growth. Often they result from a change in the inclination of the crystal boundaries perpendicular to the plane of the cross section.

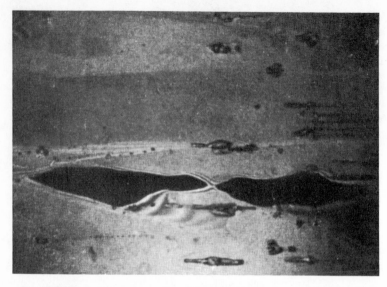

FIG. 37.   Prismatic-granular texture of congelation ice (cross section in direction
of growth). × 6. (Photograph by B. A. Savel'ev.)

FIG. 38. Prismatic-granular texture of congelation ice (cross section in direction
of growth). × 6. (Photograph by B. A. Savel'ev.)

When freezing is very rapid because of the prevalence of spontaneous crystallization, a very fine-grained ice appears which is milk-white (due to fine autogenous inclusions, namely air and salts) and has almost isometric, anhedral crystals and random crystallographic orientation. This corresponds to an *allotriomorphic-granular* texture.

Between these extreme types, there are some intermediate *hypidiomorphic-granular* growth textures with columnar crystals, which form with varying degrees of participation of both forced, orthotropic and random, spontaneous crystallization. The texture of the zone of geometric selection can be classified as *hypidiomorphic-granular*.

Crystallization differentiation. Thus far we have examined the formation of the growth textures of congelation ice which forms from pure water, but natural water always contains dissolved substances and often contains mechanical admixtures which may enter into the ice rock only as foreign *inclusions*. Consequently, the freezing of water is accompanied by the complex process of *crystallization differentiation* which to a certain extent is similar to the crystallization differentiation of magma. This results in the formation of the *structure* of congelation ice and the textural features associated with it.

During crystallization the autogenous inclusions of gases and salts are released at the interface of the newly forming ice and the unfrozen water and from the moment of their release they are identical with the xenogenous inclusions of the same composition with respect to the mechanism of interaction with the growing crystals.

The mechanism of interaction of growing crystals with bodies (i.e., the inclusions) which stand in their way is determined by the surface phenomena at the boundary of the three phases: ice, water and the body.[9]

The existence of the so-called *crystallizing force* was established in the middle of the past century. This force is manifested in the pressure exerted by the growing crystals in their direction of growth and in their ability to purify themselves. This autopurification factor consists in the effort of the new crystal lattice to eject foreign bodies (of course, with the exception of those which act as centers of crystallization). As Correns (1926, p. 81) explained, in cases where the actual or the apparent pressure of the growing crystals does not amount to an increase in volume with a change in the aggregate

---

[9] Quincke (1905) also attributes great significance to the surface tension at the boundary between a concentrated salt solution and pure water or between a concentrated and weaker solution.

state or to the growth of crystals at the expense of their environment, the "crystallizing force" is essentially the effect of surface tension at the different phase boundaries.

If a crystal is to grow, its surface must have access to a source of nourishment, i.e., it must be in contact with water. A foreign object coming into contact with the crystal obstructs the crystal's access to nourishment, curtails growth in that section of the crystal surface and eventually grows into the crystal because of the growth of the surrounding free sections of the crystal. However, as Correns pointed out, surface tension may alter this process.

Let us assume that the sum of the forces of surface tension between the growing crystal and the liquid ($\sigma_{1,2}$) and between the foreign body and the liquid ($\sigma_{2,3}$) is less than the force of surface tension between the crystal and the body ($\sigma_{1,3}$), i.e.,

$$\sigma_{1,3} > \sigma_{1,2} + \sigma_{2,3}$$

In this case, the forces of surface tension will strive to maintain a liquid film between the crystal and the body. Work equal to the product of the plane of separation and the difference of surface tensions $\sigma_{1,3} - (\sigma_{1,2} + \sigma_{2,3})$ must be expended to break this film.

If the pressure between the crystal and the body is less than the difference of the surface tensions and if the liquid film can supply sufficient nourishment to the part of the crystal surface adjacent to the inclusion, the rate of growth of that part of the crystal will keep pace with the rate of growth of the surrounding free surface and the inclusion will be forced out by the growing crystal. For the inclusion to grow into the crystal, either the liquid film between them must be broken completely or it must become incapable of supplying as much nourishment as obtained by the surrounding surface of the crystal. This may result from excessive pressure (i.e., the resistance of the body) or extremely fast crystal growth.

Correns' studies were limited to the lifting of loads by crystals nourished by a solution, when the crystallization of the dissolved substance did not break the liquid film. Conditions are somewhat different for the crystallization of a melt, since in this case the liquid film is not a means of diffusing the dissolved substance which nourishes the crystal, but is a direct source of crystal nourishment. The external, less stable layers of bound water, which can transfer oriented pressures, are mobile. Movement in films of bound water is directed toward the thinner part of the film and strives to equalize the film thickness throughout. Crystallization, like evaporation, removes from the film part of the substance which is under a pressure that does not hinder freezing at the given temperature, while the forces of surface tension strive to establish the previous film thickness by supplying liquid (Beskow, 1935).

In experiments made with solutions, the crystal often grew from below only in narrow bands along the edges of the face that came into contact with the bottom of the vessel, since nourishment could no longer be supplied by diffusion. The same occurs in the case of too-rapid freezing or when the body is too large, in which case the water film cannot supply enough substance to the crystal (Taber, 1930; Beskow, 1935). Naturally, the larger the foreign body, the greater will be the crystal surface that will have to be nourished from the sides by the same cross section of film and the smaller will be the rate of freezing required to incorporate the body into the crystal. Minute bodies are more easily expelled and displaced by the growing crystal than are larger bodies, which will grow into the crystals given the same rate of crystallization, pressure and surface tension.

Thus, the fate of a foreign body in the path of crystal growth depends on the relationship of the following factors:

(1) the magnitude of the forces of surface tension between the body, the liquid and the crystal;[10]
(2) the resistance of the body to displacement;
(3) the rate of crystallization;
(4) the size of the body.

The relationship between the forces of surface tension, ice and water for most of the widely distributed impurities is such that the ice can either capture or expel the impurities, depending on the rate of freezing. In the case of very slow freezing, all impurities except solid particles the size of grains of sand and larger are expelled by the ice, while every increase in the freezing rate leads to the appearance of inclusions in the ice.

The air inclusions are the most interesting of the autogenous impurities. In the second stage of congelation ice formation, small amounts of fresh water salts are captured by the ice primarily at the boundaries between crystals and around air bubbles; their presence can be detected during the melting of ice (Fig. 39).

According to the general rule for the macrodistribution of autogenous impurities, the quantities of both types of autogenous impurities in various parts of the rock are subject to similar changes, i.e., where there is a great deal of air there is also a great deal of salt,

---

[10] Other molecular physical-chemical interactions are involved here (orientation, polarization and dispersion effects), whose cumulative influence is also important in this case.

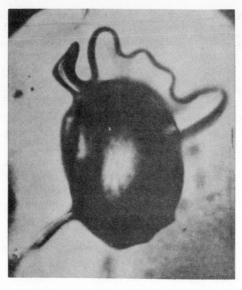

FIG. 39. Melting of ice around an air bubble due to the presence of salts.
× 52. (Photograph by B. I. Vtiurin.)

and *vice versa*. Secondary differentiation occurs only in the case of gravitational differentiation, when the air is ejected upward into the water and the salts downward.

A myriad of tiny air bubbles is released constantly at the crystallization front during freezing. If freezing takes place from below, most of the bubbles will float quickly upward. If freezing takes place from the side, some of them will fuse into larger bubbles and only then can they be torn from the surface of the ice by hydrostatic pressure or by streams of water. At the boundary of the upper layer of ice, all the air which floats up and is forced downward collects in larger bubbles, which are pressed against the ice by hydrostatic pressure and which can be torn away only by currents of water. A current of water which is not too swift and which does not hinder freezing helps form pure ice, i.e., ice without inclusions; thus, other conditions being equal, river ice is purer than lake ice (Bentley, 1907). If freezing is very slow, tiny bubbles of air may remain on the surface of the ice for a long time without growing into it. When freezing is accelerated, the tiny bubbles begin to grow into the ice simultaneously, often forming a whole layer of inclusions. Only the small bubbles (maximum 1–2 mm) remain spherical. If air continues to arrive, the bubble will grow lengthwise, assuming a cylindrical, tubular or even threadlike form (see Fig. 40). Elongation in the direction of growth is characteristic of this type of bubble, so that such bubbles indicate the direction of heat flux even more precisely and reliably than do the form and crystallographic orientation of the ice grains. Another characteristic feature of air inclusions of this origin is their distribution within the ice crystals and between crystals, independently of the position of the crystal boundaries.

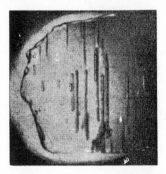

Fig. 40. Cylindrical air bubbles in congelation ice.

Frequently, instead of a single cylindrical bubble, a chain of tiny spherical or short tubular bubbles will form due to the discontinuous release of air. These chains are elongated in the direction of growth. Pear-shaped bubbles and bubbles similar to them are another variant. Most often the broad end of such bubbles, but sometimes the narrow end, faces the direction of growth, depending on whether the amount of incoming air had increased or decreased during the formation of the bubbles (Fig. 41).

The described type of air inclusion, the *oriented intergrowth type* similar to pegmatite, is as characteristic an indicator of the forced orthotropic crystallization of congelation ice as is prismatic-granular texture.

Furthermore, congelation ice contains finer spherical air inclusions, randomly dispersed within the ice crystals, which also belong to the *intergrowth* type, but they are irregular, as it were *poikilitic*.

Most of the air is expelled from the ice during forced crystallization. When protocrystallization is also involved in the ice formation, part of the air expelled from the crystals is captured by newly forming crystals which join the aggregate. Air bubbles of this origin are oval, spherical or elongated and curved, and if protocrystallization prevails they form sinuous, branching systems at the boundaries between the crystals, especially at the junction of three crystals.

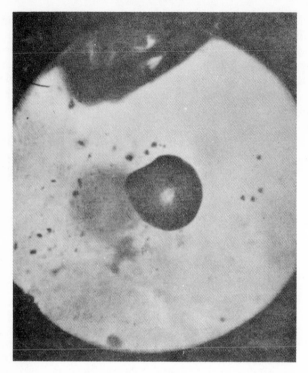

Fig. 41. Pear-shaped air bubble in congelation ice. × 10. (Photograph by B. I. Vtiurin.)

Their arrangement has no relation to the general direction of freezing (Fig. 42). This is a third type of air inclusion, the *intersertal* type, which is related genetically to spontaneous crystallization and allotriomorphic-granular or hypidiomorphic-granular texture. This type is also characteristic of the primary layer of ice which forms during considerable supercooling, especially in flowing water.

It should be mentioned that the very presence of autogenous impurities which impede the growth of crystals, facilitates proto-crystallization. Experiments in the growing of large ice crystals (Adams and Lewis, 1934) showed that the "parasitic" new crystals have a tendency to appear opposite the points of contact of a cultivated "seed" crystal with air inclusions.

The enumerated types include all the specifically autogenous air inclusions of the orthotropic crystallization stage. In all cases, apparently there is a direct relationship between the size of the inclusions, the gas content of the water and the rate of freezing.

Fig. 42.   Intersertal air inclusions (dark) in congelation ice. × 3. (Photograph by B. I. Vtiurin.)

When crystallization is slow and all the air (or practically all of it) is forced from the ice, the air which accumulates under the upper layer of ice forms large bubbles, which the buoyancy force flattens into ellipsoids or disks. Large bubbles may appear during omni-directional freezing or the release of gases from the bottom of a reservoir, even when the water surface freezes rapidly. After reaching a certain size, the bubbles begin to grow into the ice even during very slow crystallization. The air of this type of inclusion may be of xenogenous origin, but if it is autogenous it collects not only from the immediate vicinity but also from comparatively remote portions of the rock; in this sense, such intergrowth inclusions may be called xenogenous.

The *xenogenous air inclusions of an intergrowth* are characteristically large, ellipsoidal or flat at the top with strictly horizontal orientation and are independent of the ice texture (Fig. 43). If a bubble merely obstructs the growth path of separate parts of the crystal, it will grow into the ice without disturbing the ice texture; however, if it obstructs the entire surface of the crystal, the crystal will stop growing and will be supplanted by neighboring crystals.

F_{IG}. 43.   Typical forms of xenogenous air inclusions of an intergrowth and their relation to the ice texture (vertical section).

In the case of congelation ice formation, generally the amount of autogenous air which gets into the ice during the second stage of congelation ice formation varies from 0‰ to 13‰ of the total volume of rock, which, in the absence of other impurities, corresponds to an ice density of 0.9168 to 0.905 g/cm^3. The amount of air in the ice may increase somewhat during rapid spontaneous crystallization, but will not exceed 26‰ of the total volume (ice density 0.8936 g/cm^3). A higher content indicates that some of the air is of xenogenous origin. Usually, the air pressure in the ice slightly exceeds the atmospheric pressure, by the weight of the overlying water or ice.

When freezing is rapid, the insoluble solid impurities grow into the ice crystals, forming a poikilitic texture (Fig. 44), but some of

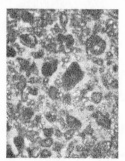

F_{IG}. 44.   Mineral particles in an ice crystal. × 100. (Photograph by B. I. Vtiurin.)

them remain between the crystals, owing to spontaneous crystallization. When crystallization is sufficiently slow, minute particles are expelled by the ice; if allotriomorphic grains appear in this case owing to growth from several centers, the mineral particles will arrange themselves along the crystal boundaries, forming a semblance of intersertal texture (Fig. 45).

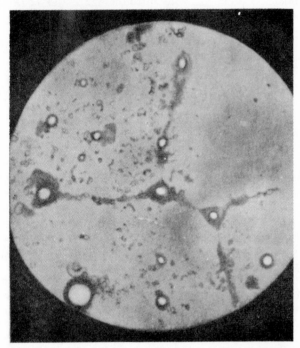

FIG. 45. Intersertal arrangement of mineral and air inclusions which had been forced out onto the grain boundaries during crystallization. × 10. (Photograph by B. I. Vtiurin.)

Since a relationship exists between the number of inclusions which remain in the ice and the rate of crystallization, a change in the rate of heat transfer leads to the appearance of a *stratified ice structure*. Each acceleration of crystallization results in the formation of a layer enriched by air bubbles and other inclusions.

FREEZING OF THE CENTRAL NUCLEUS

The third stage of congelation ice formation, i.e., the crystallization of a closed central nucleus, proceeds according to the same general laws of growth structure and texture as the previous stage, but the conditions and results of the process change essentially.

The chief differences between the third stage of ice formation and the two preceding stages are as follows:

(1) a closed system forms, in which the internal, freezing water nucleus is isolated by the surrounding ice and, consequently, a high and ever increasing hydrostatic pressure develops in it:

(2) the number of autogenous impurities increases progressively;

(3) heat leaves the central part of the nucleus in all directions.

From the very nature of these differences, it is evident that there is no sharp boundary between the second and third stages of ice formation.

What water becomes ice, its volume increases 9.08%. In a strictly closed system, freezing is retarded by increasing pressure which reduces the freezing point, but in the case of intense cooling, the pressure may reach such large values (up to 2,500 atm at a temperature less than $-22°C$) that any resistance can be overcome. As a rule, the freezing of a closed system leads to swelling, i.e., to bending of the ice roof, and then to rupture, i.e., to the formation of cracks in the ice and the effusion of the excess supercooled water onto the surface. These phenomena may be repeated often, with the resultant formation of very complex and diverse structures in the ice massif.

Air included in the ice of the central nucleus of a closed system may be under a pressure of the order of many atmospheres, so that melting of the ice is accompanied by a great number of miniature explosions with cracking and the spraying of melt water. Further, the main mass of ice does not become deformed or contain optic anomalies, since the pressure is hydrostatic.

The abundance and unique distribution of autogenous air inclusions comprise the most remarkable structural feature of ice which develops during the third stage of congelation ice formation. Usually, the ice of the central nucleus is quite cloudy owing to the presence of air and salts which penetrate each crystal, infiltrating through the regular intervals along the basal planes in the form of thin lenses and interlayers. The distance between neighboring interlayers of inclusions in a crystal decreases with increasing concentration of impurities in the remaining mother solution; often this distance is as much as $35–45\mu$ with inclusions $8–15\mu$ thick.

This orientation of the inclusions is one of the manifestations of the anisotropy of the crystal lattice of ice, in which the basal planes are least cohesive. Furthermore, the arrangement of inclusions at definite intervals (like the Liesegang rings) is an example of a *rhythmic structure* created by the periodicity of the crystallization process even when cooling is continuous. As early as 1858, Faraday pointed out that the freezing process must be a series of pulsations in which the freezing of thin layers alternates with interruptions for the removal of the generated heat. These concepts are in the best possible agreement with the occurrence of a rhythmic growth structure.

The excess air, which cannot be accommodated even in ice of rhythmic structure, accumulates in the upper part of a volume of water that freezes in all directions and collects in a single cavity, which then becomes larger as crystallization progresses. Subsequently, the increase in the volume of the cavity is not as rapid, because of the enormous pressure increase. Usually freezing terminates in an explosion that breaks the roof of the cavity or else cracks appear, through which the air and excess water erupt. The rounded upper roof of the cavity, previously occupied by compressed air, often remains after the excess pressure has been released. I. Ia. Baranov (1938) was the first to describe the formation of air cavities during the omnidirectional freezing of water.

Since the inclusions usually subdivide each monocrystal into subindividuals, i.e., plates, the central nucleus of an ice massif, which freezes last, usually assumes a concentric-conchoidal form, which can be observed with the unaided eye. Here, the radii of the main axes of the crystals converge toward the center, following the direction of heat flux. This general convergence of axes disturbs the regularity of the growth texture; the crystals crowd each other, as it were, and the orientation of the optic axes of some of the crystals may deviate several tens of degrees from radial orientation. The central nucleus usually consists of fine-grained ice, because of the abundance of inclusions and the accelerated crystallization which results from the omnidirectional, centrifugal efflux of heat. Most often the crystals become pyramidal. In other cases, an allotriomorphic-granular texture with disordered crystallographic orientation forms owing to rapid crystallization.

CHAPTER X

VARIANTS AND MODES OF OCCURRENCE OF CONGELATION ICE

Congelation ice forms under extremely diverse natural conditions. However, the petrographic study devoted to congelation ice has been so limited that no universal and detailed classification of this type of ice can be made at present. For the time being, the separation of congelation ice into several genetically independent forms must be based on the conditions of formation alone, since not enough is known about the characteristics of its composition and structure. Of course, the modes of occurrence of ice in themselves cannot be used as the basis for petrographic classification, even though they are associated with the composition and structure of the ice bodies.

Usually congelation ice is divided into three groups, according to the characteristics of the ice formation processes, which depend on the behavior of the initial material.

We have already examined the simplest cases, in which the mass of water (standing or moving) in a given volume freezes. Conditions may be complicated by the intermittent arrival of freezing water, which leads to the formation of ice of irregularly stratified structure.

The second group may be called *repeated congelation* ice, to distinguish it from ordinary congelation ice.

Finally, an ice body may form from the water contained in the pores of friable rock as a result of the singular process of crystallization differentiation which is imposed on the primary sedimentary rock. For want of a better term, we shall call this group segregation congelation ice.

ORDINARY CONGELATION ICE

The formation of ordinary congelation ice may pass through all the described stages or may stop at one of them, depending on conditions. Ordinary congelation ice may be divided into four basic petrographic types with gradual transitions between them:

(1) *primary congelation ice* with allotriomorphic-granular and hypidiomorphic-granular texture and predominantly tabular crystals; this ice forms by *protocrystallization* of supercooled and usually rapidly moving water or during freezing of snow slush;

(2) *selective congelation ice* with hypidiomorphic-granular texture and predominantly columnar crystals; this ice forms as a result of forced orthotropic crystallization or with some protocrystallization accompanied by *geometric selection*;

(3) *orthotropic congelation ice* with prismatic-granular texture. This ice forms as a result of *forced orthotropic crystallization*;

(4) *rhythmic congelation ice* with radiolitic or allotriomorphic-granular texture and concentric-conchoidal *rhythmic structure*; this ice forms during omnidirectional freezing of water in an enclosed space.

The first two types are characteristic primarily of the initial stages of ice formation, but if a calm water surface freezes slowly, orthotropic congelation, prismatic-granular ice may form with its main axes perpendicular to the surface of freezing. Complete freezing of a closed space terminates in the formation of rhythmic congelation ice; however, if the water freezes from the sides in cracks, the process cannot go beyond the orthotropic congelation or selective congelation ice formation stage or it may even be limited to the formation of primary congelation ice in narrow cracks with very cold walls.

The various types of ordinary congelation ice comprise the ice covers of water, the irregular accumulations in the main channels of rapidly flowing streams and the ice veins and irregular bodies in glaciers and in rocks with negative temperatures. The seasonal ice formations on water surfaces or in stream beds are the most widely distributed congelation ice forms in the lower boundary zone of the cryosphere. True, they often contain ice of sedimentary origin, but it plays a secondary role and can easily be distinguished from congelation ice. The structure of the ice cover of water can differ greatly, depending on the rate of flow of the water.

The ice covers of calm water. Properly speaking, only the ice covers of calm water, i.e., small lakes and other reservoirs and slowly moving rivers, are of purely congelation origin. At the time of greatest development, these covers usually consist of several layers of different structure and texture. Disregarding the snow cover or the products of its transformation, the upper layer of selective congelation ice (on an average, 15–20 cm thick) has a texture which has been transformed through geometric selection from a predominantly zonal orientation of the optic axes in the horizontal plane to a uniform vertical orientation. It has relatively small or medium-sized, vertical-columnar crystals that wedge out or expand downward. Farther down, the orthotropic congelation ice has a vertically-oriented, prismatic-granular texture. The upper selective congelation ice layer does not occur in the sections along the shoreline (occasionally it is absent throughout the ice cover) and all the vertical prismatic crystals pass through the cover from top to bottom. The structure of this ice is not directly associated with its texture.

This ice has stratified structure and the stratification is caused by the different amounts of autogenous air inclusions of intergrowth. Air-enriched strata of different thickness, indicating accelerated crystallization, occur primarily in the upper half of the cross section, somewhat below the surface of the ice. The lower half of the cross section, which crystallized under conditions of a slight or nearly constant temperature gradient, consists of pure ice with individual, randomly dispersed xenogenous air inclusions of intergrowth.

The ice covers of flowing water. As a rule, the ice covers of flowing or wind-driven water (large lakes and rivers and the sea) are complex congelation-metamorphic formations. In the first stages of development, the congelation ice formation processes are complicated by dynamometamorphic processes, viz., the fracturing, crushing and hummocking of ice with subsequent cementation of the fragments by newly generated congelation ice. The portion of the newly generated ice that fills the cracks in the ice cover should be classified as vein ice. The ice of the primary layer, which varies in thickness, has allotriomorphic-granular texture with disordered crystallographic orientation and abundant intersertal and other inclusions; next come the layers of selective congelation and orthotropic congelation ice. All these varieties of ice, particularly the first two, serve as initial material for the formation of tectonic breccia and, in part, of conglomerates with fragments ranging from a few millimeters to many meters in size, cemented by the newly generated congelation ice. Beneath the layer of ice breccia, which forms a fairly strong cover, there may be ordinary orthotropic congelation ice with a transitional layer above, but often ice tectonite builds into accumulations so large that ice can no longer form under it and the lower surface of the ice cover melts and evens out.

Very little study has been devoted to the structure of such ice covers. M. P. Golovkov (1936) made a study of this type, but did not interpret his descriptions genetically.

Stream ice. The ice of streams is a special mode of occurrence of congelation ice. This ice forms irregular accumulations on both sides of the main channel in the beds of mountain streams, when turbulent flow prevents the formation of an ice cover on the water surface. The texture of the whole mass is like that of primary congelation ice, i.e., it is allotriomorphic-granular with random crystallographic orientation and is cloudy due to inclusions.

Stream ice forms on the banks and bottom of the shallow parts of the stream bed near shore, on large boulders, and the like, due to the freezing of sludge, bottom ice, floe fragments and water sprays. Irregular accumulations of ice sometimes form banks along shore, which project in places and create bends in the river bed; sometimes they form "bridges" across the stream and sometimes they form relatively thin layers and lenses on the shallows.

There are gradual transitions between the described types of ice formations in water basins and streams.

Vein ice, or ice of unconformable injections. Three conditions are required for the formation of vein ice. There must be:

(1) cracks with access to water in water-impermeable or water-saturated rocks;

(2) water to fill these cracks; and

(3) cold sufficient to form ice.

The most favorable combination of these conditions is found in the "cold" glaciers of continental climates, where open cracks appear during glacier movement, where there is abundant melt water in summer and where the ice has a large cold reserve from winter freezing. Fissured glaciers are "fed internally" and lengthen because of the veins, i.e., the ice-filled cracks; in such glaciers, in places, vein ice amounts to as much as 10% of the total mass. Some veins are 1–2 m thick, with a dip of 20 m and a strike of tens of meters.

Glacier cracks are also caused by temperature fluctuations. Fissuring caused by freezing of the surface layer is a very important process below the firn line in slowly moving ice caps. The ice veins which form in frost cracks prevent the ice from returning to its former state when warmed and these veins, acting as wedges, promote movement, i.e., the flow of the surface layer of ice. Thus, the dilatation theory of movement, advanced by Scheuchzer in 1707 and Charpentier in 1835, is applicable in some measure to cold glaciers. The ice-cap ice contains an enormous number of narrow veins, i.e., wedges, which penetrate deep into the cap as they move together with the mass of sedimentary ice. Vein ice does not develop as well in "warm" glaciers[1] [hereafter called "temperate glaciers,"

---

[1] By "warm glaciers" we mean glaciers which are at the melting point throughout, except for the surface layer which freezes through in winter.

186 *The Petrology of Ice*

– D.K.] in regions of maritime climate, because such glaciers do not have adequate cold reserves.

The vein ice in native rock at subzero temperatures is of the same nature as the vein ice in glaciers. There are ice veins in fine-grained alluvium which differ from ordinary vein ice and are classified as repeated congelation ice. They will be described later.

The structure and texture of vein ice are functions of the crack width, the temperature and thermal conductivity of the crack walls and the temperature of the incoming water. When water arrives slowly and the water and walls of the crack are cold, the open cracks will fill with congelation ice because of the accumulation of ice incrustations on the walls. When a great quantity of water arrives and

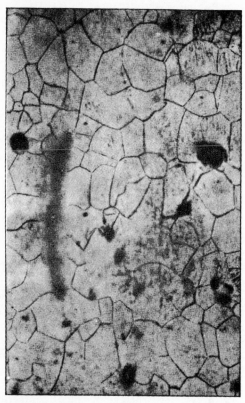

Fig. 46. Cavity on the axis of a vertical vein in glacier ice. The texture of the vein ice does not differ from that of the enclosing ice. The oval dark spots are air bubbles in the glacier ice. Actual size. (Photograph by N. V. Cherepanov.)

the temperature is high, the entire crack will be flooded with water and subsequently freeze. In many cases the two processes combine. Here we shall treat only the veins formed by the second method.

Owing to conformal forced crystallization, the texture of the vein ice in narrow cracks in the ice may not differ from that of the enclosing ice; only the number and nature of the inclusions will differ (Fig. 46). In the wider cracks there will be a textural difference manifested in a certain elongation, i.e., in the embryonic orthotropy of the crystals (Fig. 47). In still wider cracks, prismatic-granular texture develops with orientation normal to the plane of the walls. The crystals which had been growing toward each other meet in the middle of the vein, forming the axial plane of the vein, which appears as a nearly straight seam in the cross section. If one of the walls is cooled more than the other, usually the axial seam will be displaced toward the opposite wall.

If freezing is very slow and proceeds upward, the ice vein may not have any air inclusions at all. Figure 47 shows a case very similar to this. If freezing is more rapid, the ice will contain tubular air inclusions of intergrowth, which indicate the direction of freezing. They are arranged normal to the plane of the selvages, often in parallel rows, and converge on the axial seam at right angles (Fig. 48). Oval or flattened air bubbles pressed between the crystals are concentrated in the axial plane. Owing to trilateral freezing, the tubular air inclusions are arranged in the shape of a fan at the blunt lower and lateral termini of the veins, where the crack had been partially clogged with ice before being flooded with water (Fig. 49). Upward, the base of the fan passes into the axial plane of the vein. The tubular bubbles in an ice vein sometimes reach a size of 12×0.8 cm and the fan of bubbles becomes as much as 1 m wide. An upturned fan of bubbles will form if the water also freezes simultaneously from above, from the free water surface. Some veins, which formed by repeated partial flooding of the cracks over a period of several years and which, therefore, belong to the repeated injection type, consist of a number of ice stories (sometimes separated by plugs of snow origin) that terminate above and below in fans of tubular air bubbles (Fig. 50).

Nuclei of freezing. In the permafrost region and in the region of cold glaciers in continental climates, conditions which favor closed systems during freezing occur wherever water appears solely because of summer melting and is underlain by a water-impermeable frozen layer. These phenomena are most easily studied in shallow lakes that freeze to the bottom. This occurs often on glaciers and probably also on frozen ground. The general behavior of the processes in this case has been described as the third and final stage of congelation

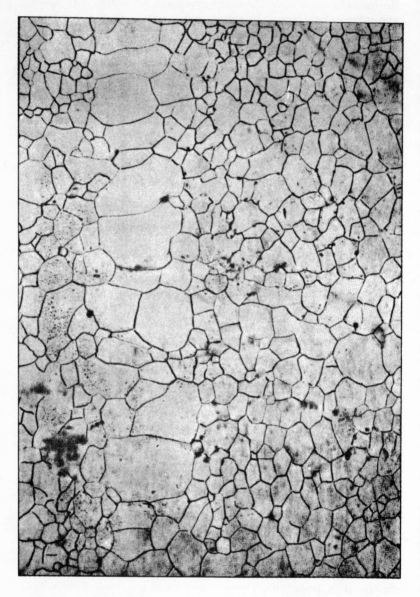

Fig. 47. Vertical congelation ice (transparent coarse-grained ice) in glacier ice. Actual size. (Photograph by N. V. Cherepanov.)

ice formation. Rhythmic congelation ice forms during this stage of ice formation. It has radiolitic or allotriomorphic-granular texture with many autogenous inclusions embedded along the basal planes

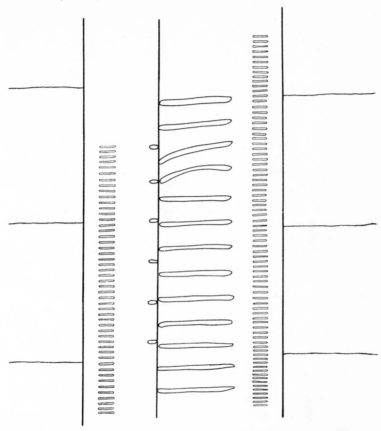

Fig. 48. Structure of a congelation vein in a glacier. The rows of fine tubular bubbles parallel to the selvages correspond to accelerated freezing. In the second stage, freezing was more rapid on the right than on the left. Drawn from nature. 1/4 actual size.

of the crystals (rhythmic structure) and thus is concentric-conchoidal. These phenomena are also associated with the formation of swelling mounds that contain air cavities and with cracking and the discharge of water onto the surface.

The nearly inaccessible central nuclei of the larger closed systems have not been investigated during the freezing of these systems and

FIG. 49.   Fan of tubular air inclusions in an ice vein. 1/4 actual size. (Photograph by N. V. Cherepanov.)

their presence can be inferred only from surface manifestations similar to the ones described above. Thus, when large masses of melt water accumulate in irregular reservoirs closed from below within cold glaciers or between the ice and the glacier bed in winter or even in spring before thawing (when the freezing has penetrated deep into the ice), water discharges along the cracks and channels onto

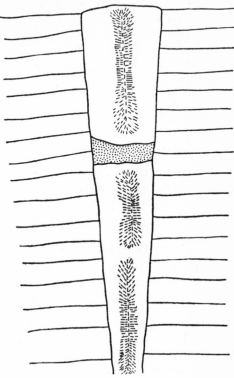

Fig. 50. Diagram of the structure of a 3-story ice vein.

the surface, forming gently sloping icing mounds (the so-called "hydrovolcanoes") and farther downslope forming streams and sheets of extruded ice.

Swelling mounds of ice form most extensively in icings, i.e., surface effusions of river or ground water, caused by the freezing of the channel. We still do not know whether a closed system and a freezing nucleus with rhythmic congelation ice forms in this case or whether the swelling is due to the pressure head of the stream, since no petrographic investigations have been made of the ice at the base of icing mounds. Probably both systems can occur in nature. In the second case, evidently the ice in the base of the icing mounds is similar to the ice of hydrolaccoliths and represents a transition to the injection type of ice.

Whatever the case may be, the upper part of an icing mound has a structure characteristic of the roof of closed nuclei of freezing. Icing mounds may reach heights of 5 m and may be from several meters to hundreds of meters in diameter, while the air cavities can be as much as 3 m high (Tolstikhin, 1941; Shvetsov and Sedov, 1942). According to Shvetsov and Sedov, the ice arch above the air cavity of an icing mound usually tapers in the apical section and they explain this by the plastic expansion of ice. Numerous cases of the explosion of icing mounds have been reported, whereby chunks of ice are hurled several tens of meters in all directions (Baranov, 1949; Shvetsov and Sedov, 1942).

REPEATED CONGELATION ICE

Repeated congelation ice differs from ordinary congelation ice in that its freezing water arrives intermittently and special structural features result. This group includes extruded ice and the perennial ice veins of frozen rocks.

Extruded Ice

Extruded ice is very widely distributed in nature as independent formations and as a component of ice bodies of complex genesis. One characteristic feature of the mechanism of formation of extruded ice consists in the freezing of water which flows more or less slowly along a solid base as individual droplets, streamlets or streams without a definite channel. Water for such ice formation is provided by the melting of ice and extrusions of water from under the ice or from under the ground. Freezing results in part from the loss of heat to the atmosphere and in part from the cold reserve of the solid base. As the ice grows, it forms the surface along which the water flows. The orientation of the surface with respect to the horizon may differ greatly, from nearly horizontal to pendent.

Although little petrographic study has been devoted to extruded ice, undoubtedly it has characteristic features which distinguish it from ordinary congelation ice that crystallizes from a continuous water medium. These differences are chiefly structural. Even if the temperature remains constant, the irregular supply of water causes stratification and the uneven spreading of the water leads to the formation of a characteristic extrusion microrelief of the layer surfaces, consisting in a series of cascade ledges separated by level sections. The larger streams, which have some heat reserve, partially melt the ice along which they flow, while freezing occurs along their periphery. Due to the frequent repetition of this process, the stratification is irregular, undulating and lenticular. The layer contacts are sometimes sharply defined (Fig. 51), often with accumulations of impurities, and sometimes they are indistinct and remelted. Sometimes the structure of the subsequent layers is the same as that of the previous layers, owing to conformal growth of the crystals of

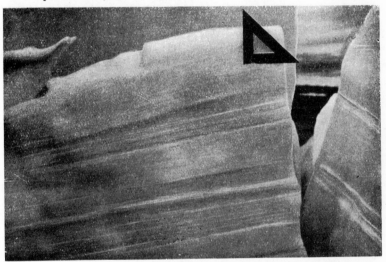

FIG. 51. Stratification of the extruded ice of a hydroeffusive. (Photograph by V. P. Sedov and P. F. Shvetsov.)

the base, and sometimes it is a new formation. In both cases, the texture is generally hypidiomorphic-granular, oriented perpendicular to the surface of freezing; however, if the water discharges onto a very cold surface, interlayers of disordered allotriomorphic fine-grained texture also form.

Extruded ice is most widely distributed in regions with a cold continental climate. Annually, by the end of summer, it forms thin covers in the lower part of the accumulation area of cold glaciers (glaciers with constantly negative ice temperatures); the extruded ice, alternating with layers of ice of different structure, acts as a source of nourishment and thus is a perennial formation. Sheets of extruded ice which form in winter and are fed by river or ground water become considerably thicker. The greatest discharges of water result from the freezing, or reduction of the cross section, of a stream of river water or ground water which encounters the least resistance upward and breaks through to the surface, usually along the cracks in the swelling mound which forms. The smaller discharges also come from swelling mounds, which form during the omnidirectional freezing of an enclosed volume of water in a layer of seasonal thawing or in unfrozen areas, "taliks,"[2] amidst frozen layers.

The Russians who live in the region of these surface extrusions call them "naleds." Some researchers began to use the term "naled" for ice covers formed from the freezing of water discharged onto the surface (Tolstikhin, 1941). Shvetsov and Sedov (1942) proposed that the products of the freezing of river and lake icings (naleds) be called "naled ice covers," while the products of the freezing of "naleds" formed from ground waters be called "hydroeffusives." If we wish to retain our concept of ice as a rock, we can hardly make this distinction and the very appropriate term "hydroeffusive" should be applied to all formations resulting from the freezing of "naleds," i.e., those formed from river, lake and ground waters that discharge onto the surface.

The large hydroeffusives are some of the most complex congelation ice rocks. Basically, they consist of extruded ice with lenses of ordinary orthotropic congelation, prismatic-granular ice, infiltration ice (impregnated with snow water) and the rhythmic congelation ice of the nuclei of omnidirectional freezing. In the region of the Siberian cold pole there are giant hydroeffusives 5 m and even 10 m thick and 27 km long, containing up to 500,000,000 m^3 of ice (Fig. 52); the Ulakhan-Taryn in the Moma River Basin is an example of a giant hydroeffusive (Tolstikhin, 1941; Shvetsov and Sedov, 1942). With some exceptions in colder years, most of the hydroeffusives are annual formations which melt each summer.

Extruded ice also coats the walls and floors of caves, glacier precipices and cliffs and the walls of glacier crevasses. Often extruded ice forms rows of half-columns on perpendicular walls, in addition to more or less thick continuous covers, while in caves and on overhanging walls it forms stalactites, stalagmites and, as a result of the fusion of these two, ice columns.

Vertical and horizontal sheets of extruded ice have similar characteristics, but the hanging forms have some special features. One may get an idea of their structure from the study of icicles, which are

---

[2] ["Talik: a deposit of unfrozen ground above, within, or beneath permafrost. Also called a 'tabetisol,' " *Glossary of Arctic and Subarctic Terms*, ADTIC Publication A-105, 1955, p. 80.—D.K.]

analogous to stalactites. When growth is very slow and continuous, the stalactites are monocrystals with horizontal or inclined optic axes perpendicular to the edge of the precipice (Hess, 1904, p. 12; Golovkov, 1939, p. 21). However, in most cases of interrupted growth, sooner or later polycrystalline layers with their main axes perpendicular to the stalactite surface begin to grow; this leads to

Fig. 52.   Giant hydroeffusive in the Indigirka River Basin (summer). (Photograph by V. P. Sedov and P. F. Shvetsov.)

the formation of a radiolitic aggregate. As the lower end of the stalactite begins to grow, the main axes of the crystals become inclined downward more and more and sometimes become vertical. The texture of the upper part of stalagmites is radiolitic, while the layers growing to the base have a vertically-oriented texture. The ice of the axial shaft of a stalactite icicle is cloudy (due to inclusions), while the outer concentric layers consist of purer ice (Futterer, 1901).

Often extruded ice fills ice cracks, forming ice veins. Evidently, it is also found in the native rocks of the permafrost region. Fine-grained variants with random allotriomorphic texture are often found among the *extruded vein ice* types which form under conditions of rapid freezing. Melt studies of this ice show it to be a homogeneous amorphous mass (Fig. 53). A still more characteristic feature of veins with extruded ice is that the uneven incrustations on the walls often stop up a crack before the entire lower part of the crack is filled with ice. As a result, air pockets remain along the axis of the vein, like those shown in Fig. 46. Otherwise, the only difference between extruded vein ice and ordinary vein ice is its irregularly stratified structure.

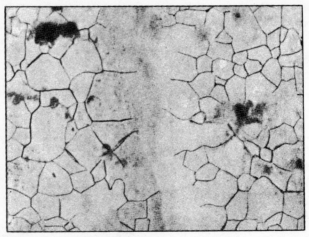

Fɪɢ. 53.   Vertical vein of fine-grained extruded ice (appearing in the photograph as a homogeneous vitreous mass) in glacier ice. Actual size. (Photograph by N. V. Cherepanov.)

Perennial Vein Ice

Perennial vein ice differs considerably from the extruded vein ice described above and results from the annual filling of frost cracks in frozen rock with ice over a long period of time. The volume of the rocks changes annually, owing to the seasonal temperature fluctuations; the rocks contract when cooled and expand when heated. Cooling splits the monolithic rock massif into a series of polygonal blocks. When a cold wave penetrates the rock, the cracks expand and when a heat wave penetrates it, they contract.

The following are required for the formation of perennial ice veins:

(1) frost cracking must extend beyond the active layer (otherwise the ice would melt out each year);

(2) the cracks must fill with ice;

(3) the enclosing frozen rock, split by the ice veins, must consolidate or extrude upward during the subsequent expansion due to heating (otherwise the ice will be extruded and melt under pressure and the vein will not be able to survive).

Observations show that perennial ice veins develop only in cold continental climates with light winter snow and primarily in finely dispersed new precipitations which freeze in a loose state soon after deposition. Large veins are found in clays, argillaceous soils and peat. Other conditions being equal, the veins are much smaller in sandy loams. They occur but rarely in pure sand and then they are no more than 0.1–0.5 m thick. However, when ice is abundant, veins can develop even in coarse clastic rocks.

Genetically speaking, various kinds of rocks enclose ice veins: alluvial, diluvial, lacustrine, fluvioglacial and marine; the formation of perennial ice veins is most highly developed in flood-plain alluvium. When climatic conditions are sufficiently favorable, ice veins grow in river-bottom land and, on a smaller scale, in the troughs and diluvial trains of slopes, but, as a rule, vein formation ceases after the terrace has emerged from the flood-plain stage or the slope has consolidated. Ice veins do not grow on the old elements of the relief.

The first thought that comes to mind when considering the connection between the development of perennial ice veins and the flood-plain regime is that flood water is the material which fills the frost cracks and since the flood waters do not reach the higher elements of the relief, veins cease to grow on them. However, observations show that in some cases ice veins grow even without water nourishment, owing solely to depth hoar which forms in the cracks, while veins do not appear in watershed areas and high terraces even when there is more than enough surface water to fill the cracks. The best conditions for the development of ice veins occur in high flood plains which are rarely flooded and where there is practically no accumulation of precipitation. The climate has to be more severe for veins to form in low flood plains.

The compressibility and plasticity of frozen rocks are much more important. They enable the rock to contract, collapse and extrude upward when wedged by ice veins. Freshly deposited, finely dispersed syngenetically frozen precipitation possesses these properties to the highest degree. Coarsely dispersed rocks, beginning with sand, are practically incompressible and have a higher coefficient of viscosity than does ice. Ice veins do not form on ancient terraces and watersheds, since frost cracks which would penetrate deeper than the active zone do not form there. Deep frost cracking is enhanced by an increase in the ice content of the enclosing rocks and the rocks of the active layer, since ice has a coefficient of thermal expansion which, on an average, is ten times greater than that of other rocks. High moisture content explains the great depth of cracking and growth of ice veins in flood plains and other areas where fresh precipitation accumulates.

A vein which forms in one year is from 1–2 mm to 1.5–2 cm thick and wedges down to a depth of several meters.[3] This process is repeated year after year in the same place. New cracks pass through the ice, which has less tensile strength than the cold frozen rock, and the vein grows from the center, because of the new layers of ice intruding it. The vein acts as a wedge and the enclosing frozen rock collapses into folds and is extruded laterally in the form of cylinders.

Often the formation of perennial ice veins is accompanied by the simultaneous accumulation of precipitation, because of which the veins not only widen but also grow upward as the upper surface of the enclosing layer rises. With this in mind, one can distinguish the following types of perennial ice veins (Gallwitz, 1949):

(1) epigenetic, which form in deposited rock with a constant surface height;

(2) syngenetic, which develop in precipitation as it is being deposited and as the surface is rising.[4]

Perennial veins may become 6–8 m wide and, with syngenetic

Fig. 54. Syngenetic perennial ice veins. Cliff height 30 m. (Photograph by E. M. Katasonov.)

---

[3] Under the most favorable conditions, the maximum depth of cracking at present is 5–7 m, but during the era of greatest development of perennial vein ice it was 9–10 m on an average and 12–15 m maximum.

[4] See also A. I. Popov (1953, p. 29).

growth, 20–30 m deep, in places even deeper (Fig. 54). In vertical cross section, the epigenetic veins are wedge-shaped (see Fig. 58), while in plan view they form a polygonal network. Changes in the depth of cracking and the depth of summer melting, and especially syngenetic growth simultaneous with the accumulation of precipitation, cause a diversity of perennial ice vein forms which can often be highly complex. In the case of very intense expansion of the veins, the nuclei of frozen rock in the cells of the space lattice become comparatively narrow columns, "earth veins" in the ice, and when the ice melts they emerge in the form of alluvial cones, known in Yakutia as "baidzharakhs." A cross section of an ice vein network with an irregular outcrop surface reveals fantastic configurations of ice beddings (Fig. 55).

Fig. 55. Outcrop forms of a network of syngenetic ice veins in the same outcropping as in Fig. 54. (Photograph by E. M. Katasonov.)

In most cases, the ice of perennial veins is yellowish, owing to the host of minute mineral particles brought into the frost cracks by the water. Such ice contains a large amount of xenogenous air (up to 60% of the total), which comes from the pores of the depth hoar. The density of this ice varies approximately between 0.880 and 0.908 g/cm^3; without mineral inclusions it is 0.878–0.903 g/cm^3, as in the case of infiltration ice. The air bubbles constitute 25–42‰ of the volume, while the mineral particles comprise from 2‰ to 10‰ and more of the volume. Owing to oxidation of the relatively large

amount of plant remnants, the air in the ice usually becomes a nearly
oxygen-free mixture of inert and biochemical gases.

The ice has a characteristic vertically stratified structure, because
of the alternation of layers with different amounts of mineral and
air inclusions. The stratification is irregular, it is undulating below,
interlacing, with vague, diffuse layer boundaries, since the contacts

FIG. 56.   Stratification of perennial vein ice. Reduced 1.8 ×. (Photograph
by B. I. Vtiurin.)

are remelted by water (Figs. 56 and 57). Sometimes cavities
(characteristic of extruded vein ice) form within the veins, owing to
clogging of the cracks by the freezing ice. The layers are usually
fan-shaped; along the axis the veins are vertical, along the margins
they tilt toward the center (Fig. 58). Xenoliths of the enclosing rock,

Fig. 57.   Stratification of perennial vein ice. Reduced 1.8 ×. (Photograph by B. I. Vtiurin.)

compressed between curved layers of ice, are found in the lower part of perennial veins. Individual layers pass downward beyond the limits of the main body of veins, forming apophyses in the enclosing rock.

The ice texture is allotriomorphic-granular or hypidiomorphic-granular (Figs. 59–61). The crystals are limited horizontally by the width of the cracks; above they may be 1–2 cm wide and taper down to 1 mm and less. Often the crystals are somewhat larger vertically than horizontally in vein profile, giving the impression of a column. Actually, in most cases the crystals are flattened in the plane of the layers and are platy. The main axes of the crystals in different parts of the veins vary from distinctly ordered horizontal orientation across the layers to random orientation (Fig. 62). According to the laws already stated concerning the growth of crystals onto solid walls, the first type of orientation occurs when the temperature of the enclosing rock during crystallization is low, and the second type

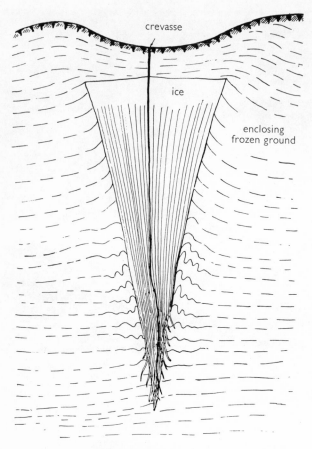

FIG. 58.   Sketch of the structure of a perennial ice vein.

occurs when the temperature is high (close to zero). However, the
picture may be complicated considerably by the influence of depth-
hoar crystals, which act as centers of crystallization for the water
which fills the cracks in the event of incomplete remelting and usually
this makes the orientation more random.

The main axes are vertically oriented at the upper end of the
veins (Fig. 63) and the crystals are columnar. The stratification
becomes quite indistinct in this part of the vein and the number of
mineral inclusions decreases considerably. Characteristically, the
gradual transition from vertically-upward to horizontal crystallographic orientation of the deep part of the vein does not occur as it

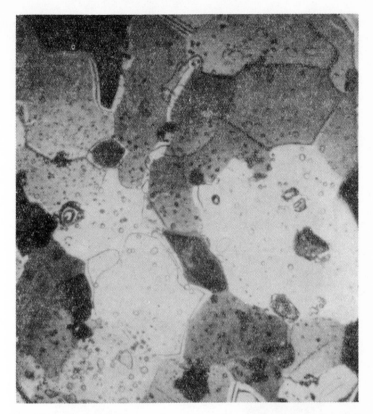

Fig. 59. Allotriomorphic-granular texture of a perennial ice vein. × 5. (Photograph by B. I. Vtiurin.)

does in the case of geometric selection; there is random orientation in the transitional zone, which subsequently becomes ordered owing to the increasing number of crystals with horizontal axes (Figs. 64 and 65).

Such is the primary texture of perennial vein ice. Later, owing to mechanical influences, it may become cataclastic. There is a regular relationship between the regime of a given section of flood plain, the lithology of the sediments and the character of the ice veins that form in them, namely: the lower the flood plain is, the closer it is to the river bed and the coarser the sediments are, the thinner will be the layers of vein ice and the smaller the crystals, the greater will be the mineral impurity content and the smaller the gaseous impurity content, the more ordered will be the crystallographic orientation, the higher will be the pressure of the gases in the ice, and the more strongly developed will be the optic anomalies and the cataclastic phenomena.

Perennial ice veins which have ceased growing form the main mass of the so-called *fossil ice*, which is widely distributed in regions of cold and dry continental climate. Owing to the complexity of the form

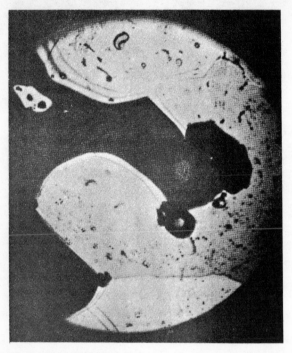

FIG. 60.   Allotriomorphic-granular texture of a perennial ice vein. × 7.5.
(Photograph by B. I. Vtiurin.)

and composition of perennial ice veins, their origin was long the subject of controversy. The prevailing opinions favored glacier (Tol', 1897; Sumgin, 1940a) or snow origin (Tolmachev, 1903; Grigor'ev, 1932 and 1946, *et al.*). Figurin (1823) was the first to suggest that this phenomenon might be caused by the accumulation of ice in frost cracks and later this idea was developed by Baer in 1842 and by Bunge (1903) and Leffingwell (1919). Petrographic investigation has confirmed the hypothesis that fossil ice is of vein origin, a hypothesis based on the observations of contemporary processes.

In addition, extensive material has been gathered on the extinct ice veins of the periglacial regions of Quaternary glaciation. These veins have subsequently been replaced by other rocks. The data on these extinct veins agree with the data presented above and indicate that this was a very widely distributed phenomenon (Moskvitin, 1940 and 1947; Gallwitz, 1949).

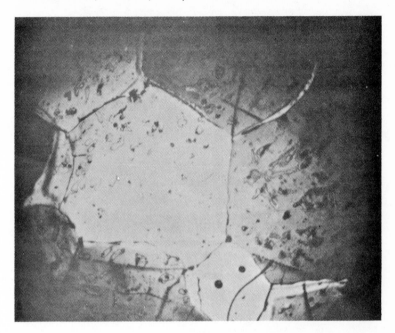

FIG. 61. Hypidiomorphic-granular texture of a perennial ice vein. × 16.5. (Photograph by B. I. Vtiurin.)

SEGREGATION CONGELATION ICE

The segregation congelation ice group, which forms within friable rock when the rock freezes, is the most difficult group to analyze structurally and genetically, since practically no study has been made of the structure of this ice and since the conditions and process of formation are much more complex than those of the previously examined types of congelation ice.

Segregation congelation ice formation is a unique process of crystallization differentiation, which takes place in a highly complex

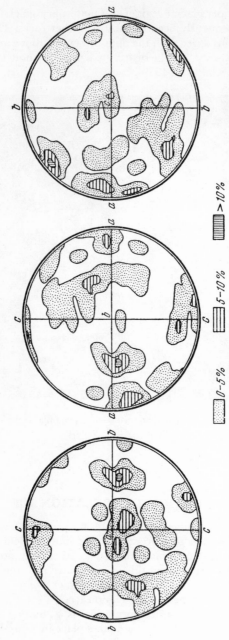

Fig. 62. Stereogram of the crystallographic orientation of perennial vein ice. Random orientation of the principal axes. c—vertical direction; bc—plane of the vein.

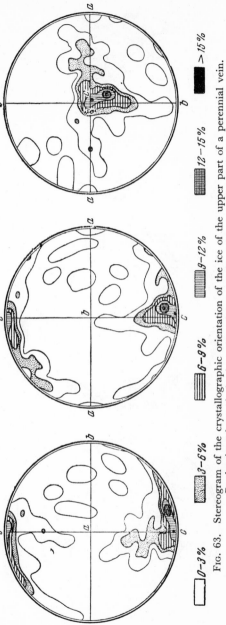

FIG. 63. Stereogram of the crystallographic orientation of the ice of the upper part of a perennial vein. Predominantly vertical orientation of the axes. Symbols same as in Fig. 62.

0–3% 3–6% 6–9% 9–12% 12–15% >15%

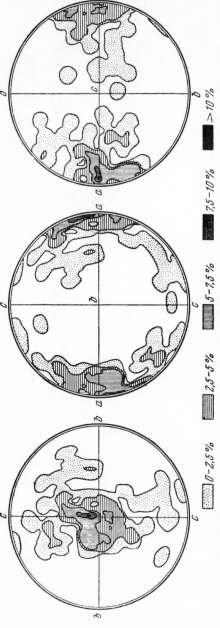

Fig. 64.   Stereogram of the crystallographic orientation of the ice of a perennial vein, 2 m deeper than in Fig. 63. Predominant orientation of the axes—normal to the plane of the vein.

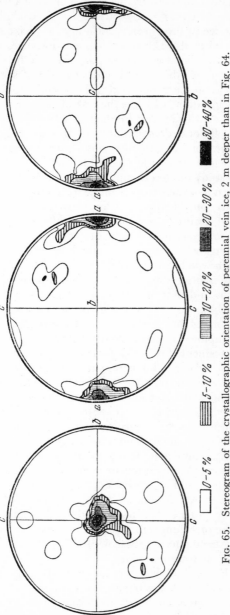

FIG. 65. Stereogram of the crystallographic orientation of perennial vein ice, 2 m deeper than in Fig. 64. Clearly defined dominant orientation of the axes normal to the plane of the vein.

polyphase system, in moist friable rock. The ice bodies are one product of this process and the various frozen enclosing rocks are
another. The ice in these frozen enclosing rocks cements the grains
of the other minerals. There are frequent instances where the ice
crystals continue directly into the polymineralic frozen rock as ice
cement. Obviously, the genesis and structure of segregation congelation ice cannot be understood without studying the processes of
frozen rock formation, which is the task of cryopedology.

Ice formation during the freezing of ground has attracted the
attention chiefly of pedologists and construction engineers because
of the damage done to structures and communication lines by the
swelling of the ground. Various physical research methods have been
employed to study this freezing process, but such studies have almost
completely ignored the structure of the frozen rock which forms. For
the most part, only texture (in the petrographic sense) has been
studied, which in itself does not provide sufficient data for judging
the internal processes of the rock. At present, cryopedology, as the
study of frozen rock, is still in the premicroscopic stage of development, through which petrography passed in the 1860's.

Thus, at present only very schematic descriptions can be given of
the conditions and processes of segregation congelation ice formation, only insofar as this is required for understanding the few
available reports of the mode of occurrence and insofar as the present
state of development of cryopedology permits.

Friable, uncemented rock at a positive temperature is a polyphase
system, comprised of solid mineral particles or of a skeleton, of a free
and a bound solid water surface or, more exactly, of an aqueous
solution of salts and other materials and, finally, of air with water
vapor in the communicating pores or in isolated bubbles. The bound
water is a film of complex structure; the layers near the binding
surface are solids, modifications of high-pressure ice or quasi-
crystalline forms similar to high-pressure ice, while the outer layers
are under less molecular pressure and are in the liquid state. In
theory, the force field of adsorption, approaching zero asymptotically, propagates over an infinitely great distance from the binding
surface, but in practice it is manifested for a distance of just a few
microns in the mechanical properties of ice (shear modulus) and for
a distance up to 40 microns (Beskow, 1935) in the thermal properties
(reduction of the freezing point).

Completely "dry" rock or soil does not exist in nature, because a
film of bound water always remains on the surface of the rock or soil
particles. This film is thick enough so that its outer layer will be in
equilibrium with the atmospheric water vapor. As the film becomes

thinner, its retaining power increases and less atmospheric vapor pressure is required to maintain equilibrium. Therefore, when the atmospheric humidity decreases, the film of water bound by the surface of the solid particle will become thinner, but will not disappear unless there is no atmospheric water vapor whatsoever. A similar process of diminishing film thickness is observed when the temperature drops below zero, but in this case the water becomes ice I instead of vapor.

When heat is lost after a certain amount of supercooling takes place and ice embryos form at 0°C, only the free fresh water under normal pressure in the large rock pores will freeze. The rest of the water, which is subjected to higher external or internal pressures, will freeze gradually with a further temperature decrease, as its freezing point is reached. The higher internal pressure in such cases is due to the attraction of the solid particles or ions of the dissolved substances. The same thing happens in the case of heating, when partial melting of the ice occurs over a considerable range of negative temperatures. Tsytovich (1945) calls this situation, which follows directly from the laws of physicochemical equilibrium, the *principle of the equilibrium state of water in frozen ground*. Actually, the main mass of water bound by the surface of the solid particles, which corresponds for the most part to the sorbed film thickness, freezes within a temperature range of a few degrees below zero, while the strictly liquid part of the film perhaps may not exist at temperatures below −22°C. The remainder will be in the solid phase.

The relative amount of moisture in the bound state is a function not only of the nature of the absorbing complex and the mineralogical composition, but also of the rock pore size or the specific surface and, thus, of the size of the component particles. The amount of bound water will increase with decreasing particle size. In dispersed rocks (sediments)[5] with fine pores, where all the water (or a good part of it) is bound by the skeleton surface, freezing takes place in the relatively thick transitional frozen-thawed layer, not just in the plane of the crystallization front which separates the frozen from the thawed rock. Within this transitional layer, freezing begins in the large pores and the outer parts of the sorbed films and, as the temperature decreases, it extends to ever finer pores and to the more

---

[5] [The author uses the term "rock" (*poroda, gornaia poroda*) to indicate any consolidated material, including frozen ground and frozen sediment, i.e., the soil and mineral matter plus the frozen and unfrozen water in the mass. I have retained this term in the translation, because of the complex system Prof. Shumskii builds around it, although here and in what follows "sediment" would probably be more appropriate. – D.K.]

stably bound parts of the film. The transitional layer will become thicker as the temperature gradient and the rate of freezing decrease, and when the cold source (under natural conditions, the earth's surface) is relatively warm, all the "frozen" dispersed rock will contain a considerable quantity of liquid, loosely bound water and will not leave the transitional, frozen-thawed state. In comparatively coarse-grained friable rock, beginning with sand, the amount of bound water is so small that the delayed freezing of this bound water has practically no effect on the properties of the rock and the processes of structure formation.

The boundary between the particle size of sand and dust (0.05–0.1 mm)[6] is critical in another respect, viz., it is approximately the size limit of the solid mineral particles which growing crystals can expel during very slow freezing and low external resistance. This is due chiefly to the small area of the crystal surface covered by such mineral particles; the crystal surface must get enough nourishment from the segregating water film to insure growth. However, in soil and friable rock there is another variable which is decisive for the behavior and outcome of the freezing process, namely, the presence of enough water to insure ice crystal growth. The freezing process itself, which is associated with the temperature gradient, reduction of the thickness of sorbed films and an increase in the volume of the freezing water, is accompanied by a quite considerable redistribution of moisture in the rock.

The problem of moisture migration in friable rocks during freezing is highly complex and has not yet been solved completely.[7] The flow of liquids and gases always causes pressure differences, but the reason for the appearance of a pressure gradient differs in the different states of moisture in friable rocks. Apart from the water vapor in air pores, solid ice I and firmly bound "water," we may distinguish two different moisture states with respect to the migration mechanism, namely, loosely bound water and free water.

Lebedev (1935) established experimentally that *loosely bound water* migrates toward the thinner parts of the bound water film. The film thickness evens out, like a free water surface seeking its own level because of gravity, but in this case the forces acting on a unit mass (binding forces) are greater than the gravitational forces and the

---

[6] In pedology the boundary between sand and dust particle sizes is 0.05 mm, in sedimentary rock petrography it is 0.1 mm.

[7] The literature on this problem is extensive (Beskow, 1935; Lebedev, 1935; Tsytovich and Sumgin, 1937; Sumgin *et al.*, 1940; Fedosov, 1940; Gol'dshtein, 1948, and others). We have not presented all the points of view here, but merely those we consider to be the most reasonable.

migration of the film does not depend on the direction of the gravitational force. When the outer part of the bound water film freezes, the film becomes thinner, which causes pellicular migration in a direction opposite that of the temperature gradient, and the loosely bound water is attracted toward the layer of crystallization. Outside the crystallization layer, the loosely bound water which runs off along the films may be replenished by supplies of free water, when such are available.[8]

There may be various reasons for the appearance of a pressure gradient in *free water*, but few of them are directly related to freezing; in particular, the gravitational movement of free water and capillary attraction (due to meniscus forces) are unrelated to freezing, except in the special case of the formation of "freezing pores," caused by the expansion of freezing water.[9] Capillary attraction proceeds from the moister portions of the pores, with less curved meniscuses, to the drier portions, with more curved meniscuses. If there is a temperature gradient, a new migration factor appears, viz., a surface tension gradient directed toward the temperature gradient, which causes the water to run in the opposite direction, i.e., toward a greater surface tension with the same meniscus curvature. However, even this thermal factor, which induces the migration of water toward the crystallization front, is not associated with freezing as such and is also effective in the positive temperature range. Migration results directly from freezing only when the rock contains a large amount of free water that fills all the pores. In this case, reduction of the volume of the skeleton and of the air bubbles entrapped by the water during the temperature decrease (according to Gay-Lussac's law) cannot compensate for the expansion of the water as it becomes ice.

---

[8] This process is quite similar to pellicular migration toward thinner parts of the film because of evaporation and has nothing in common with the direct uptake of water by the "crystallizing force" of ice, as depicted by Taber (1930, *et al.*). The migration occurs in films sorbed by the solid mineral skeleton of the rock, not by the ice.

According to Gol'dshtein (1948), pellicular migration is caused by the difference of osmotic pressures resulting from the increased concentration of the solution due to the freezing of the outer layers of film. However, the salting of ground swellings has indicated that this factor does not play any decisive role. Gol'dshtein admits that salting eliminates ice production even when the salted ground freezes. Freezing occurs even though the difference in concentrations and osmotic pressures created by freezing of an identical amount of water increases as the initial concentration of the solution increases.

[9] The first hypothesis of the migration of water in freezing ground, formulated by the Russian engineer V. Shtukenberg in 1885, was based on this secondary phenomenon.

In this case, the *water is forced out of the freezing layer* and, consequently, migrates in the direction of the temperature gradient or, to be more accurate, in the direction of least resistance, which may not coincide with the direction of the temperature gradient.

Thus, in the final analysis, the dispersion and moisture content of the rock determine the direction and intensity of moisture migration in friable rock during freezing. All or most of the water is bound in dispersed rocks with a great specific skeletal surface and fine pores, and during complete saturation the amount of water may considerably exceed the volume of the skeleton. The growing ice crystals expel the rock particles, simultaneously taking water from the outer part of the bound film, and the water migrates in a direction opposite to that of the temperature gradient, toward the layer of crystallization, providing a constant fresh supply of nourishment for ice crystal growth.

However, in coarse-grained rocks with a small specific skeleton surface and large pores, the bound water occupies only a small part of the rock volume and even under favorable conditions the pellicular migration cannot have any noticeable effect. When the moisture content is sufficiently high, all the excess moisture appears as free water which freezes in the rock pores between the skeleton particles. Since each particle has a large surface, the ice crystals at the contacts with the skeleton particles, which are nourished by the film of loosely bound water, cannot grow at the same rate as the crystals in the pores between the particles, which are nourished by free water, and the crystals grow through the rock, along the pores, instead of expelling it or displacing it. Furthermore, the pressure on the contacts between the particles of coarse-grained rock is so great that a film of quite mobile bound water cannot remain between them, since the weight of the overlying layer in the coarse-grained rock is distributed over fewer points.

Unless such comparatively coarse-grained rock is saturated with water, there will be practically no migration of liquid water during freezing. The only migration will be along the air pores in a vapor state (distillation and sublimation), but because of the enormous heat of vaporization, the migration will be more a factor of heat transfer than of moisture migration. The main mass of water freezes without migrating, forming a cementing mineral skeleton of ice grains; these ice grains fill all the pores and are no larger than the skeletal particles, in fact usually they are smaller. Thus, the frozen rock texture becomes intersertal.

During freezing, the free water in a water-saturated, coarse-grained rock, forced out by the growing ice crystals, migrates from the crystallization front in the direction of least filtration resistance in an open system or toward a deformable wall in a closed system. If numerous centers of crystallization appear, abetted by mineral particles which act as nuclei of freezing, the freezing water-saturated rock will also acquire intersertal texture with ice-cement crystals no larger than the pores and particles of the skeleton. However, during very slow and strictly forced crystallization in water-saturated rock, a *poikilitic texture* can develop, in which the skeletal particles are included in the large crystals of the ice cement which has grown along the pores.

The intensity of migration increases as the moisture content of the freezing rock increases in both cases of water migration caused by the freezing of friable rock, namely, (1) when bound water is attracted toward the crystallization layer in dispersed rock and (2) when free water is forced away from the crystallization front in coarse-grained rock. In coarse-grained rock, the maximum moisture content permitting migration during freezing is close to complete water saturation, while in dispersed rock it corresponds approximately to the maximum molecular moisture content. The relationship between the rate of migration and the rock particle size is directly opposite in the two types of rocks described above. In coarse-grained rock, the rate of migration of free water from the crystallization front increases with increasing pore size (and, consequently, particle size), since the coefficient of filtration increases sharply in this process, i.e., the resistance to the escape of water decreases. In dispersed rock, other conditions being equal, the rate of pellicular migration of the water film toward the crystallization layer increases with decreasing skeleton particle size, since the specific surface of the particles increases in the process and, consequently, the number of nourishing water films per unit volume of rock also increases. If the migration of water during freezing is actually more intense in less dispersed, dusty ground than in clays, evidently this will be due, in part, to differences in the thickness of the films of bound water.

In dispersed ground, the pores are smaller than the normal thickness of the film of bound water. Therefore, in the "water-filled" state (A. E. Fedosov's [1940] term for the state in which the pores are filled with water) the rock continues to absorb water and "swells" to a water-saturated state, until the film of bound water, displacing the skeleton particles, approaches normal thickness. Therefore, if the moisture content is the same in the water-filled state, the films of bound water will be thinner in more dispersed than in less dispersed ground; the outer layers of the film will be bound more firmly, they will be less mobile and, despite their larger specific surface, will not be able to insure sufficiently rapid migration. Further, the water-binding capacity of rocks varies with their mineral composition; bentonite clays, in particular, can bind not only the surface water but also deeper water (penetrating within the crystal lattice and separating it), which creates differences in both the film thickness and the mobility of the bound water.

However, bound water is so viscous that it can move but very slowly and for only a short distance—in Gol'dshtein's (1948) opinion, merely a few centimeters. Therefore, migration cannot be very fast if the rock is so dispersed that all its water is bound. Conditions are more favorable for migration in rocks which have an adequate supply of bound water in addition to their free water (in particular, gravitational water or a combination of capillary and gravitational water), which nourishes the sorbed films outside the crystallization layer.

The formation of *segregation ice*, with the resultant *uniform swelling* of quite considerable portions of the rock, is associated with the attraction of water to the crystallization layer in dispersed rocks which freeze as open systems. The formation of *injection ice*, with the resultant *differential swelling* of the rock, is associated with the expulsion of water from coarse-grained rocks and often with the expulsion of supersaturated fluid (quicksand-like)[10] masses in rocks which freeze as closed systems, i.e., masses surrounded by an impervious (frozen) shell. In both cases, the ice bodies form amid polymineralic frozen rock as a result of the above-described processes of crystallization differentiation in friable moist rock. However, in the first case the ice is *separated out* in the crystallization layer, while in the second it is *intruded* under the pressure of water expelled along the planes of weakness in deformable freezing rocks, with subsequent total or partial freezing of the water lens.

Segregation Ice

If the process of segregation ice formation is regarded as crystallization differentiation superposed on the primary sedimentary rock, frozen rocks with segregation ice should be classified as *taxites* (or if they have a regular alternation of strata, *eutaxites*), while the segregation ice bodies should be classified as *constitutional schlieren*.

For the aforementioned reasons, segregation ice forms only in friable dispersed (fine-grained) rocks, i.e., in clays, argillaceous soils and, less often, in adequately moistened sandy loams not too far below the diurnal surface (at not too great a pressure) and with a

---

[10] [Hereafter called "sandsnow"; see footnote 4, chap. XIII. – D.K.]

slow rate of freezing. Under the most favorable conditions, the friable rock particle size critical for segregation ice formation is approximately 0.1 mm (Beskow, 1935). This limit decreases abruptly when the external pressure or the cohesion between the rock particles increases and especially when the freezing process is accelerated and the moisture content decreases, so that during very rapid freezing the finest clay forms a macroscopically uniform rock without ice inclusions.

The influence of the rate of freezing is defined more exactly by the relationship between the rate of heat loss and the rate of water influx: as the cooling rate increases, the rate of influx of water which releases the latent heat of crystallization should also increase, permitting the continuous forced growth of segregation ice crystals, which separate the rock. If the cooling rate exceeds the rate of water influx, new centers of crystallization will appear in advance in the pores and intercept the migrating water. Thus, new segregation ice crystals will begin to grow at some distance from the previous ones. If the rate of cooling decreases, the segregation ice bodies and the spaces between them will become larger and the crystallization differentiation more complete; however, if the rate of cooling increases, the ice bodies produced will be smaller and closely spaced, because there will be less time for the migration of water during the freezing process. In the extreme case, during very rapid cooling, crystallization differentiation will not occur in general and the moisture will be fixed *in situ* as minute crystals of ice cement evenly distributed in the rock. The migration of water[11] will also be prevented by reduction of the moisture content, by an increased dispersion with the same moisture content and, generally, by any reduction of the mobility of water in the rock.

Efflorescences of ice on a soil surface, which have been described frequently since 1821 (see Dobrowolski, 1923, pp. 387–390), comprise the first type of segregation ice. It forms during the onset of freezing of moist dispersed rocks and appears during the slow cooling of the earth's surface, e.g., during nocturnal radiation frosts, when the surface soil temperature remains positive and the air temperature drops below zero. A continuous crust of *columnar-fibrous ice* (Chirvinskii, 1936) or discrete *ice stalks* (Bonshtedt, 1921) may form on

---

[11] Some researchers liken moist water-impermeable rocks, which do not allow the migration of water, to closed systems. Hence, the difference between closed and open systems becomes relative, depending on the relationship between the rates of freezing and migration of water. In contrast, in the case of freezing, we shall use the term "closed system" to mean a volume of water-permeable rock within which water completely surrounded by a water-impermeable shell can migrate.

supermoist soils. These are columnar crystals, as much as 10–12 cm high and 1–2 cm in diameter, which lift stones and other objects from the surface. Sometimes a network of plate crystals [called *ice druses* by Baranov (1949)] and various other types also develop. All these forms differ from the sublimation ice crystals of rime and hoarfrost on the soil surface in that they form from the freezing of ground water which rises to the surface and they grow from below, at the contact with the moist soil. Thus, the process is typically segregational.

The ice crystals within finely dispersed rocks nucleate primarily in the larger pores, where the water is less firmly bound. The embryos are randomly oriented and attempt to grow primarily in the basal plane. However, the growth differs for different crystals, depending on their spatial orientation, their position with respect to the local irregularities of the enclosing rock and the neighboring ice crystals, the relationship between the moment of origin of the embryo with respect to its neighbors and the properties of the rock, which include the initial moisture content and the rate of heat loss. These factors influence the *selection* of ice crystals during freezing. Some of the crystals grow to a considerable size, separating the mineral skeleton of the rock and combining in groups of relatively large aggregates, others remain small, cementing the rock particles. The crystals which nucleate first are generally the ones which grow. They use the local moisture supplies from the surrounding sections of rock.

In supermoist flowing rock, the crystals grow at the expense of their environment, easily displacing the mineral particles in any direction. Under these conditions, the embryo has indifferent orientation; all crystals that nucleated early enough grow along the basal plane, forming a disordered lattice of tabular monocrystals with rock cells between them: the lattice becomes finer and denser as the rate of freezing increases. The lattice of monocrystalline ice schlieren grows in a fairly narrow zone of freezing, depending on the magnitude of the temperature gradient, but in time this freezing zone moves deep into the massif. The crystals, whose basal planes are oriented in the direction of freezing, penetrate into the still unfrozen rock, until crystals of other orientation form in it (which requires greater cooling) and develop preferentially. Thus, a disordered reticulate frost structure forms layer by layer throughout the rock mass: the dominance of ice schlieren oriented in the direction of the temperature gradient increases as the rate of freezing decreases (Fig. 66).

Evidently segregation ice formed from the rock's own moisture supply, redistributed within only a very thin layer, is characteristic for such structures. Under these conditions, the enclosing rock plays the passive role of a medium in which the ice crystals develop according to their own laws. The texture of the frozen rock is determined chiefly by the orientation of the ice crystals which develop in it.

The conditions of segregation ice formation change substantially as the initial moisture content decreases and the rock consistency

Fig. 66. Segregation ice schlieren in sandy loam. × 0.5. (Photograph by B. I. Vtiurin.)

changes from fluid to plastic. The main change consists in the development of an ever increasing resistance to the displacement of the rock in all directions, except normal to the surface of the massif, i.e., vertically in most cases. Further, the growth of ice crystals and the dehydration of mineral particles under these conditions result in the appearance of cracks in the rock, and the conditions under which moisture is supplied to the growing crystals also change.

Owing to the differences in the resistance of the enclosing rock to displacement in various directions, selection occurs in the case of crystals which exceed the limits of development within the pores; further growth is confined to crystals whose basal planes are oriented more or less parallel to the surface of the massif and thus are also parallel to the isothermal surfaces in most cases. Consequently, a number of other factors also assume new importance. Since crystals nucleate simultaneously on practically the same isothermal surface when their preferred growth is in this plane, the crystals tend to fuse into polycrystalline ice schlieren, parallel to the surface of the massif. Furthermore, the probability of simultaneous nucleation of crystals on the same isothermal surface and the probability of the formation of continuous ice layers over a great distance will increase as the temperature gradient increases and the rock becomes thinner and more uniform. The role of the isothermal surfaces in limiting the spatial possibility of nucleation and crystal growth decreases with decreasing temperature gradients.

Heterogeneities and disruptions of the continuity and of the plane of weaker cohesion in plastic rock assume great importance as centers of nucleation and preferred growth of ice crystals whose basal planes are oriented parallel to the planes of weakness. The ice schlieren appear primarily in cracks, along the planes of latent embryonic schistosity of argillaceous soils and clays, along the boundaries of layers, around stones, in worm holes, etc., while irregular ice pockets form in porous arable soil. A very regular stratified frost structure forms in banded clays. The influence of the primary rock structure before freezing is so great that if the direction of stratification differs sharply from the direction of the isotherms, two systems of ice schlieren will form, oriented in both directions, with gradual transitions between them.

When the plastic rock is separated by the growing ice crystals, accompanied by dehydration of the mineral particles and settling of the rock, cracks occur oriented primarily in the direction of preferred growth of the tabular crystals, parallel to the freezing front, but often deviating from that direction. The removal of moisture may also cause cracks before the zone of freezing. These cracks are situated at right angles to the other cracks, in the direction of freezing. The more dispersed the rock is, the more widespread the crack formation will be. Often a discontinuous system of cracks is observed before the freezing zone; one after another, these cracks become filled with ice and sometimes penetrate several centimeters into the rock, which is warmer than 0°C (Fig. 67). These phenomena disrupt the regularity of the incipient stratiform structure.

If the crack curves, the crystal which caused the crack may change its direction of growth and follow the direction of the crack, which causes a disparity between the orientation of the crystallographic and geometric axes of the crystals. In other cases, new crystals form in the cracks, quickly filling the cavity which has formed, and abut the original crystals which caused the cracks.

Thus, when the enclosing rock has plastic consistency, it ceases to act as a passive medium for ice crystal development. Instead, it interacts with the crystals and, owing to its inhomogeneity, exerts a substantial influence on the nascent cryogenic structure.

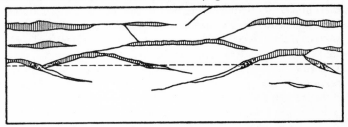

Fig. 67.   Cross section of the freezing zone boundary in clay. The ice crystallizes primarily in the open cracks which form below the freezing line. (After G. Beskow, 1935.)

The appearance of stratified cryogenic structures parallel to the isotherms may be accompanied by a considerable influx of water from the lower horizons to the zone of freezing, with the formation of relatively thick ice schlieren. A prime requisite for this is equilibrium between the amount of heat delivered to the cold source and the amount of heat generated during crystallization by the water which migrates to the zone of freezing. The rate of water supply should increase as the rate of freezing increases. If this equilibrium is disrupted by the acceleration of freezing or the reduction of water influx after the nearer horizons have been deprived of moisture, freezing will extend to the rock pores below the ice schlieren and new schlieren may begin to form there. These new schlieren will also become thicker owing to the influx of water, if the necessary equilibrium is re-established.

Evidently, in most cases the freezing of plastic rocks consists in an alternation of (1) interruptions of the crystallization front at levels where thermal equilibrium is established (where ice schlieren form) and (2) discontinuous changes in the position of the crystallization front after the nearest moisture supplies have been exhausted and equilibrium has been disrupted (Taber, 1930; Beskow, 1935; and others). Generally, conditions for maintaining thermal equilibrium and for the formation of thick ice schlieren improve as the rate of freezing decreases. The migration of moisture from other horizons

and the resultant thermal equilibrium can scarcely play an important role in the formation of reticulate structures in supermoist rocks.
However, the nature of the relationship between the size of the ice
schlieren and the rate of freezing remains the same: the schlieren and
the cryogenic structure produced by them will become thinner as
the rate of freezing increases.

In most cases, the schlieren of segregation ice vary from a few
millimeters thick to 1–2 cm; sometimes they become 20–30 cm
thick. Thicker, lenticular schlieren (up to 1 m thick) are found only
in areas of considerable local supermoistening: in peat bogs, beneath
a peat or moss cover at the mineral rock interface and around
melted bodies of underground ice of other origin.[12]

As a rule, segregation ice contains practically no impurities; it is
pure and transparent, and its density is close to the specific gravity
of pure ice. However, all transitions from pure ice to frozen rock
with ice cement are encountered, because individual particles and
relatively large inclusions (xenoliths of the enclosing rock) freeze into
the ice schlieren during crystallization. When the xenoliths become
larger, it is difficult to draw the line between individual ice schlieren
with inclusions and rock with reticulate structure, i.e., rock which is
permeated by a network of ice schlieren and which is superficially
quite similar to breccia with basal ice cement.

Often small lenses of segregation ice contain only minute spherical
air inclusions, while thin cylindrical and filamental inclusions,
elongated in the direction of crystallization, can be observed in the
thicker schlieren. Sometimes one finds ice schlieren which are
penetrated by a large number of vertical cylindrical air inclusions
and thus are white.

The texture of segregation ice can be quite diverse, depending on
the conditions of its formation, and evidently its texture is regularly
associated with the structure of the frozen layer. Most often the
texture is hypidiomorphic-granular with a more or less preferred
orientation of the main crystal axes normal to the plane of the
schlieren. In this case, the crystals are tabular in the thin schlieren
and columnar in the thicker schlieren. Allotriomorphic-granular
texture with approximately isometric and randomly oriented
crystals is less common. Fine-grained crystals (up to a fraction of a
millimeter in diameter) and coarse-grained crystals (2–5 cm and
more) are found in schlieren. The prevailing crystal size in the plane
of the schlieren is 5–10 mm and the largest that have been observed

---

[12] Taber's (1943) value of 3.6 m for segregation ice thickness in Alaska is not valid,
since Taber erroneously attributed segregation origin to perennial ice veins.

are 20 × 9 cm. If the schlieren become considerably thicker than the diameter of the crystals in the plane of the schlieren owing to orthotropic crystallization, a prismatic-granular texture with columnar crystals will form, and in the fine-grained variants, even needle crystals will form.

Segregation ice is the second major type of underground ice; its total mass is not as great as that of perennial vein ice, but it is more widely distributed. The range of segregation ice distribution practically coincides with the range of dust and clayey frozen rock distribution.[13]

Segregation ice is of great practical importance, since its formation causes the swelling of ground and its melting results in considerable settling, which leads to the destruction of installations built on "frost-danger" soils. Furthermore, segregation ice formation often breaks off plant roots and destroys seeds.

Injection Ice

Concordant ice injections, in contrast to the non-concordant vein ice and to segregation ice, result from the freezing of free water or of a mass of liquefied ground (sand snow) intruded under pressure along the boundaries of water-impermeable rock strata. There may be two different sources of pressure on the water which moves and deforms the enclosing rock, and the role of rock freezing differs accordingly. In some cases, the freezing merely disrupts the established hydrogeologic regime, reducing the cross section of a stream of ground water or forming a barrier of water-impermeable frozen rock in the path of this stream. Under such conditions, freezing plays a passive role and the hydraulic pressure head of the stream of underground water acts as the pressure source. In other cases, a closed system may develop during freezing. This consists of a volume of water-permeable moistened rock bounded on all sides by a water-impermeable shell. The free space of the pores in this water-permeable rock cannot compensate for the increased volume of water that is converting into ice. Under such conditions, the freezing itself creates the pressure head of the water or the fluid mass. Under increasing pressure, the water takes the path of least resistance, i.e., it flows toward the thinnest sections of the water-impermeable layer

---

[13] The ice described by Kachurin (1946) as infiltration-solifluction ice, in particular, should be classified as segregation ice. In this case, the only difference between infiltration-solifluction ice and the other segregation ice types lies in the origin of the initial material, water, not in the mechanism of the ice separation process and the resultant mode of occurrence and structure.

which has frozen from above, tearing it away and exfoliating it from the underlying thawed rock as water lenses or layers, which subsequently freeze. A flat, intrusive layer forms when the flexural strength of the frozen roof is great and when the bond between the roof and the underlying rock is weak. Otherwise, the roof bends more sharply and a mound with a planoconvex nucleus forms, corresponding to a laccolith. Various forms can occur, depending on the relationship between the strength of the frozen roof and the firmness of its lateral attachment to the base and the amount of incoming water. These may be intrusive layers or lenses that are steeply convex upward, i.e., laccoliths, or various transitional formations, sometimes with several swellings of the most varied sizes.

When the influx of water is great compared with the area of the swelling, the roof does not endure and is broken by "endogenous" cracks in the apical part of the mound. The water or fluid mass discharges through these cracks onto the surface and the laccolith becomes a "hydrovolcano," producing a surface icing or a "mud volcano" (a "frozen-soil salse").

Sometimes rupturing of the roof is accompanied by the eruption of fountains of water or liquid mud several meters high and sometimes there are explosions which scatter fragments of the roof.

The cracks may re-form quickly if the water which fills them freezes, and if the water pressure persists, the rupturing and eruptions will be repeated. The process will cease if the pressure head decreases or if the roof becomes stronger through freezing; in this latter case, the injection may be directed toward another spot where the roof is more pliable, and a group of swelling mounds will form.

The processes of differential swelling and the formation of injection ice differ and have different results under different cryopedologic and hydrogeologic conditions. Injection ice schlieren may appear in a layer of seasonal freezing and melting or at the lower surface of a progressively freezing thin stratum. The first type consists of seasonal or partially seasonal, ephemeral formations (Fig. 68); the second type consists of perennial formations.

Ice injections in the form of lenses up to 1 m thick and 10 m in diameter are sometimes encountered in the zone of seasonally frozen ground at the egress of ascending springs. The ice injections are much more widely distributed and are larger in the layers of seasonal melting in the permafrost region. Agreement has never been reached on the question whether underground icings ("naleds") result from the freezing of closed systems or from the freezing of descending streams of suprapermafrost water.

Fig. 68. A seasonal hydrolaccolith which has thawed. (Photograph by P. F. Shvetsov and V. P. Sedov.)

S. A. Pod'iakonov (1903), V. N. Sukachev (1911), K. Nikiforov (1912) and D. A. Dranitsyn (1914) supported the first point of view and M. I. Sumgin (Sumgin *et al.*, 1940; Tsytovich and Sumgin, 1937, and others) reproduced this phenomenon in the laboratory and formulated a mathematical theory of differential swelling for the freezing of closed systems. L. P. Prasolov and S. A. Iakovlev in 1911, R. I. Abolin (1913), N. I. Tolstikhin (1932), I. Ia. Baranov (1940) and other hydrogeologists supported the second point of view.

Undoubtedly, both types of injections exist and apparently are linked by gradual transitions, which often make it difficult to distinguish the two types accurately. Furthermore, the numerous specific descriptions which have appeared thus far indicate that the swelling phenomena associated with the freezing of streams of suprapermafrost water occur on a larger scale than those of the closed systems and dominate quantitatively. Seasonal swelling mounds with ice nuclei are widely distributed, chiefly in regions of dissected relief, at the foot of slopes, in the valleys of small rivers and in the drainage basins of ephemeral streams. They reach heights of 2–3 m. Differential swelling is weakly developed in flat regions without clearly defined streams of suprapermafrost water and, in most cases, is due solely to the formation of small intrusive ice strata.

In regions of thin frozen rocks with complex tectonic structure, perennial ice injections form at the points of emergence of subpermafrost water. N. I. Tolstikhin (1932) was the first to describe these injections as hydrolaccoliths. The roof of such injections may become very thick (as much as 15 m) and sometimes consists not only of frozen Quaternary deposits, but also of native rock strata. The swelling mounds at the egress of ascending springs become as much as 10–12 m high, sometimes even 15–17 m.

The most important ice injections are the perennial injections which form during the freezing of taliks,[14] which are closed from below and lie beneath lakes that are shoaling or have dried up. S. G. Parkhomenko was the first to apply the Pod'iakonov and Nikiforov hypothesis to these formations and he called them "ice laccoliths" (1929). Later V. N. Andreev (1936), V. N. Saks (1940), M. I. Sumgin (1940) and others followed Parkhomenko's lead. This type of swelling mound is known in literature by the Yakut term "bulgunniakh," which corresponds to the American Eskimo term "pingo." Bulgunniakhs [hereafter called pingos – D.K.] grow gradually over a long period of time in frozen lake basins and rise at a rate which varies from the barely perceptible to more than 0.5 m per year. In most cases, pingos range in height from a few meters to 20–25 m (Figs. 69 and 70) and in the northern regions they may become 40–70 m high (Parkhomenko, 1929; Leffingwell, 1919, pp. 150–151). Large pingos on alluvial plains are considerably higher than the highest elements of the surrounding terrain over extensive areas. Pingos become several tens and hundreds of meters in diameter. Their crests may be 2–8 m thick, their ice floor or ice nucleus lies 5–10 m below the surrounding surface. As a rule, pingos are adapted to alluvial strata and the injection ice schlieren that comprise their nuclei lie on the contact between the blanketing bottom deposits of argillaceous soil and sandy loam and the underlying channel sands and gravels or near the contact within the bottom-land or channel horizons. In closed taliks, the water moves almost exclusively in the water-permeable channel alluvium. The freezing of this water is connected with pingo formation.

The planoconvex nuclei of the swelling mounds consist of solid ice lenses, sometimes with interlayers parallel to the roof, i.e., xenoliths of the enclosing frozen rock or relatively thick ice strata, which alternate with the frozen rocks. Sometimes the ice lens is solid in the center but stratified on the periphery, becoming a packet of tapering

---

[14] [See note 2, this chapter. – D.K.]

FIG. 69. A bulgunniakh (hydrolaccolith) in a thermokarst pit. (Photograph by B. I. Vtiurin.)

FIG. 70. A close-up view of the same hydrolaccolith. (Photograph by B. I. Vtiurin.)

and wedging layers. Ice veins which penetrate the roof and upper part of the nucleus appear in the apical part of quite convex mounds.

Growing mounds are underlain by melted, water-bearing rocks or water lenses and in most cases the water has a hydraulic pressure head. Large chambers with ice arches form in seasonal mounds after the water has drained out. "Narrow black burrows," which are the outlets of a network of water channels, can be seen along the edges of these chambers (Nikiforov, 1912). Air pockets with an ice arch up to 3 m high are found in the apical part of the mounds.

Evidently the difference in the structure of mounds with nuclei of solid ice or icy frozen rock is caused by the relationship between the rate of incorporation of water and the freezing rate. If only part of the incoming water freezes, there will always be a water lens beneath the freezing layer and pure ice will form when this water lens freezes. If the ratio of the rate of intrusion of water to the rate of freezing is time-dependent, the freezing of the water lens will be followed by the freezing of the water-bearing rock in the base, after which water will again be intruded, etc., and thus injection ice schlieren will alternate with icy rocks. The same thing happens when the frozen roof is ruptured periodically and water pours out onto the surface, after which the cracks re-form and the underlying rock freezes before new water is intruded. When the rate of water influx decreases sufficiently, only ice rock with minute segregation schlieren will form. To a certain extent, the pressure migration of water, which increases the moisture content of the rock before freezing, helps form these segregation schlieren. Thus, there can be gradual transitions from injection to segregation ice.

As a rule, injection ice is very pure and transparent. Xenogenous solid impurities in injection ice are found only at the base of the schlieren as tongues and streams of minute mineral particles which rise inside the ice and bend in places. Evidently, these particles are lifted by the movements of the water. Sometimes plant rootlets, stems and twigs with lumps of dirt that penetrate into the ice massif are found at the contacts.

The injection schlieren ice also contains a small quantity of air inclusions of the most diverse dimensions and shapes, which form a confused stratification parallel to the roof, various vertical, oblique and irregular agglomerations, etc. The large injections also contain groups and clusters of large, irregular, curved and vertically elongated bubbles. The injections can also have branching systems, horizontally flattened bubbles, spherical, cylindrical and filamental bubbles, etc., i.e., all genetic types of primary inclusions, indicating the great complexity and diversity of the crystallization processes. The apical parts of the ice laccoliths are often enriched by large air inclusions, especially if freezing from the sides and below has played a considerable role, due to the concentration of autogenous gases in these places. The formation of extensive air cavities is an extreme case of such concentration.

The gas pressures in the swelling mound nuclei and in the inclusions in them may be very high. When a closed system freezes, the pressure increase is actually limited only by the resistance of the rigid shell. However, in some cases, explosions and catastrophic eruptions of water and compressed air can apparently produce a vacuum inside the mounds, due to the rapid freezing of the supercooled water in the cracks of the roof, and establish a lower pressure after the explosion. For example, I determined air pressures of 0.44 and 0.50 atm in a small ice laccolith with a large quantity of air inclusions in its apical part ($28-34\%_{00}$ of the volume: density of the ice $0.885-0.891$ g/cm^3).

Very little study has been devoted to the texture of injection ice. The literature indicates a vertical prismatic-granular texture, but this is based on fleeting visual observations. A few accurate studies have revealed allotriomorphic-granular texture with very large grains, from 1–2 to 16 cm (on an average, only a few centimeters in diameter), and with random crystallographic orientation. In some cases, a weakly defined tendency toward linear vertical and zonal horizontal orientations has been observed, but this does not change the general character of the texture. These data, like the structural features, indicate that large masses of intruded water freeze, without orthotropic crystallization in most cases.

Sedimentary Ice

CHAPTER XI

DEPOSITION OF THE SNOW COVER

Sedimentary ice rocks comprise two groups:

(1) the widely distributed *atmospheric precipitations* which are analogous to *chemical sediments* in water reservoirs;[1]

(2) the secondary, *clastic* ice rocks, which are *mechanical deposits* of the products of ice fragmentation.

Solid atmospheric precipitation deposited on the earth forms ice rocks, which are classified as *snow cover*,[2] although the initial material and the features which appear during the deposition process may differ.

The snow cover is formed from atmospheric ice crystals and inter-growths of both sublimation and congelation crystals, ranging from snowflakes to ice rain. Supercooled atmospheric water plays a very large role in the formation of solid precipitation; ice crystals nucleate only by the freezing of droplets, but then grow by sublimation of vapor from the droplets onto the crystals and by the freezing of droplets on the crystal surfaces (granulated snowflakes, graupel, hail and some types of hoarfrost) or independently (ice rain). Nevertheless, *idiomorphic sublimation crystals*, predominantly *skeletal*, are the main component of the snow-cover material and determine its general structural features. Of the irregular congelation ice crystals,

---

[1] Sublimation and condensation in the atmosphere, the freezing of water vapor, are analogous to the precipitation of salts from solution. Genetically speaking, the subsequent mechanical deposition of precipitations of the free atmosphere is of secondary importance.

[2] Of course, the products of the freezing of liquid precipitation on a solid surface, i.e., glazed frost and frost deposit, are not included here among the solid atmospheric precipitations, since they form congelation ice rock similar to extruded ice.

only snow hail and the analogous hoarfrost can play any essential role in the formation of the snow cover, since the other types of congelation hydrometeors are relatively rare and, besides, hail falls only during warm weather and melts immediately.

Therefore, sedimentary rock of atmospheric origin is a friable and porous aggregate of ice crystals or their fragments usually called *snow* (precipitated or deposited snow, as opposed to falling snow). Thus, the snow cover, or deposited snow, is a special highly porous form of ice rock which differs from ice in the petrographic sense, in that ice is a solid, nonporous rock.

Idiomorphic and particularly skeletal atmospheric ice crystals are a form of free growth which is stable only during quite considerable supersaturation with water vapor. When forming accumulations on the earth's surface, they encounter conditions unfavorable for their steady state and soon begin to undergo metamorphism.

The question arises: where should one draw the line between sedimentary ice rock and the metamorphic rock deriving from it?

Although there is considerable disagreement concerning non-ice rocks, the prevailing concept in petrography is that sedimentary rock becomes metamorphic under the influence of volcanic heat or orogenesis. As long as the rock is not affected by these processes, it remains sedimentary and all the processes which occur in it are *diagenetic*, not metamorphic, i.e., the rocks regenerate without the participation of external agents. Clearly, this criterion is untenable for ice rocks, in which water plays the role of magma. Geologists who do not wish to treat ice as a special case classify all ice as sedimentary rock (F. Iu. Levinson-Lessing, 1940, p. 24; N. I. Tolstikhin, 1936; L. V. Pustovalov, 1940). However, we cannot agree with this generalization, since even slight surface freezing and melting leads to a profound change in the snow structure, i.e., to firnification, which must be classified as a metamorphic process.

Although it is difficult to draw a sharp boundary between sedimentary and metamorphic ice rocks, there is little doubt as to which processes play the leading role in the change of structure and composition during these stages of evolution. *Sublimation processes* play the leading role in snow. They are an extension of the processes of snow crystal formation under changing conditions, which are also the basis for the diagenesis of the sedimentary ice rock. If melting does not occur, the diagenetic stage lasts for a long time, so that in most cases the snow cover continues to be sedimentary rock for more than a year.

All in all, there is a deep affinity between diagenesis and subsequent metamorphism consisting in common sources of energy and

the physical nature of the processes. They are links in a single chain
of transformations of snow into ice, i.e., metamorphic ice formation.
Consequently, it is convenient to examine the diagenetic stage
together with the other stages of metamorphic ice formation.
Similarly, we shall examine the formation of clastic ice rocks in
connection with the processes of the dynamic metamorphism of
ice.

In this chapter, we shall restrict ourselves to an examination of the
processes of snow-cover deposition and the resultant structural and
compositional features of sedimentary ice rock, or to be more exact,
the features of precipitation which has not yet become rock.

The properties of a freshly deposited snow cover are a function of
the properties of the deposited material and of the conditions of
deposition. According to P. Niggli, all the changes experienced by a
snow cover in this first stage of its formation can be classified as
autometamorphic.

The snow cover is deposited by precipitation of ice crystals from
the upper layers of the atmosphere or by the growth of crystals on
the earth's surface. As a rule, the snow cover is formed by atmospheric precipitation, while rime and hoarfrost comprise only thin
layers in it.

Rime and "light" sublimation hoarfrost grow on solid surfaces
primarily as layers of relatively sparse leaflets and tufts of plate

FIG. 71.   Layer of heavy hoarfrost on the surface of a snow cover.

crystals with more or less horizontal optic axes. The denser layers form "heavy" hoarfrost, which is produced in part by the freezing of supercooled droplets (Fig. 71). The hoarfrost keeps the snow surface from being blown away by the wind.

The density and texture of the precipitating cover depend on the properties of the initial material. Skeletal dendritic crystals, provided they are not fractured during deposition, form a fluffy porous layer, while the solid crystals, particularly graupel and heavy hoarfrost, form comparatively dense layers.

Air temperature plays an important role in the deposition of the solid precipitation that falls from the upper atmosphere. At low temperatures, the snowflakes are brittle, do not freeze together upon contact with each other, break easily and are blown about by the wind. High temperatures and dendritic forms promote cohesion of the snow crystals, permitting regelation at the points of contact, and at the same time increase their plasticity. If the air temperature rises slightly above the melting point for a short time during a snowfall, the peripheries of the snowflakes begin to melt. Wet snow forms, with separate droplets on the ends of the spurs (rays), the corners and the edges of the snowflakes, because of which the snow combines into large clusters as it falls and even a strong wind cannot blow it about on the surface of the snow cover. When melting is more intense and the snowflakes become covered with a continuous water film, they immediately begin to convert into ice grains. We shall describe this process in our examination of the metamorphism of sedimentary ice.

Thus, very sharp differences can appear in the characteristics of the precipitating snow when the temperature is low, whereas these differences smooth out near the melting point because the snowflakes are more plastic and because regelation occurs immediately. These factors prevent extreme friability and porosity and keep the snow from being transported and densely packed.

The properties of the freshly fallen snow cover are a function primarily of the force of the wind during deposition. In calm weather, the snow is deposited in an even, fluffy layer, in which the individual crystals scarcely come into contact with each other. In a dead calm, dendritic stars may form a cover with a density of 0.01 g/cm^3 near the surface. The lowest known density of snow, viz., 0.004 g/cm^3, was recorded under these conditions at Sodankylä, Finland, in the winter of 1917–1918.

Porosity is associated with great structural freedom of the crystals, and this can scarcely be maintained in an aggregate. Usually the crystal orientation is completely random, but sometimes the orientation of plate snowflakes is primarily horizontal.[3] A very friable snow cover rarely evolves naturally, since the slightest wind will redeposit it; however, in sheltered areas (e.g., forests), a freshly fallen snow cover is generally similar to the one described.

In the presence of a wind and fairly low temperatures, snowflakes are transported for considerable distances in the ground layer of air before being deposited. The turbulent air motions sometimes cause the snowflakes to rise, sometimes to drop suddenly, and the snowflakes execute a number of jumps and hits against the snow surface. In the process, they break into minute angular fragments. An ice particle will be transported about until it enters a depression of like size and form among the particles which are firmly attached to the surface. This results in tight initial packing, owing to which the freshly deposited snow immediately becomes less porous and loses some of the structural freedom of its particles, because they are held by neighboring particles. Direct wind pressure does not play a vital role in the wind packing.[4]

Snow deposited during a heavy snowstorm[5] sometimes has a density of as much as 0.50 g/cm^3, which corresponds to a porosity of the order of 45% and a volume of enclosed air bubbles of as much as $2\%_0$. The wind does not affect the nature of the crystallographic orientation of the grains; as a rule the orientation is disordered, as in snow deposited in the absence of wind. Also, there are indications that in some cases the main axes are dominantly vertical, because the wind presses the plate crystals flat against the surface (de Quervain, 1948).

Owing to frequent changes of the initial material and conditions of deposition, even the snow deposited during a single snowfall is thinly stratified (layer thickness of the order of several millimeters). Although the stratification may not be immediately visible, it may exist all the same. Often the stratification is latent and becomes visible only as a result of wind action, since different layers have different resistances to wind erosion (Fig. 72). More distinct and thicker stratification results from interrupted deposition, during

---

[3] Observations by N. A. Morozov during his long stay in Schlüsselburg Fortress (Veinberg, 1936, p. 90).

[4] G. Seligman (1936; 1947, p. 70) holds that wind packing plays a secondary role in the densification process that accompanies the deposition of snow and that sublimation of ice between crystals, caused by a moist wind, plays the main role. Undoubtedly, sublimation can be important, but microscopic studies, which can distinguish between the results of the two influences, indicate that wind packing is the more general and effective factor.

[5] According to the author's measurements.

which the entire deposited layer and the surface of the layer, which is particularly sensitive to external influences, undergo considerable changes. Often layers of different age are separated by an ice crust, i.e., by various kinds of melt and wind crusts. These are white crusts, which form as a result of eolian packing and polishing of the surface by wind-blown snow and by sublimation or bridging of the crystals

FIG. 72. Transverse sastrugi and eolian stratification of the snow. (Photograph by N. V. Cherepanov.)

of the surface layers. Under the prolonged action of moist winds, the surface of the ice crust changes from porous to solid, retaining its white color because of air inclusions. The wind crust may become as much as 1 cm thick.

When the snow can be blown about to a considerable extent, the snow cover becomes uneven owing to the formation of dunes and drifts, which may become 0.7–1.0 m high in exposed places and many meters high at obstacles. The surface forms of the snow cover have much in common with those of sand, but are even more diverse, because snow particles can freeze together and consolidate when forming a snow cover.

A great variety of banks, drifts, cornices and ridges form at obstacles (Figs. 73 and 74) and there is also an enormous variety of free-surface forms, e.g., the accumulative dunes and banks and the erosional sastrugi.[6] Both types can run counter to or with the wind direction (Figs. 72 and 75) and there are also intermediate forms.

Occasionally, when the temperature is low and there is shifting snow, one finds snow barchans[7] on a level surface; less often, when the temperature is high, one finds snow cylinders rolled by the wind.

FIG. 73.   Snowdrifts at an obstacle. (Photograph by N. V. Cherepanov.)

FIG. 74.   Snow cornices overhanging an ice cliff. (Photograph by N. V. Cherepanov.)

The accumulative forms become partially destroyed by cross winds (Fig. 76). The products of their disintegration are deposited under the shelter of the projecting remnants of the dunes, forming snow drifts. The snow cover assumes an irregular, hilly microrelief, consisting of snow of different generations, from old, very hard snow to freshly transported snow as loose as sand. The stronger winds not only abrade and erode the surface formations, but they expose the older layers to a great depth, creating the erosional sastrugi and various corrasional depressions. In this case, the microrelief is often

---

[6] ["Sastruga (pl. sastrugi) : the Russian term for a wind-deposited or wind-eroded irregularity, often sharp edged, on a generally featureless snow surface," *Glossary of Arctic and Subarctic Terms*, ADTIC Publication A-105, 1955, p. 69. – D.K.]

[7] ["Barchan: a crescent-shaped mound of windblown sand or snow, the arms of the crescent pointing downwind," *ibid.*, p. 9. – D.K.]

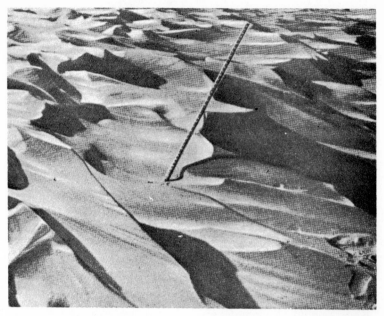

Fig. 75. Fresh, longitudinal snow dunes. (Photograph by N. V. Cherepanov.)

Fig. 76. Partially destroyed snow dunes. (Photograph by N. V. Cherepanov.)

completely inverted. Subsequent snowfalls bury the complex accumulative-erosional snow microrelief, which results in exceedingly irregular stratification, both oblique and diagonal, with drift lenses, ridges of buried dunes and sastrugi, wind crusts and others.

Another important feature of regions exposed to the wind is the great irregularity of snow deposition on the various elements of the relief. As a rule, during a snow storm, the layers of air near the ground receive a boundless number of snow particles from above or from the snow cover and transport as many of them as can be kept in a suspended state at a given wind velocity and particle size and shape. When the rate of motion increases, more particles are transported, and when it decreases, some snowflakes settle to the surface. Consequently, the acceleration of the wind and not its absolute velocity is the decisive factor in the distribution of snow which is falling from the atmosphere or being transported as blowing snow over the elements of the relief. On a level area, where the average wind velocity is constant with respect to the neighboring areas, the snow removed by the wind is compensated for by snow brought in by the wind. Snow is redeposited, but the average depth remains constant due to drifting. However, the snow cover is blown away from the convex elements of the relief, where the lines of air flow converge and the wind velocity increases, while the snow accumulates and is deposited on the concave elements, where the lines of air flow diverge. Thus, in the case of dissected relief, not only are there regional differences in the depth of the snow cover as a function of the amount of precipitation, but there are very great local differences in the thickness of the entire snow cover and of individual layers deposited by winds of different directions.

The described differences in the conditions of deposition lead to the formation of various *facies of the snow cover*, which differ in thickness and density, structure and texture.

In general, the fresh snow cover has *stratified structure* and *porous agglomerate texture*, usually with random crystallographic orientation. Its density may vary within very broad limits, from 0.01 to 0.50 g/cm^3; this corresponds to porosities of approximately 99% to 45% and to a volume of enclosed air bubbles of 0‰ to 2‰. Most often a fresh snow cover weighs from 0.07 to 0.18 g/cm^3.

The basic types of fresh snow are:

(1) *facies of non-eolian deposit, fluffy snow*, characterized by a unique *idiomorphic-crystalline*, mostly *skeletal-crystalline* agglomerate texture, low density, high porosity and great structural freedom of the crystals, regular and indistinct stratification;

(2) *eolian facies*, solid, *storm-driven snow* with *clastic* agglomerate texture, high density, relatively low porosity and little structural freedom of the particles, irregular, thin and more clearly defined stratification.

There are gradual transitions between these types.

Secondary differences are created by the properties of the precipitating material (e.g., powdery snow, graupel, hoarfrost) or by the temperature (moist snow with individual water droplets on the ends of snowflakes). As soon as wet snow with a continuous water film appears, firnification and aging of the snow cover occur.

The thickness of the precipitating layers and of the snow cover as a whole is another very important facies difference, although it does not appear in the texture until later, during the metamorphism of the snow layer.

Metamorphic Ice

CHAPTER XII

REVIEW OF THE PROCESSES OF ICE METAMORPHISM

Once formed, primary congelation or sedimentary rocks always undergo some change because their structure does not conform with their environment. The metamorphic process is an expression of the complex struggle between internal and external factors.

The motive force of the metamorphic processes may be provided by the energy of the ice rock itself, by the external influences on the ice or by the interaction of these factors.

The principle of least free energy. The internal sources of energy, included in the rock itself, lead to molecular processes governed by the thermodynamic laws of equilibrium, according to which any system tends toward a state of least free energy.

When the internal energy U is constant (isothermal process), the free energy expended on molecular processes $\psi = U - TS$ becomes bound energy TS, i.e., it increases the entropy S. Since temperature T enters into the bound energy formula as a factor of S, the intensity of the molecular processes increases as the temperature increases. The energy of the thermal vibrations of the atoms decreases so much in the crystal lattice of ice at $-70°$ to $-72°C$ that the molecular processes practically cease. Hence, the temperature range $-70°C$ to $-72°C$ is the so-called *temperature of recrystallization* of ordinary ice, above which the amorphous and cubic modifications of ice cannot remain stable. This temperature also coincides with the boundary of the metastable state of supercooled water and the "triple point of spontaneous nucleation" of ice crystals.

A crystalline substance can accumulate free energy in two forms: (1) the surface energy of crystal individuals or their fragments and (2) the internal free energy of the material under stress.

Rounding and collective perecrystallization.[1] The free energy of a supersaturated vapor or supercooled liquid expended on creating the surface of crystalline individuals during their growth or the mechanical energy of the brittle fracture of crystals may act as the source of surface energy. The magnitude of the surface energy is directly proportional to the surface area of the crystals, and also depends on the relative development of the various faces and on the properties of the ambient medium, which has an influence on the magnitude of the surface tension.

For the individual crystal, the principle of minimum free energy signifies the tendency toward the *equilibrium form*. The equilibrium form of an isotropic substance is a sphere, which has the smallest specific surface of all the geometric figures. The spherical form is approximated (1) by removal of the material from the more convex surface segments, where the surface tension is greater and where the forces binding the molecules and the body are weaker, i.e., where the molecules have greater free energy and (2) by simultaneous deposition of the material on the concave or less convex segments. This relationship is expressed quantitatively by W. Thomson's formula (see Chap. IV). The equilibrium form of anisotropic crystals differs somewhat from a sphere, because the surface tension of the various faces differs; however, this difference is not great and thus we shall call the process of approximating the equilibrium form "rounding off."

In the case of rock, which is a polycrystalline aggregate, the principle of minimum free energy also indicates a tendency toward a reduction of the number of crystals and, finally, fusion into a monocrystal. This is the process of *collective perecrystallization*, by which small crystals with surfaces of greater curvature are absorbed by larger crystals, for the reasons stated above. For anisotropic crystals, the process is also complicated somewhat by the difference in the surface tension of the faces, but this does not change the general trend of the process.

At first, both processes induced by surface energy, viz., the

---

[1] [Perecrystallization. Throughout the second half of the book, Shumskii makes a point of distinguishing between two aspects of recrystallization. He uses the terms *rekristallizatsiia* (Latin prefix re- plus the Russianized form of crystallization) to mean recrystallization in the solid phase only and *perekristallizatsiia* (Russian prefix *pere-* [meaning re-] plus the Russianized form of crystallization) to indicate crystallization (1) in the solid phase, (2) by transition through the liquid phase and (3) by transition through the vapor phase and by migration along the crystal surfaces. On the advice of Prof. Shumskii and leading American and British glaciologists and crystallographers, I have translated *rekristallizatsiia* "recrystallization" and *perekristallizatsiia* "perecrystallization." See also Table 3, this chapter. – D.K.]

rounding off of the crystals and collective perecrystallization, are very intense, but soon decrease and approach zero asymptotically. The curvature of the ice crystal surfaces at temperatures near the melting point exerts a substantial influence on the perecrystallization processes at curvature radii up to 0.1–0.2 mm (Bader, 1939, p. 16), while the influence becomes negligible for radii of the order of one centimeter. Therefore, rounding off is rapid only in the presence of skeletal or angular crystals in general, while collective perecrystallization is rapid only when very small crystals are present. Subsequently, however, both processes practically cease.

The formation of non-oriented structures is a characteristic feature of perecrystallization caused by surface energy, as is clear from the mechanism itself. In using the term "perecrystallization" thus far, we have not specified the mechanism of the process, keeping in mind that each of the examined types of perecrystallization can be realized in three ways, depending on conditions: (1) in the solid phase, (2) by transition through the liquid phase and (3) by transition through the vapor phase and by migration along the crystal surfaces.

Recrystallization. Any perecrystallization that takes place in the solid phase is called recrystallization. The recrystallization processes include devitrification of amorphous material when annealed, i.e., when the material is heated above the temperature of recrystallization and converts from one polymorphous modification into another, after the corresponding metastable boundary has been crossed. We do not have the space here to discuss the hypotheses of the atomic mechanism of recrystallization, which include the quantitative aspect of the phenomenon. What is essential for us is that the types of recrystallization caused by surface energy, i.e., *recrystallization rounding* (more exactly, approximation of the equilibrium form) and *collective recrystallization*, are realized by the transfer of molecules from one crystal space lattice to another lattice immediately adjacent to it. There is a continuous exchange of molecules between the lattices of neighboring crystals at temperatures above the recrystallization temperature, so that the phenomenon called recrystallization is merely the result of a change in the balance of molecular exchange in favor of one of the crystals.

Recrystallization is manifested in the spatial displacement of the boundary between contiguous crystals, observed in ice by G. Tammann and K. Dreyer (Tammann, 1929; Tammann and Dreyer, 1929). Tammann and Dreyer's experiments show that the rate of displacement is 8 μ/min at -6°C and reaches 14 μ/min at -2°C, i.e., along approximately 4×10^5 basal planes of the lattice per minute. As the grain boundaries shift, salts accumulate in them, retarding recrystallization.

It follows from the above that the direction of the displacement of the crystal boundaries is determined by two factors:

(1) the curvature of the contiguous surfaces (concave surfaces grow at the expense of the convex surfaces contiguous with them);

(2) the mutual orientation of the space lattices (the basal planes of ice tend to incorporate molecules from the planes of a prism or pyramid, advancing on the latter).

These two factors taken together express the processes of recrystallization rounding and collective recrystallization. In the Tammann and Dreyer experiments there was another very important factor, not related to surface energy, which we shall discuss below.

Sublimation perecrystallization. As a rule, ice recrystallizes at negative temperatures. Simultaneously, material is redeposited between the non-contiguous crystal surfaces through the vapor phase, i.e., by sublimation perecrystallization accompanied by the migration of material along the crystal surfaces.

The existence of a surface migration, already established for metals, was proved for snow by the change in the form of snowflakes immersed in a water-insoluble liquid (paraffin oil) at a temperature of $-5°C$, by which the vapor phase was excluded (de Quervain, 1945; Winterhalter, 1947). Surface migration is possible only at temperatures close to $0°C$. At $-10°C$, no change was observed in the snowflake over a period of months, but the influence of the sublimation processes could be detected even at temperatures around $-80°C$.

Among the sublimation perecrystallization processes caused by surface energy one may distinguish *sublimation rounding* and *collective perecrystallization*.

Temperature gradients contribute considerably to sublimation perecrystallization accompanied by the transfer of an enormous amount of thermal energy in the direction of redeposition of material. The saturated-vapor tension is greater in the warm than in the cold sections of the rock. In the case of porous rock, this results in vapor diffusion in the direction opposite to that of the temperature gradient.

The incomplete saturation resulting from diffusion leads to volatilization in the warm parts of the rock, while supersaturation in the colder sections leads to sublimation. This process, which can be induced by an external thermal effect and thus is classified as thermometamorphic, activates sublimation perecrystallization, which would have practically ceased much earlier had there been no temperature fluctuations. The activation is manifested in increased volatilization from surface projections and from small crystals in the warm horizons of the rock, and also in increased sublimation in the surface depressions and on large crystals in the cold horizons (Koloskov, 1945). In general, all perecrystallization processes are accelerated by external influences which remove the material from the equilibrium state (for instance, recrystallization is enhanced by mechanical shaking, temperature changes, etc.).

A further increase in the influence of external thermal energy, which creates greater water-vapor supersaturation in the cool layers of quite porous rock adjacent to warm layers, promotes the growth of idiomorphic and even skeletal depth hoar crystals. In this case, the potential-energy level of the ice increases. Thus, the growth of depth hoar should be regarded as a phenomenon of retrogressive metamorphism, namely, *sublimation diaphthoresis*.

Recrystallization and sublimation perecrystallization are a natural complex of processes which occur in the ice rock, when there can be no liquid phase on the active crystal surfaces.

Regelation perecrystallization. We shall use the term regelation perecrystallization to mean the perecrystallization of ice with a transition through the liquid phase. Literally, the word *regelation* means "repeated freezing," and not "freezing together" as it is frequently translated. These terms have been confused because Tyndall (1858) began to use regelation to indicate the freezing together of contiguous ice surfaces (discovered by Faraday in 1850) and for which he accepted J. Thomson's explanation of 1857. According to Thomson, this freezing together is caused by the partial melting of ice under pressure and the subsequent freezing of the water after the pressure has been removed. Faraday, who established that ice surfaces freeze together at 0°C even in the absence of pressure, explained this phenomenon on the grounds that the solid phase is more stable within the body than at its surface. At present there can be no doubt that ice surfaces can freeze together at very low temperatures without participation of the liquid phase, although more slowly, owing to the sublimation of ice in narrow cracks and owing to recrystallization processes. If the crystallographic orientation is uniform, the constituents will eventually fuse into a monocrystal, but if the orientation is not uniform, the bond between the constituents after they have frozen together "dry" will become as strong as it is between the crystals of a polycrystalline aggregate. Thus, in Tyndall's interpretation, regelation is just one of the various kinds of adfreezing and one must not equate these concepts, as did Veinberg.

In the strict sense of the word, regelation indicates repeated freezing, whether the preceding melting was caused by a heat influx or by a pressure increase. Of course, if the ice melts completely and then the water refreezes, the new ice should be regarded as congelation ice; in this case, the origin of the water has no bearing on either the processes of formation or the structural features of the ice. Often extruded ice and vein ice are formed from melt water, but their formation processes must not be classified as regelation metamorphism.

Regelation perecrystallization should be restricted to the redeposition of material in the ice rock itself through the liquid phase, i.e., it should be restricted to the processes of melting, migration and the freezing of melt water in the pores or cavities of the ice.

As already noted, very thin films of liquid salt solution at the crystal boundaries appear at negative temperatures even in fresh ice. Therefore, some of the processes regarded as recrystallization actually involve a transition to the liquid phase, but this does not change the essence of the matter. The transfer of molecules from the thermodynamically less stable parts of the crystal surfaces to the liquid film reduces the concentration of the solution and causes a corresponding amount of material to be deposited on the more stable parts of the surface. The redistribution process involves the diffusion of salts in solution and a considerable redistribution of heat. Thus, it is slower than direct recrystallization (see Tammann's observations reported in this chapter).

The regelation perecrystallization processes take place incomparably faster when there is an intensive repeated external influx of energy causing the temporary appearance of a considerable supply of free melt water in the rock cavities, in addition to the water bound by the salt solution. In this case the surface melting of the rock caused by the influx of heat in one form or another is the main factor which activates the perecrystallization process.

The melt water which penetrates into the rock pores from above, melting the peripheries of the surface projections and completely melting the small grains, crystallizes primarily in the surface depressions and on the large crystals. This leads to extremely fast regelation rounding and collective perecrystallization, which are classified as thermometamorphic processes. No phenomena analogous to sublimation diaphthoresis were observed during regelation perecrystallization of the type described, because they require great supercooling which cannot be realized inside the ice rock without rapid pressure changes. The latent heat of sublimation has been suggested as a possible source of heat during the regelation processes. The crystallization of 1 gram of water vapor produces 677 calories of heat, which, at 0°C, is sufficient to melt 8.5 grams of ice. Using this as their basis, H. W. Ahlmann and A. Tveten (1923) assumed that sublimation in snow is accompanied by melting of the peripheries of ice particles, and V. E. Khar'kov (1944) attributed great significance to this, considering "sublimation peripheral melting" to be one of the main factors involved in the formation of firm bonds between the crystals of a snow cover. However, they forgot that sublimation is governed by the outflow of heat from the subliming surface, because an increase of temperature to the thermal level of volatilization will halt the process. It is difficult to assume sufficiently large pulsations accompanied by the production of a heat excess with respect to inertia, because the thermal factor plays a decisive role. Peripheral melting can occur only during the distillation of water vapor onto a melting surface; however, this will be condensation melting, not sublimation peripheral melting. Actually, condensation melting plays an important role on the ice surface, but its effects are the same as those of radiational or convective melting. According to A. A. Shakhov (1948), "sublimation peripheral melting" is one of the lacunae of snow physics, but in our opinion it has never been proved that such a lacuna actually exists.

Dynamic metamorphism. The processes associated with the energy of a stressed state are classified as dynamometamorphic, in contrast to the processes examined above.

The internal free energy of a stressed substance is the portion of the deformation energy produced by directed pressure or by some other orienting force which is absorbed during the isothermal process or, in other words, the work expended on changing the form but not the volume of the body. The degree of conversion of the mechanical energy of the substance into free energy is a function of the elasticity of the deformation. The work expended on the plastic deformation and volumetric change of the body becomes thermal energy.

In the case of a stressed substance, the principle of least free energy signifies a tendency toward relaxation, i.e., a lessening of stresses, which, as a rule, is attained by perecrystallization. J. Thomson (1861) announced the general concept of growth of the less stressed crystals or parts of crystals at the expense of more heavily stressed crystals or parts of crystals in the same system. This proposition was confirmed by J. W. Gibbs in 1877 for crystals in contact with a melt or a solution and was established in detail by E. Riecke (1894). It is now known as Riecke's principle. G. Tammann developed the Thomson concept for contiguous crystals on the basis of experiments with various substances, particularly with ice (Tammann and Dreyer, 1929; Tammann, 1930).

Paratectonic perecrystallization. The mechanism and results of the perecrystallization of a stressed substance may differ considerably under different circumstances. If the deformation takes place at temperatures below the recrystallization temperature, the perecrystallization will not occur simultaneously with the deformation but only after annealing, i.e., after heating above the recrystallization temperature, which can be observed during the cold working of metals. In contrast, the deformations experienced by natural ice correspond to the hot working of metals, during which perecrystallization and deformation occur simultaneously. In the case of rocks, one distinguishes between pretectonic, paratectonic and posttectonic perecrystallization, according to the time relationship between perecrystallization and the tectonic movements. Paratectonic perecrystallization can be observed in ice and may continue for some time after movement ceases, until the internal stresses relax. In what follows, we shall use the term "paratectonic perecrystallization" in its genetic rather than its chronological meaning, to designate all types of ice perecrystallization caused by the internal free energy of a stressed state.

Paratectonic perecrystallization is only one aspect of the adaptation of rock to deformation and, naturally, it changes according to the reaction of the rock to deformation as a whole. If the stress does not exceed the elastic limit in the liquid or vapor phase, the paratectonic perecrystallization may be the only type of adaptation of the rock to deformation and then it will be the basic mechanism of movement; pseudoviscous flow will occur, which consists of melting or volatilization from the stressed parts of the surface, migration of the substance and its deposition on unstressed parts, according to Riecke's principle. Thus, one may distinguish regelation and sublimation paratectonic perecrystallization in connection with pseudoviscous flow.

Pseudoviscous flow is primarily a mechanism of compression and lateral extrusion. In pure form, this process should lead to flattening of the grains and the whole mass of rock in a plane perpendicular to the direction of pressure, which results in the transverse crystallization schistosity which can be observed in gneiss and plutonic rock.

The lack of transfer of directed pressure and the local removal of oriented stresses are a characteristic feature of pseudoviscous flow which gives it a superficial resemblance to the true viscous flow of fluids (Seng, 1937, p. 239). Nothing similar is observed in ice rock. Pseudoviscous flow does not play any significant role in the behavior of ice, because in most cases the stresses exceed the elastic limit of the aggregate during deformation. Further, there may be intergranular or intragranular movements in this case, depending on the degree of structural freedom of the crystals, i.e., there are relative displacements of entire crystals or motions along the internal glide planes of the crystal—in other words, plastic deformation.[2] In both cases this may result in an oriented structure. In the first case, the orientation conforms to the external shape of the crystals, which turn their long or flat side parallel to the direction of movement induced by the given deformation. These phenomena can be observed in snow. In the second case, which is characteristic of ice, the orientation is associated with the internal crystallographic directions, i.e., the basal plane (which is the glide plane) is parallel to the direction of movement. Since the crystals themselves are not rotated in this process, regular orientation may result only from paratectonic perecrystallization.

Experiments with metals (Tammann, 1922, p. 203) show that slight deformations result in the growth of some crystals (the less stressed ones) at the expense of others (the more stressed). In this case, the size of the average crystal increases, the number of crystals decreases and the orientation becomes ordered.

Recrystallization proceeds differently after intense deformations: embryos of new, unstressed crystals appear among the deformed material. These new embryos grow at the expense of the old and, consequently, the number of crystals increases, while the orientation becomes random, or even ordered, but with a considerable scatter of the individual grains.

For the sake of brevity, we shall call the first type of recrystallization *migratory* (after Dorsey, 1940) and the second type, which is most widely distributed among metals, *primary* (after Cahn, 1949, p. 121).

Migratory recrystallization. Only migratory recrystallization has been detected in ice. In this case, the crystals with basal planes oriented close to the direction of movement, and thus under less stress during the deformation process, grow at the expense of the less favorably oriented and more strongly stressed crystals. Thus, there is a tendency for the crystals to be oriented with their main axes perpendicular to the direction of movement and this tendency also develops after prolonged movement in a single direction. In this case,

---

[2] Evidently, ice crystals are incapable of twinning mechanically, which would provide an additional degree of freedom for intragranular adaptation to pressure, nor can they become other polymorphic modifications.

the crystals become larger and less numerous; thus, paratectonic migratory perecrystallization produces the same effect as collective perecrystallization, except that it continues to be effective for larger crystal sizes. Even in this case, the limit of development (practically unattainable) of the aggregate is a monocrystal, but a monocrystal with its basal plane parallel to the direction of movement, while in the case of collective perecrystallization the orientation is random.

As in the case of collective perecrystallization, migratory perecrystallization may take place in the solid phase or, with an intermediate transition, it may pass through the liquid or vapor phase. Hence, one may distinguish between *migratory recrystallization, paratectonic regelation* and *sublimation perecrystallization.* Properly speaking, these processes are an expression of Riecke's principle (although this principle does not include migratory recrystallization as such), but structurally they differ sharply from the perecrystallization which occurs during pseudoviscous flow, because the rocks must adapt to deformation of a different type, to internal gliding in the crystals.

The main types of migratory paratectonic perecrystallization are recrystallization and regelation, which differ but little in their results. The recrystallization type prevails at negative temperatures and the regelation type at temperatures near zero.

In contrast to regelation perecrystallization during pseudoviscous flow, the examined type of regelation perecrystallization, which is widely developed in "temperate glaciers," is not associated with the migration of water over any great distance, but actually amounts to a transfer of material across the liquid films between neighboring crystals.

Regelation perecrystallization according to Riecke's principle should not be confused with melting and freezing that are influenced by time variations of hydrostatic pressure, which, in a given section of rock, can be caused by the impossibility of lateral expansion due to the resistance of the surrounding rock to plastic deformation. This process has nothing in common with the elasticity of form and Riecke's principle. One need but recall that ice has a very low elastic limit and crushing strength and thus when pressure is exerted on it (and lateral expansion is possible) ice will deform plastically before melting, even at a temperature of the order of minus one thousandth of a degree, while it will crush before melting at temperatures below $-0.25°C$.

Films of salt solution or "adiabatic" water between ice crystals prevent direct recrystallization and result in the substitution of regelation perecrystallization according to Riecke's principle, but their actual occurrence is not connected with oriented stress. Water, which appears as a result of melting under unilateral pressure, soon migrates and freezes at the point of least pressure, while the water subject to hydrostatic pressure (most of the water of intercrystalline films) has no egress and does not freeze until the pressure decreases with time.

Sublimation paratectonic perecrystallization is far less important than the first two types, because it is observed primarily in porous rocks where the crystals have relatively great structural freedom and where the adaptation to deformation proceeds basically along the line of intergranular movements which relieve the crystals from stress.

Polygonization. Evidently, there is no primary recrystallization in ice rock. In all probability this can be explained by the inadequate elastic stresses in ice crystals at temperatures near the melting point. Instead, a still different type of recrystallization takes place in ice. Recently, it was detected in metals and called *polygonization* (Cahn, 1949).

Polygonization consists in the disintegration of overstressed curved crystals into a series of finer crystals with fairly straight boundaries between them and with a crystallographic orientation corresponding to the orientation of a given segment of a primary curved crystal. A group of finer crystals with similar orientation forms instead of a single crystal. This situation is characteristic of the so-called cataclasites, thus it is quite possible that in many cases cataclasis amounts to polygonization. With increasing flexure, the primary crystal separates into an ever greater number of blocks and the difference in the crystallographic orientation of the peripheral blocks also increases.

The new crystal blocks are fairly free of elastic flexural stresses and thus the polygonization will also be a molecular mechanism which reduces the free energy reserve of the substance. However, from the point of view of the general trend of the perecrystallization processes, which strive to convert a polycrystalline aggregate into a mono-crystal, polygonization is retrogressive metamorphism, i.e., *diaph-thoresis.*

The rounding off of crystals, collective perecrystallization and paratectonic perecrystallization are the molecular processes which occur in polycrystalline ice due to the internal sources of energy and which advance it toward a state of least free energy. However, if the first two processes have an already established energy source, para-tectonic perecrystallization will draw its energy from the stress of the deformation which occurs simultaneously with it. Of course, a powerful external energy source could easily increase the free energy of the ice rock, rather than reduce it, if one considers the state of the rock before deformation, and this increase would be expressed in the reduction of the crystal size.

In polygonization, as well as in primary recrystallization, we encounter cases where the molecular processes, obeying the general principle of least energy, cannot completely counteract the external energy flux and, in transforming the excess energy from one form to another (from the energy of the stressed state to surface energy), still produce a rock with a larger supply of free energy than it had before. Thus, the quantitative increase in the intensity of deformation becomes a qualitative change in its influence on the rock structure.

Dislocation metamorphism. A further increase of oriented stress leads to the direct fragmentation of crystals by brittle fracture, instead of indirect fragmentation caused by elastic stresses and molecular processes; cataclasis and mylonitization occur, with the movement of fragments along the surface of breaks, which do not necessarily follow either the boundaries or the internal glide planes of the crystals. *External energy* is the direct source of these *dislocation metamorphism* processes, which *increase the free energy supply* of the rock.

In the opinion of the author, this provides the general answer to one of the most perplexing problems of glaciology, viz., does glacier movement promote or prevent the growth of glacier grains? P. L. Mercanton (1950) states that no satisfactory answer has been given since F. Hugi (1830) established the granular structure of glaciers. The reason for this is that the answer may be different in each specific case and that it must be based on detailed petrographic study.

Regelation dynamic metamorphism. Since ice is very plastic and near the melting point, strong shear deformation often leads to the appearance of zones of higher plasticity rather than to cataclasis. Perecrystallization is accelerated in these zones with partial conversion to the liquid phase. Probably the heat of friction accounts for the melting. On the other hand, the ice also melts in sections where sufficiently high hydrostatic pressure develops. These are the phenomena of *regelation dynamic metamorphism*, which is a special substitute for dislocation metamorphism. These phenomena cannot be considered ordinary processes of perecrystallization, because whole sections of the rock melt with ensuing crystallization that is spontaneous in part and unaffiliated with the structure of the enclosing rock.

These phenomena also differ from those of congelation ice formation in that they are genetically associated with the processes which occur within the ice rock.

Rapid freezing after melting caused by excessive pressure may produce fine-grained ice, which increases the supply of free energy in the rock, as in the case of cataclasis, polygonization and the growth of depth hoar. All these processes may be classified as diaphthoresis, caused by external energy sources.

The examined processes of rock dynamic metamorphism (from pseudoviscous flow with perecrystallization after Riecke's principle to mylonitization and internal melting) form a continuous series, in which each successive member reflects the reaction of the rock to an ever increasing stress. Most of the members of this series are phenomena of flow or *plasticity*, but cataclasis is a phenomenon of the brittleness of polycrystalline ice. Obviously, these phenomena are considerably more complex than the corresponding ones in monocrystals (see Chap. III). The intergranular adaptations may combine with both paratectonic perecrystallization, in the presence of the liquid phase, and with dislocation (disruption) metamorphism, which destroys the cohesion between the grains of "dry" ice.

Table 3 summarizes the processes of ice metamorphism.

Owing to the specific mechanical and thermodynamic properties of ice, the processes of ice metamorphism show less of a sequence of changes with depth than do non-ice rocks. For the most part, the metamorphic zones overlap in the case of ice. For example, beginning with the surface or near-surface layers, processes occur in ice which are characteristic of the epizone, the katazone and the palingenetic zone of the earth's crust. In the case of ice, fluidity, which is characteristic of the katazone, begins to occur at a depth of no more than 15 m; the open cracks are usually concentrated in this surface crust. However, in dilation zones the cracks penetrate to depths of 80 m and more, dissecting the glacier throughout, and thrusts are a common phenomenon in the bottom layers of glaciers, even in glaciers hundreds of meters thick. Further, there may not be any temperature stratification at all (as in the case of temperate glaciers, which are at the melting point throughout).

In ice rock, differentiation due to the properties of the rocks themselves is more important than the standard zonality of the metamorphic processes. Sedimentary ice is the only form of ice rock which can become quite thick on the earth's surface, and in the first stage of development, it can easily be distinguished from compact ice. Snow and ice are two completely different rocks with respect to their structure, physical properties and the metamorphic processes which occur in them. Owing to the porosity of fresh snow, its mechanical properties correspond to those of a viscous fluid and differ from it only in compressibility. Ice shows a definite tendency to flow

TABLE 3

CLASSIFICATION OF THE PROCESSES OF ICE METAMORPHISM

Energy source			Types of metamorphism			
			General characteristics	Recrystallization and dislocation metamorphism (in the solid phase)	Regelation metamorphism (through the liquid phase)	Sublimation metamorphism (through the vapor phase with surface migration)
Internal energy of the rock	Free surface energy of the crystals		Rounding of the crystals (approximation of equilibrium form)	Recrystallization rounding	Regelation rounding	Sublimation rounding
			Collective pere-crystallization	Collective recrystallization	Collective regelation pere-crystallization	Collective sublimation pere-crystallization
	Free internal energy of the stressed state	Dynamic metamorphism	Paratectonic pere-crystallization	Migratory recrystallization	Paratectonic regelation pere-crystallization (according to Riecke's principle)	Paratectonic sublimation pere-crystallization (according to Riecke's principle)
				Polygonization (recrystallization diaphthoresis)		
External energy			Dislocation metamorphism	Cataclasis and Mylonitization	Regelation dynamometamorphism of friction and pressure	Sublimation diaphthoresis (growth of depth hoar)

under its own weight on an inclined surface at an average thickness of about 12–15 m, while this tendency appears at a snow depth of 5 cm (de Quervain, 1945). Plastic transformations can change both the shape and volume of snow, but the volume of ice remains practically constant. Finally, both liquid and gaseous material can migrate in snow, owing to its porosity, while "healthy" ice is an impenetrable rock.

In view of this, we must make a special study of the metamorphism of snow before it becomes ice (taken in the petrographic sense, i.e., a rock without open pores) and special studies must also be made of the metamorphic processes of both congelation and sedimentary-metamorphic ice.

We shall call the first group of processes *metamorphic ice formation*, in which dynamic metamorphism also plays a role, although a secondary one. On the other hand, the metamorphism of ice consists almost exclusively of the processes of *dynamic metamorphism* and the *thermal metamorphism* of ice is of very limited importance.

CHAPTER XIII

METAMORPHIC ICE FORMATION

Metamorphic ice formation transforms disordered, porous accumulations of barely connected ice particles into solid aggregates of ice crystals impermeable to air and water. This transformation is brought about by (1) mutual displacement of the crystals, (2) surface changes of their form and dimensions and (3) internal deformations of the crystals. As a result, the open pores disappear and the crystals become closed and grown together and increase perceptibly in size.

To a considerable extent, the pores disappear because the crystals assemble mechanically, i.e., because of the compression of the rock manifested in *settling*, but often this is also caused by the filling of the pores with ice that migrates primarily downward as melt water. During ice formation, a large part of the air from the pores is forced upward, but some of it (from 1% to 30%) is trapped in the ice and remains there as enclosed bubbles. Thus, air is "captured" by the ice and the volume of enclosed air inclusions increases from approximately 0.1–0.2% of the total volume in new snow to 1.3–13% in ice.

As the role of settling increases during metamorphism, the amount of air included in the ice increases and as infiltration and freezing of the melt water increase, more air is forced out from the ice.

The entire process of ice formation can be expressed as a time curve of rock settling, which is close to a hyperbola for non-eolian deposition of dry snow and constant external conditions. At first, settling is very rapid and then decelerates, asymptotically approaching zero at the greatest possible density.[1] R. Haefeli made calculations for dry snow with an initial density of 0.074 g/cm^3 under a load of 0.1 kg/cm^2. It takes 0.85 year (311 days) for the snow to settle to a density 10% less than the maximum density, 2.21 years for it to settle to a density 5% less than maximum, and 10.5 years to settle to a density 1% less than maximum (neglecting the partial conversion of air pores into enclosed bubbles). Thus, under the conditions described, metamorphic ice formation is quite a long process.

---

[1] A. A. Shepelevskii (1938) and R. Haefeli (1939) attempted to depict the snow settling process or the time variation of density quantitatively.

Actually, the conditions are considerably more complex and may show infinite variety. If a factor such as the initial wind packing could be calculated as a simple displacement of the initial point of the settling process on the abovementioned theoretical curve and if downhill creep, which imposes shear on the compression strain, does not exert an essential influence on the shape of the settling curve, the deposition of new layers of snow and, especially, partial melting would change the state of affairs completely.

Settling, i.e., densification, is just one indication of change in the rock texture along with the shape and size of the crystals and of the intervening pores, the strength of the bonds between the crystals, etc. All these properties of the rock experience various changes, which have not yet been studied to any great extent, but which reveal some definite regularities.

Intermediate stages in the transformation of snow into ice have long been differentiated. A. B. Dobrowolski (1923, p. 647) characterizes them as follows: "First, the primary masses of snow become fine-grained *firn snow*, not as blindingly white [as the primary snow] because they have less air, next they become coarse-grained and still duller, then *firn ice* and finally they transform into actual *glacier ice* with ever larger and purer grains."

According to A. B. Dobrowolski, firn ice consists of transparent ice grains fused by a cement of cloudy ice, similar to conglomerates and sandstones, while actual glacier ice is an uncemented pure-grained rock, like marble. This difference is by no means characteristic: usually, the entire mass consists of grains of different sizes with air bubbles scattered between and within them. There is no definite criterion for distinguishing between the so-called "firn ice," as the first stage of sedimentary-metamorphic ice, and glacier ice. Thus, only three basic groups of sedimentary ice rock can be differentiated: *snow, firn* and *ice*.[2]

The German word "firn" or "ferner" first meant "last year's" in general, but now is used to mean old snow (more accurately, last year's snow, as opposed to this year's snow). Since the term has become firmly established in glaciology, it should be defined accurately. Of course, age must not be taken as the criterion for definition, since the intensity of the metamorphic processes differs greatly under different conditions. If the change which the snow

---

[2] The special class "firn glaciers" should be abandoned along with the concept "firn ice," since there is no basis for distinguishing either as a special group. This is particularly important, because the special classification "firn glaciers," alongside cirque glaciers and hanging glaciers, often found in standard morphological descriptions, are a confusion of various principles of classification.

experiences on alpine firn fields during the summer is taken as the criterion, the term "firn" should be applied to granular snow in general, whatever its age and density. The loss (due to sublimation processes) of the last vestiges of the idiomorphic structure characteristic of snow should be taken as the line of demarcation between snow and firn and the loss of the communicating pores, typical of firn, should be taken as the boundary between firn and ice.

Snow may become firn at densities of approximately 0.35 to 0.60 g/cm³ and firn may become ice at densities of 0.80 to 0.90 g/cm³, depending on conditions. Thus, the process of metamorphic ice formation may be separated into three fundamental stages:

(1) diagenesis of the snow cover, including all processes that take place in the snow;

(2) firnification, i.e., the transformation of snow into firn;

(3) actual ice formation, i.e., the transformation of firn into ice.

Although the processes of sedimentary ice metamorphism are highly diverse, they may be distinguished clearly on the basis of whether they occur in the liquid phase, including melting and freezing, or only in the solid and vapor phases. Sublimation metamorphism and recrystallization comprise a natural complex of processes of cold metamorphic ice formation, while regelation perecrystallization comprises the "warm" type of metamorphic ice formation.

THE "COLD" TYPE OF METAMORPHIC ICE FORMATION

Diagenesis of the snow cover

Diagenesis includes all processes which occur in the snow cover in the absence of high temperature and the subsequent appearance of a considerable amount of melt water or in the absence of high pressure, which prevents the retention of loose, porous structure. The diagenetic stage, during which the main features of the sedimentary rock are preserved, usually persists through the cold season and is interrupted by melting. In the regions of continental glaciation, but only in such regions, diagenesis continues until the rock becomes buried deep below the surface, where the nature and conditions of the processes change substantially. In this case, the diagenetic stage may last some years.

The basic conditions which determine the complex of processes that occur in the snow cover are:

the relative proximity of the melting point; consequently,

the high pressure of the saturation vapors of ice;

the great plasticity of the crystals; further, in most cases,

the great initial porosity of the precipitation, which allows water vapor to circulate in the pores and accounts for the great free surface of the crystals, which is active with respect to the sublimation process;

the small area cross section of the contacts between crystals; consequently,

the large local stresses at the contacts; and, as a result,

the great structural freedom of the crystals in the aggregate; further,

the skeletal forms of snow crystals which appear in an atmosphere supersaturated with water vapor become unstable after passing into an environment in which, on an average, the pores are merely saturated with water vapor; and, finally,

the large and frequently changing vertical temperature gradients in the upper layers of the snow, which activate the sublimation processes.

The above list indicates that *sublimation perecrystallization* and *settling* play the leading role in the diagenetic processes and that regelation and recrystallization at crystal contacts are secondary. Recrystallization merely increases the cohesive strength of the contacts somewhat. Collective and migratory recrystallization do not occur in snow or, to be more exact, they do not produce any noticeable result because the area of contact is small and because the contacts are frequently destroyed by differential movements of the crystals during settling. Evidently, regelation at the crystal contacts can play a larger role, but only at temperatures close to zero (above $-0.25°C$; see Chap. XII[3]); otherwise regelation will not be as important as the mechanical fracturing of the contacts.

The settling and sublimation processes are closely related in snow. At first, the great porosity creates conditions equally favorable for both processes. Sublimation rounding, which initiates the sublimation processes, greatly facilitates the relative rotation and slipping of the crystals in a porous aggregate. However, as Bucher (1948) emphasizes, sublimation perecrystallization and settling subsequently begin to become antagonistic and counteract each other to a certain extent because of the following.

---

[3] I. V. Kragel'skii (1942, p. 13) performed an interesting experiment which proved that regelation does not occur in snow at negative temperatures. No signs of melting were detected when snow containing methylene blue was strongly compressed, even though the snow was pressed into a solid lump. Under these same conditions, snow under a sliding wooden runner stained intensely due to melting. Unfortunately, the author did not indicate the initial snow temperature.

It is quite apparent that settling and densification, in reducing porosity, weaken the sublimation processes. The reverse relationship has also been established. The structural freedom of the crystals in a porous aggregate accounts for the great fluidity of snow, which is 10^4 to 10^5 times that of ice (the coefficient of viscosity of new snow near $0°C$ is about 10^8 poise), and, what is more, the differential movements of each structural unit in a given volume increase the fluidity. Therefore, fine-grained snow is more plastic than coarse-grained snow and sublimation perecrystallization, which increases the grain size of the snow, also increases viscosity and retards settling and densification.

Settling and sublimation perecrystallization are so antagonistic that one process may be completely suppressed under conditions that favor the other. Thus a given snow layer or snow cover as a whole may develop in one of two opposite ways, depending on the conditions during the initial stage of diagenesis, i.e., the development may tend towards *densification*, with dominance of settling, or it may tend toward *loosening*, with dominance of sublimation perecrystallization. The first type of development leads to a rapid increase of density without grain growth, while the second type leads to a rapid increase of crystal size without changing the initial density. In most cases, the second type of development terminates in processes of *sublimation diaphthoresis* which, under favorable conditions, leads to the appearance of sand snow[4] in some layers. This sand snow is very brittle, coarse-grained, highly viscous, weakly bonded and is replete with depth-hoar crystals.

Snow may settle by two means: (1) normally, by gradual plastic transformation, which generally does not destroy the structure although it derives primarily from the differential movements of the crystals, and (2) by abrupt, sudden sagging, accompanied by breaking of the primary structure, by quaking and by rapid removal of air from the snow. The second type of settling is often noted during and immediately after non-eolian deposition of snow, but in such cases it is not accompanied by any spectacular phenomena. In the subsequent stages of evolution of the snow cover, the tendency toward loosening finally ends in the discontinuous settling of the snow, which

---

[4] [The Russian term here, *sneg-plyvun,* means, literally, "snow quicksand" and is admittedly a translation of the German *Schwimmschnee.* The SIPRE translation of Bader's article containing the term *Schwimmschnee* (SIPRE Translation 14, *Snow and its Metamorphism,* 1954) calls it "depth hoar," but Shumskii uses another, distinct term for depth hoar. The *Glossary of Arctic and Subarctic Terms,* ADTIC Publication A-105, 1955, p. 70, translates *Schwimmschnee* as "sand snow." I have accepted the latter translation in order to make this distinction. – D.K.]

occurs when the fragile and brittle layers become buried at such a depth that they cannot withstand the increasing load of subsequent deposits at higher levels. In such cases settling is often accompanied by a loud noise and sizable quakes.

Snow diagenesis consists of two more or less distinct stages which correspond approximately to the stages of early diagenesis (syngenesis and diagenesis of the precipitation) and epigenesis (late diagenesis) of other sedimentary rocks.

The early diagenetic stage of snow. During early diagenesis, a first approximation of equilibrium with the medium is attained under conditions which have changed sharply since the deposition of snow particles. This stage is characterized by very rapid sublimation rounding and settling processes and by the regelation process at temperatures close to zero. The time involved is small, usually of the order of several days. In most cases, early diagenesis results in the freezing together of the snow, sublimation rounding and smoothing of the thin primary stratification, which occur in all facies of the snow cover.

The earliest result of diagenesis, which appears no more than 1–2 days after deposition, is the *freezing together* of the snow cover, its transformation from a sediment (an accumulation of barely contiguous ice particles surrounded by a film of absorbed air) into a sedimentary rock more or less firmly fused into a randomly spaced lattice of crystals. The cohesive strength of the snow particle contacts amounts to 0.5–1.0 kg/cm^2 and more (de Quervain, 1948), depending on the mutual crystallographic orientation, so that the contacts can be destroyed and differential movements of the crystals can occur only when the contact areas are small and the stresses large. Eolation and redeposition of the snow cease after the snow particles have frozen together, and the snow cover cannot be corraded and deflated except by strong winds. A moist wind and a snow temperature that is low compared with the temperature of the ground layers of air considerably enhance the freezing together of the surface layer and lead to the diffusion of water vapor from the air into the snow and to cementation of the concave contacts and the narrow pores between the crystals. On the other hand, a dry wind and volatilization from the snow surface prevent the freezing together of the surface layer and may even lead to secondary loosening of the surface snow.

Rounding of the snow particles, primarily sublimation rounding but also regelation rounding at temperatures around 0°C, are the main processes of the early diagenesis stage. To a considerable extent, rounding also results in smoothing of the thin primary snow stratification. We refer to the stratification of a single snowfall, which does not disappear without a trace in the stage described but merely becomes indistinguishable or difficult to distinguish visually and is manifested for a long period of time in the different cohesive strengths between and within the layers.

Owing to volatilization, rounding of snowflakes may begin as the snowflakes fall through the lower layers of the atmosphere, before they are deposited, but in most cases slow, continuous growth begins there. However, air in the pores of the snow cover is vapor-saturated only with respect to the surfaces of crystals which have a predominent, quite large radius of curvature, while the narrow projections, edges and branches are subject to volatilization. Prolonged observations of the processes of metamorphism (Bader, 1939; de Quervain, 1945) have shown that the microrelief of the snowflake surface disappears first, then the edges and the plane faces round out and finally the lateral branches of the skeletal crystals disappear or are disjoined by volatilization of the narrow sections situated primarily at the base of the branches. The material which evaporates and migrates along the surface is deposited chiefly on the concave sections and in the narrow pores, in part cementing the contiguous crystals.

As a result, the fine particles (up to 0.4 mm) become quite round and the larger particles become irregular with rounded edges, but retain their plane faces to a certain extent. *Fine-grained snow* forms and its grain size depends on the size of the deposited snowflakes or the products of their fractionation. Ordinarily, the grains vary from 0.1–0.2 mm to 1 mm in diameter and combine into relatively compact complexes; each grain is in contact with 3–4 neighboring grains and the entire structure is that of an irregular space lattice rather than spherical packing.

The destruction of the lateral branches during the rounding process greatly facilitates the rapid settling of the snow. However, settling during the early diagenetic stage is not characteristic of all the facies of the snow cover; snow packed tightly by the wind does not settle or settles but very little until it becomes buried deep beneath the surface. The upper layer of a non-eolian snow deposit usually settles in a series of small discontinuous motions accompanied by the fracturing of the crystals and then settles smoothly but rapidly and pseudo-plastically, owing to differential movements and rounding of the crystals.

In the Alps, on an average, a surface layer of dry new snow with a density of 0.15 g/cm^3 settles at a rate of 13% of its initial thickness per day, so that in three days settling increases the density from 0.15 to 0.25 g/cm^3 (Hughes and Seligman, 1939).

However, the rate of settling depends not only on the initial wind packing but also on the snow temperature, which also exerts a great influence on the plasticity of the snow and especially on the magnitude of the loading from above, i.e., on the quantity and frequency of solid precipitation. A relatively high temperature causes rapid settling and densification, while low temperatures decrease plasticity to a considerable extent and cause the snow to settle slowly. If the new snow remains on the surface of the snow cover for a long time and is not loaded, it will settle but little during the rounding process and, *vice versa*, it will densify rapidly if covered by thick layers of precipitation.

In addition to the specific surface changes caused by wind action and an intensive energy and material exchange with the atmosphere (wind crust, sublimation cementation and loosening due to volatilization, melting, etc.), temperature conditions and especially loading during the stage of early diagenesis exert a decisive influence on the entire further development of the snow, pre-determining whether the dense or the loose type will develop.

In regions of maritime climate where the snowfalls are frequent and abundant at relatively high temperatures, conditions are such that a snow cover almost entirely of the dense type will develop, while the loose type of snow cover will form in regions with a cold climate and little snow. In regions with strong winds and dissected relief, local differences of this same type occur between the facies of the foot of slopes, where thick layers of snow are deposited, and the facies of the uplands, where the snow deposits are light.

For these same reasons, during the early diagenetic stage a secondary differentiation will be created in the layer of each snowfall imposed on the primary thin stratification. The lower part of each snow layer will tend to develop as the dense type and the surface part as the loose type. The properties of the snow will change discontinuously at the boundary of two layers, and this discontinuity will increase with increasing time between snowfalls; it will also be greater after abundant snowfalls and high temperatures, which cause greater densification of the lower part of the layer, than after light snowfalls and low temperatures (Bucher, 1948).

The differences created in the described stage are more distinct during the subsequent development of the snow cover.

As a whole, during early diagenesis the snow has *fine-grained, porous agglomerate texture*, latent stratified structure and stratiform composition produced by the alternation of relatively thick layers of different snowfalls.

The epigenetic stage of snow. The epigenetic stage of snow is characterized by the termination of snow-particle rounding (although vestiges of the skeleton texture still remain) and by dominance of *collective sublimation perecrystallization*. Correspondingly, the rate of snow settling should decrease and only the increasing pressure of the newly deposited layers can prevent its rapid attenuation along the hyperbolic curve. During the settling process, the snow grains become more and more constricted by their neighbors and the structural resistance which bonds a grain increases; thus the internal deformations of the crystals begin to play a role, small at first, along with the intercrystalline differential movements, and Riecke's *paratectonic sublimation perecrystallization* also begins to play a role.

Laboratory experiments (de Quervain, 1945) have shown that snow diagenesis practically ceases at the stage of rounding and volatilization of the smallest grains, when the temperature is constant and there is no gradient. Further collective perecrystallization can occur only if temperature fluctuations and spatial temperature gradients are also involved.

As noted previously, the temperature gradient causes ice to migrate through the vapor phase in the direction of the thermal flux, so that the entire sublimation process is a means of accelerating the transfer of heat in a porous ice rock. As the snow becomes more porous, its thermal conductivity decreases, the temperature gradient which can occur in it increases and vapor migrates more easily in it; thus conditions for the development of the sublimation processes improve.

The temperature gradient in the snow is always normal to the surface. The diurnal and particularly the aperiodic temperature fluctuations, attenuated and with a certain inertia, penetrate several tens of centimeters into the snow cover. The direction of migration of the vapors changes continually in this layer. Only the seasonal temperature variations penetrate deeper. During most of the lifetime of a snow cover, the surface temperatures are relatively low and the heat flux is directed upward; thus there is sublimation migration of ice from the lower to the upper layers. The direction of the sublimation migration is reversed in the spring and summer because of heating from above, but this is brief compared with the winter regime.

Data on the magnitude and spatial distribution of sublimation migration differ greatly. A. S. Kondrat'eva's (1945) laboratory experiments with snow having a density of 0.32–0.45 g/cm^3 and a constant temperature gradient of 27°C/m along a 41-cm profile, showed a 0.016 g/cm^3/day loss in the first "warmest" quarter of the profile and a gain of 0.004 g/cm^3/day in the last, coldest quarter of the profile. Bader's theoretical calculations (Bader, 1939) gave a transfer value of the order of 1 mg/day/cm², i.e., a value 100 times smaller, with the following distribution along the profile: loss only at the "warm" end, uniform deposition of half of the material within the layer and deposition of the other half at the "cold" end. Shumskii measured the magnitude of sublimation loss from the lower 7-cm layer of snow for the six winter months, under natural conditions, in a half-meter layer of snow and thus in the zone of diurnal and aperiodic temperature fluctuations. He found the sublimation loss to be 0.022 g/cm³ (change in density from 0.374 to 0.352 g/cm³), accompanied by a density decrease of 0.008 g/cm³ when the open pores were not considered, which corresponds to a 2.43% loss of ice from the total volume of the rock, a 2.1% increase in the volume of the pores and a 0.33% increase in the volume of the enclosed bubbles.

Migration caused by convective air currents is superposed on the sublimation migration caused by diffusion of water vapor in the direction of the heat flux. Slow air currents, apparently caused by fluctuations of atmospheric pressure, have been observed in the pores of the snow-firn layer of central Greenland (Sorge, 1935), but they could scarcely have any perceptible influence. The circulation of air parallel to the stratification in the snow layer of mountain slopes plays a more substantial role. Usually this circulation is concentrated below and above the snow crusts (Neher, 1939).

The intensity of the sublimation perecrystallization, which is affected by variations of the temperature gradients and air currents, is highly dependent upon the porosity and air permeability of the snow. This is why secondary differentiation, noted in the first stage of the snow cover due to the different rate of settling, becomes more intense during the epigenetic stage. Now, the snow development quite clearly follows the type (densification or loosening) indicated in the stage of early diagenesis.

This happens because in snow which has been densified by compression from the very beginning, the fine grains converge, the pores are very thin and meandering and do not leave room for sublimation growth of the grains. The air permeability of such snow is slight and collective sublimation perecrystallization is difficult to achieve. Only intergrowth can occur, i.e., cementation of the grains into more or less compact complexes. Further, because of the additive nature of snow fluidity based on intergranular movements, the fine-grained aggregate remains relatively plastic. Therefore, once begun, the tendency toward densification continues, new snowfalls lead to new compression and the formation of dense, hard fine-grained snow.

On the other hand, in snow which has not settled (or which has not been wind-packed), high porosity and great air-permeability lead to intensive collective sublimation perecrystallization and, consequently, to rapid growth of the grains. A friable and brittle porous medium-grained or coarse-grained snow forms. Its grains are cemented as groups into fairly large intergrowths, but at the same time the narrow strips between the individual intergrowths become volatilized and the snow becomes weaker than it was initially. Furthermore, the growth of the grains considerably increases the viscosity of the aggregate, which in turn decreases settling even in the later stages, despite increased loading. Therefore, in this case, too, once the tendency toward loosening has begun, it continues until interrupted by melting or mechanical disruption of the structure under the increasing pressure of the upper layers.

Central Greenland is an example of the general evolution of a snow layer toward densification. Here the snow grains, which reach an average diameter of 1 mm (0.9–1.1 mm) during the first year, as opposed to 0.5 mm (0.1–0.8 mm) in new snow, do not show any further growth for decades, as shown, for example, by Sorge's (1935) study of a 21-year-old layer. The thick layers of snow at the foot of steep slopes in regions with a cold climate and strong winds are a still more typical example of this kind of development. Here, a very hard, fine-grained snow forms in one cold season (grains 0.5–1.0 mm), density up to 0.56 g/cm^3 and porosity 40.3%, i.e., the same degree of densification attained in central Greenland in 21 years and at 15 meters below the surface. Typical development of snow toward loosening was observed under the same climatic conditions on deflation areas with a thin snow cover. In this situation, in one cold season the grains and durable intergrowths grew to a diameter of 3–6 mm, while the snow density did not exceed 0.35–0.38 g/cm^3, which is somewhat greater than the initial value for wind packing.

Since temperature affects the plasticity of snow, densification develops most typically in a moderate maritime climate, while loosening develops primarily in regions of cold continental climate. This explains the apparent anomaly that snow is generally coarser-grained during very cold weather than during a mild winter, provided the mild frosts are not interrupted by thaw periods.

In most cases, the development of a snow layer includes both densification by settling and grain growth, but one or the other tendency prevails to a greater or lesser extent. Therefore, a vertical profile of snow shows a downward increase of both density and grain size, but considerable fluctuations are imposed upon this general variation.

A differentiation, although less well defined than in the above cases, occurs within any snow layer, due to differences during the stage of early diagenesis: the lower part of each layer develops along the lines of densification while the upper part develops as the loose type. Consequently, the structure and properties of the snow in vertical profile show irregular variations due to the differences in the abundance and temperature of the individual snowfalls. The lower part of each snowfall layer is denser, smaller-grained, more plastic and stronger than the upper part, while the upper part is relatively loose, coarse-grained, non-plastic and brittle. The properties vary discontinuously at the boundary of two layers and often this boundary is also marked by a snow crust. The differences in thermal conductivity, which create large temperature gradients and promote local activation of the sublimation processes, also help create this effect.

In the densification type of development, the textural changes merely amount to compression of the pores, convergence and partial sublimation intergrowth of the grains. In the case of loosening, sublimation intergrowths form, partial volatilization occurs and the strips between the intergrowths disappear, but the important thing is that the grains grow. Grain growth is accompanied by partial *restoration of the idiomorphism* of the crystals. After the crystals have been rounded in the early diagenetic stage, often plane faces redevelop as the large crystals grow. These faces are chiefly monohedra, prisms and pyramids, but their percentage relationship differs from that of atmospheric crystals (de Quervain, 1945).

Further development toward loosening, which usually takes place only in layers of temperature discontinuities, leads to the appearance of a large number of idiomorphic and skeletal cup-shaped and particularly bowl-shaped *depth-hoar* crystals. Often the main axes of the hemimorphic, hollow, bowl crystals are oriented vertically, with the narrow end up, in the direction of the thermal flux. The size of the depth-hoar crystals is limited to the size of the cavity enclosing them: in snow they are rarely larger than 5–8 mm and only once has a prismatic crystal as large as 3 cm long been found, in a large snow cavity (Paulcke, 1934).

As a rule, the appearance of depth hoar, which is a manifestation of *sublimation diaphthoresis*, is associated with the sublimation removal of part of the substance, with great loosening and the formation of large pores and cavities. The snow becomes very brittle, so that it disintegrates into individual crystals and crystal intergrowths at the slightest touch, even then remaining non-plastic. Paulcke applied the not very apt term "fluid snow," i.e., sand snow (*Schwimmschnee*) to this type of snow.[5] In using this term, one must keep in mind that

---

[5] [See preceding footnote. – D.K.]

sand snow becomes fluid only after its structure has been destroyed, which may happen easily since this snow is hard and brittle. The density of sand snow usually varies between 0.2 and 0.3 g/cm³, which corresponds to 67–78% porosity, and since it is coarse-grained and has large pores, its air permeability considerably exceeds that of all other types of snow.

The lower layers of the snow cover just above the soil surface, where the maximum temperature gradients occur, are the most favorable levels for sand snow development and the least favorable are at the layer boundaries within the snow cover. In some cases, this process is also aided by the convective circulation of air above and below the impermeable snow crusts on the slopes. In the bottom layers of the snow cover, the sand snow layers are usually no more than 10–30 cm thick and only in rare cases are they more than 1 m thick; as a rule, they are no more than a few centimeters thick within the snow layer.

The above described differences in the trend of snow development during the epigenetic stage are clearly manifested in Bader's diagram (Fig. 77) of the relationship between porosity *n* and air-permeability *k* (see p. 108). Old snow may be less porous and denser than young snow, because it is hard and fine-grained when compacted in a fresh state under heavy loading. The air permeability of such snow remains approximately as low as that of new snow (new snow is not very permeable to air, even though it is very porous, because it has skeleton texture and thus its pores meander greatly). On the other hand, when the loading is slight in the stage of early diagenesis, the old snow does not become very dense, but becomes coarse-grained and very permeable to air at average porosity. This is the loose type of development, an extreme case of which is the sand snow.

Old snow has *porous agglomerate, fine-grained to coarse-grained texture*, always with traces of the primary *skeleton* texture, while in part sand snow has secondary *idiomorphic-crystalline* texture. The following size limits of the various groups of snow grains can be established: small, < 1 mm; medium, 1–3 mm; large, > 3 mm. Thus, most types of granular snow correspond to psephites (gravel) and only the finest grained snow corresponds to psammites (sand). Under the microscope large grains of old snow usually appear as fairly *tight* clusters of several (up to 10–15) particles of different crystallographic orientation, often with interpenetrating pores. The density of old snow varies from 0.2–0.3 g/cm³ for sand snow to 0.5–0.6 g/cm³ for some kinds of fine-grained snow. These densities correspond to porosities of 78% to 36%.

When sublimation intergrowths form, some of the pores in the

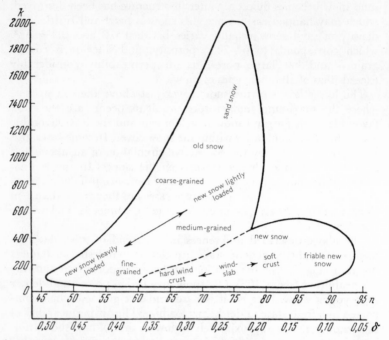

FIG. 77.   Classification of snow by the relationship between porosity *n* and air permeability *k*. (After H. Bader, 1939.)

snow become blocked and form isolated bubbles. The hypogenous new bubble formations differ from the primary air inclusions in the snowflakes in that their form and arrangement are irregular, and often they are larger as well. Primary air bubbles are rarely found in grains of snow. The volume of enclosed air bubbles in old snow amounts to 0.2–0.7%. Since most of these are hypogenous new formations created by diagenetic processes, the average air pressure in the bubbles is close to the atmospheric pressure at the given hypsometric level.

Determinations of the crystallographic orientation of grains in a natural snow cover, made in the Alps and on the Ross Ice Shelf in Antarctica, have not revealed any signs of ordered structure. Only laboratory experiments have revealed the possibility that ordered orientation develops as a result of the natural weight of the snow (de Quervain, 1948). The porosity of the snow allows reciprocal movement of the particles, but the shape of the crystal determines the ordering of the structure during deformation. During deformation, the planes of the plate crystals turn parallel to the direction of movement; consequently, during shearing they turn in the shear plane, during compression they turn perpendicular to the direction of pressure (because of the possibility of lateral expansion) and in the case of tension they turn parallel to the direction of the stress. Vertical pressure forces act in a horizontal snow cover, leading to compression and settling of the snow, while an additional shear force parallel to the slope acts in the snow cover of slopes, causing downhill creep. In both cases, plate crystals should become so oriented that their main crystallographic axes are normal to the snow surface. Actually, such ordering cannot proceed far, because the crystals tend to change form and become isometric. In the epigenetic stage, vertical settling is much slower in a horizontal snow cover than in a fresh non-eolian snow deposit, despite the heavy loading. This process gradually decelerates with time. In the center of the Greenland Ice Sheet (Eismitte station, Wegener Expedition of 1930–31), at a depth of 2–3 m, where the snow density is about 0.4 g/cm^3, continuous settling proceeded at a rate of 0.011–0.012% of the initial layer thickness per day, i.e., more than a thousand times slower than in fresh snow, while at a depth of 5–7 m, the density was 0.45–0.49 g/cm^3, and the rate of settling only 0.0065–0.008% per day. The snow in the first of these layers was 3–4 years old, in the second 6–9 years old and the load increased 0.031 kg/cm^2/year (Sorge, 1935). A similar rate of snow settling was observed under analogous conditions on the Ross Ice Shelf in Antarctica (Wade, 1945).

The snow cover of slopes experiences shear deformation parallel to the slope simultaneously with vertical compression-settling. Measurements show that the rate of creep of a surface layer of snow along a slope in the Alps is 1.0–1.5 cm/day (Neher, 1939). Due to creep, the snow cover on moderately steep slopes can be in apparent equilibrium only when tension acts on the upper part of the slope and tangential compression acts at the foot of the slope; in this case the tension zone is larger than the compression zone and the tensile stress is greater than the compressive stress. This is the opposite of what generally occurs in ice. If the snow cover becomes thicker toward the lower part of the slope, the tension zone may reach as far as the foot of the slope (Haefeli, 1939).

Since vertical and tangential stresses, shear and tension occur and increase as snow accumulates, there is danger of fracture and destruction of the snow cover structure if the cover develops without consolidating. Densification increases snow strength and maintains adequate plasticity. Thus, such snow reacts to increased loading by slowly deforming plastically, by settling and by creeping downhill.

Loosening has exactly the opposite effect. The combination of low density, large grain size and few contacts between the grains makes the snow weak and very rigid, not allowing plastic deformation. Thus, in the final analysis, this type of development must lead to fractures which disrupt the equilibrium of the snow cover, provided the process is not interrupted by melting before the corresponding load increases occur.

Sudden settling of snow, accompanied by escaping air which sounds like a loud sigh, is the least harmful result of the destruction of the friable layers by vertical pressure. The same thing occurs during the fracturing of cavities formed by the uneven settling of the lower layers of snow under strong ice crusts. In the snow of central Greenland, firnquakes caused by the fracture of loose interlayers can occur simultaneously over an area of more than 100 km², accompanied by a noise like thunder, with perceptible surface quaking (Koch and Wegener, 1930; Sorge, 1935). The instantaneous settling observed at Eismitte during a firnquake amounted to 1–2 cm in a 2.5 m layer. The settling travels at the speed of sound and is accompanied by an acoustic pulse. Evidently, after a porous aggregate has been fractured, the snow crystals no longer cohere and the entire upper layer appears to lie on a "cushion of air," as during the sudden flow of subsoils, when the mineral particles seem to be suspended in water for a time. Settling is accompanied by an air discharge, which, in part, travels along the rupturing porous horizons.

On slopes, fractures of the friable layers caused by vertical pressure or tangential stress cause avalanches of the "windslab" type, while sudden settling during the early diagenetic stage causes loose-snow avalanches.[6]

Firnification and Ice Formation

Firnification and ice formation of the "cold" type are widely distributed over vast expanses of the Antarctic and Greenland continental ice sheets, and occur on a considerably larger scale than the "warm" type of metamorphic ice formation. However, the intensity of study of these two types has been inversely proportional to their importance in nature. Thus far, the processes of the "cold" stage of firnification have been investigated only by E. Sorge (1935, 1939) at the Eismitte station in central Greenland and by F. A. Wade (1945) and A. D. Howard (1948) on the Ross Ice Shelf in Antarctica and, generally speaking, no one has yet observed the processes and results of cold ice formation.

---

[6] With regard to avalanches, see G. K. Tushinskii (1949) and E. Bucher (1948).

Firnification. "Cold" firnification is a continuation of the diagenetic processes, but under somewhat different conditions. The
main differences between the physical conditions of firnification and
diagenesis involve the accumulation of a thick layer of new precipitation, which has a two-fold effect on the behavior of the metamorphic processes. Its passive role consists in preventing temperature
fluctuations in the layers which have descended, while its active role
is manifested in the ever increasing pressure on the lower layers.

In the snow and firn of central Greenland, the amplitude of the
annual temperature wave decreases to 1/10 of its surface amplitude
(35°C) at a depth of slightly more than 5 m, while at 9 m it decreases
to 1/40 of its surface value and at 18 m to 1/1000 of its surface value,
i.e., at this depth the temperature is nearly constant ($-28.68°C$),
having a very small vertical gradient. Since the development is
basically of the densification type, the rock becomes less porous with
depth and the pores become narrow and meandering; this considerably reduces the air-permeability of the rock. Furthermore, the total
wall surface of the pores decreases, because a considerable portion of
the crystal surfaces border on each other and not on the pores.

Thus, all the factors which further the sublimation processes
rapidly become less effective with depth below the diurnal surface.
Therefore, the rate of sublimation perecrystallization decreases
greatly at a depth of a few meters and then disappears completely.

Owing to increasing pressure and the increasing area of contact
between the grains, *recrystallization* plays the main role in the metamorphic processes. The transition is gradual and thus a clear line
cannot easily be drawn between the two types of processes. Nevertheless, some discontinuity in the behavior of the metamorphic
processes was discovered at Eismitte, where a more detailed study
was made.[7] The curve of the relationship between the density of the
rock and its depth below the surface (Fig. 78) shows a distinct bend
at 7 m, i.e., at the level of layers about nine years old. The rates of
settling and densification are nearly constant both above and below
that level, decreasing very slowly with depth, so that in first approximation densification with depth can be considered linear in both segments of the cross section. However, the rate of densification above
the 7-m level is 0.017 g/cm^3/year and only 0.005 g/cm^3/year below
it, i.e., about 30% of the rate in the upper part of the cross section.

---

[7] The Wegener group at Eismitte, although it was in a precarious situation,
carried out incomparably more complete and painstaking work than the well protected American Antarctic expeditions. The main difficulty with Sorge's glaciological investigations is that he did not have a polarizing microscope.

The reasons for the sharp decrease of densification at 7 m lie in the difference between the types of development in the different parts of the snow layer. Although the general development is toward densification, the upper parts of the layers of some snowfalls follow

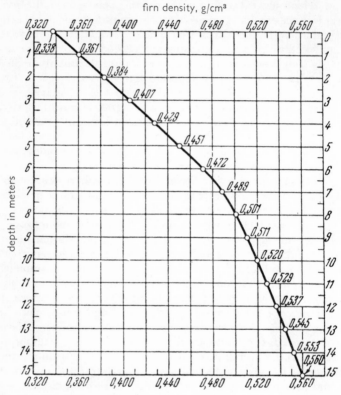

Fig. 78. Density curve of snow and firn along a vertical profile in central Greenland. (After E. Sorge, 1935.)

the loose form of development. As a result, the structure of the relatively friable and brittle layers is destroyed and firnquakes occur. This destruction proceeds layer by layer with depth; the weaker layers break nearer the surface, the stronger layers resist the increasing load longer. The process ends at a depth of 7 m at a pressure of about 0.3 kg/cm^2 and an average density of 0.49 g/cm^3. The loose layers are not preserved below 7 m and plastic compressive deformation is the sole cause of densification. Hence, the friable layers are no longer fractured and thus the rate of densification decreases sharply.

Loose development with sublimation perecrystallization is a distinctive feature of snow, genetically associated with conditions at slight depths, namely, low pressure and large temperature fluctuations. The intervention of an alien factor, i.e., the pressure increase characteristic of deeper zones of metamorphism, results in mechanical fracture and a forced transition from the surface, loose type of development to the deep type of densification, thus transforming snow into firn. This ceases at a depth of 7 m. Temperature fluctuations and sublimation perecrystallization cease at approximately this same depth and the last vestiges of idiomorphic sublimation texture disappear during the crushing of the friable layers.

Thus, firnification is always associated with the disruption of the process of sublimation perecrystallization characteristic of the diagenetic stage, but in a "warm" regime the disruption is due to the intervention of melting, while in a cold regime it is manifested in the mechanical crushing of the layers loosened by sublimation. Sudden settling of old snow, which causes windslab avalanches on slopes, marks the onset of "cold" firnification, which is interrupted by melting in the warm regions.

Ice formation. In a layer of cold firn, the ice formation process is continued by densification and recrystallization. The grains of cold firn with a density of 0.5–0.6 g/cm^3 have so little structural freedom that the firn reacts to pressure by effecting intergranular movements and, to a considerable extent, by plastic deformations of the crystals along the internal glide planes and also, in part, by crushing of the crystals.

In this connection, *paratectonic recrystallization*, largely *migratory*, plays a considerable role in the firn recrystallization processes from the very beginning. Collective recrystallization and rounding are probably of secondary importance, since the crystals are so small.

The type of deformation experienced by the rock determines which kind of structure will result from migratory recrystallization. As will be shown below, downhill flow should result in oriented structure and considerable growth of the crystals. However, the distribution of such conditions in regions of cold metamorphic ice formation is strictly limited. Shear stresses do not operate in the firn layer of continental ice sheets, because the surface inclination is slight and the differential movements are due solely to vertical pressure. Owing to the porous structure of firn, and also of snow, large differences are created in the resistance to deformation in different directions at each given point. Therefore, although the pressure in the firn generally is not distributed hydrostatically at depths of less than 20 m (thus the vertical pressure is greater than the lateral pressure), the deformation at each given point of a porous firn lattice is subject to local differences in resistance and tends toward hydrostatic compression of the pores.

Accordingly, the differential deformations of the converging firn grains do not have any sort of ordered orientation. No signs of horizontal elongation of the grains or of schistosity were detected either in Greenland or on the Ross Ice Shelf, and the crystals remained more or less isometric. Therefore, the relationship between the stressed state of neighboring crystals may change during the settling process, favoring one crystal at one time and another crystal at another, and approach an equilibrium state of hydrostatic pressure distribution. Naturally, under these conditions there will be no preferred growth of some crystals and disappearance of others and, thus, there will be no dominant crystallographic orientation.

At Eismitte, the firn grains maintained an average size of 1 mm (0.9–1.1 mm) to the maximum depth investigated (15 m), at which the ice was 21 years old. On the Ross Ice Shelf, the grain size was 1–1.5 mm in the upper 8 meters and 1.5–2.0 mm at a depth of 8–11 m, the largest grains being no more than 3 mm in diameter. Thus, in general, these crystals were smaller than those of snow which follows the loose type of development through sublimation perecrystallization. No signs of ordered structure were observed in "cold" firn. At Eismitte, the summer layers differed from the winter layers in that they inherited somewhat larger grains from the snow. This, together with the weaker cohesion between the layers of individual snowfalls, created a cryptostratified structure.

While firn is being compressed, the bridges between the pores gradually close, the contiguous crystals grow together and the pore remnants become bubbles enclosed in the ice. Upon further densification and simultaneous constriction of the remaining open pores, the bubbles begin to compress and the air pressure in them increases with respect to the atmospheric pressure at the given level. Shumskii found the first measurable indications of an increase of atmospheric pressure in frozen firn of somewhat different genesis and a density of 0.69 g/cm^3 at a depth corresponding to a vertical pressure of 0.6 kg/cm.^{2}

In Greenland, one may expect that noticeable compression of the air included in the firn will begin at a depth of about 11 m, where the vertical pressure is about 0.5 kg/cm^2 and the density 0.53 g/cm^3. Thus, even at a depth of about 10 m, the air begins to participate somewhat in the transfer of pressure and to reduce the rate of settling of the firn.

Opinions vary greatly concerning the depth at which all the pores in cold firn become closed and the firn becomes ice. Hess (1933) refers to some seismic measurements made by the Wegener expedition, which show a reflecting surface (evidently the firn-ice interface) at depths of 50–100 m, but then he estimates the firn at Eismitte to be 450 m thick. Ahlmann (1933, 1935, 1936), in his geophysical classification of glaciers, estimates the firn of high-polar glaciers to be at least 200 m thick. Sorge (1935), who extrapolates his densification curve in different ways, believes that a density of 0.900 g/cm³ can be reached at depths ranging from 63.6 m to 1000 m.

All estimates which deal in values of hundreds of meters are fantastic, because they ignore the plasticity and strength of ice. Compression of even minute air bubbles begins with a load of 1.2 kg/cm², in ice having a density of 0.9 g/cm³ at a temperature of −10°C. Only the elasticity of the air included in the cavities in the ice can account for the persistence of these bubbles. Consequently, at a pressure of 1.2 kg/cm², even the tiniest open pores will close in time, and the firn will become ice.

The densification of glacier snow and firn with depth is a process of re-establishment of equilibrium, which is continually disrupted by the gradual increase of load due to new deposits of precipitation. Since the loading increases, settling does not become damped asymptotically as the maximum density is approached, but proceeds at a rate proportional to the increase of load, until all the pores close. The curve of the rate of densification from snow to firn to ice should have two bends, corresponding to two critical points, viz., the transformation of snow into firn and the transformation of firn into ice. In both cases the rate of densification decreases discontinuously. In the first case, this is due to the destruction of all the friable interlayers and the termination of spasmodic settling of the snow and in the second case it is due to the closing of all the pores and thus the air enclosed in the ice assumes the pressure of the ice. In the areas outside these critical points, the curves can be interpolated and extrapolated and their accuracy will be limited only by the size and accuracy of the initial curve segment.

We do not know which density corresponds to the transition from firn to ice during the "cold" type of ice formation. However, judging by the general law that the density at the moment the pores close decreases as compression increases during the ice formation process, we can estimate roughly that "cold firn" will become ice at a density no greater than 0.8 g/cm³.

Extrapolating Sorge's curve of densification to a density of 0.8 g/cm³, we find the firn-ice boundary at Eismitte to be at a depth of the order of 50 m. There are no accurate data on the densification of firn in the Ross Ice Shelf. Densification is more rapid there than in Greenland, but it varies greatly in the different layers. At a depth of 10.7 m below the surface at the base of the shelf, the density is 0.64 g/cm³. Proceeding from the data on the height above water level (28.7 m) and the thickness of this floating shelf (232 m), we find the average density of the ice to be 0.84 g/cm³. On considering the rate of densification in the investigated 11-m layer, Howard (1948) concluded that a density of 0.84 g/cm³ is reached at a depth of just 30 m. Thus, the lower boundary of the firn should be even nearer the surface. Evidently, this value is too small, but in any event it is much closer to the truth than the Hess and Ahlmann estimates.

Texture. Evidently, ice formed by compression and recrystallization of "cold" firn differs from the cold firn only in that it does not have pores and that the air pressure in its bubbles is greater than in the cold firn. We shall call this *primary-recrystallization* ice to distinguish it from ice which forms during the process of flow. Eventually primary-recrystallization ice becomes flow ice.

Cold *recrystallization firn* and the primary-recrystallization ice formed from it have crystalloblastic texture. This is characterized by relatively small (1–3 mm) isometric grains and thus is *granoblastic*; in firn it is porous-granoblastic. There is no regular crystallographic orientation whatever. The porosity of the recrystallization firn varies from approximately 46% (density 0.49 g/cm³) to 0%, while the volume of air in the enclosed bubbles varies from .07% to 12.5–13.0%.

Primary-recrystallization ice has more air inclusions than any other type of ice, except perhaps the rhythmic congelation ice nuclei of freezing. On reviewing the characteristics of the types of sedimentary-metamorphic ice, one may conclude that the numerous fine, branching and penetrating air bubbles of primary-recrystallization ice are its most characteristic feature. These bubbles are vestiges of firn pores and form a meandering, branching network. They are arranged intersertally with respect to the ice crystals. At normal pressure, the volume of air included in the primary-recrystallization ice amounts to 12.5–13.0% of the rock volume, but the actual volume of air bubbles is smaller because the air is under higher pressure. The described types of firn and ice have crypto-stratified or massive unstratified structure.

THE "WARM" TYPE OF METAMORPHIC ICE FORMATION

The "warm" type of ice formation processes differ from those examined above in that liquid water plays a role. The three-phase system ice-water-water vapor is in equilibrium only at the triple point and is much less stable than a system of "dry" ice and water vapor at negative temperatures. In a 3-phase system there are 3 degrees of freedom instead of 1, with respect to the 2-phase lines: ice-water, ice-water vapor and water-water vapor. Here, the leading role is played by the regelation processes, which change the rock structure very rapidly, but settling and other processes of firn deformation behave quite differently, while vaporization and condensation of water are added to the sublimation processes.

Melt water from ice is the main source of water for the perecrystallization process (particularly regelation perecrystallization), but rainwater and icing ("naled") waters, which penetrate the snow cover from below or from the sides, and the supercooled water droplets of low clouds and fogs may also participate.

The snow cover melts from the surface, provided the heat arrives from atmospheric air and condensing water vapor, or in the layer nearest the surface (maximum thickness 10–20 cm), if the heat source is radiant energy. The only requirement imposed on melting is that more heat arrive than is lost to the deeper layers of snow and to the atmosphere: therefore, a horizontal snow cover can experience radiation melting at air temperatures as low as $-5°C$ (Kuz'min, 1947), but if the air is very dry, the heat may be used up on volatilization, and melting will not occur even at air temperatures as high as $+15°C$ (Troll, 1942).

The temperature of the lower layers of the snow is negative when melting begins. They have a "cold reserve" and warm to the melting point chiefly because of the release of latent heat during the freezing of water which percolates down from above. Hence, not all melting, by any means, results in the loss of ice. The effect of melting on porous ice rock may vary greatly, depending on the intensity and duration of melting, the initial rock structure and the possibilities and conditions of melt water runoff.

In porous ice rock, the reactions at the water-solid interface can be classified as two categories of phenomena: the first group includes the phase transitions between water and ice, regulated by the thermal energy of the material (see below) and the second, indirect group which results from the surface interaction of water and ice, consists in the change in form of the water-air interface near ice walls, i.e., in the formation of concave meniscuses (the water wets the ice) and in capillary phenomena.

Owing to the meniscus forces, the mobility of the water varies with the amount of water in the rock pores. Capillary water may exist in three states in rock (Dolgov, 1948):

(1) the discrete, immobile state, consisting in droplets bounded by concave meniscuses around the points of contact of the solid particles;

(2) the slightly mobile, beaded state, consisting of droplets connected by narrow constrictions in the continuous film on the walls of the pores; this water can be drawn up slowly from the moister sections with less curved meniscuses into drier sections with more curved meniscuses, independently of the force of gravity;

(3) the mobile state, in which the narrow pores are completely filled and the capillary suction can overcome the force of gravity up to a certain pore diameter.

The meniscus forces are weaker in the larger pores and the water passes into the gravitational state, percolating down and assuming hydrostatic pressure. When it encounters a layer relatively impermeable for water, it accumulates as an underground lake and if there is a gradient, it forms a ground-water stream with predominantly horizontal movement.

If capillary water is present, some of the pores will be filled with air, but even in pores filled with gravitational water usually there are some air bubbles "entrapped" by the plugs of capillary water, in addition to the air dissolved in the water.

The water in snow and firn moves downward because of either capillary or gravitational forces, depending on the rate and duration of melting. When the lower layers of snow are cold, intensive vaporization, diffusion and sublimation of water vapor into the lower layers of the snow will be added and if melting is slight, most of the water will be expended on these processes. This will cease if the whole layer becomes wet, because the vapor pressures of ice and water are nearly identical at 0°C.

The penetration of water into a rock with air-filled pores is called *infiltration*, in contrast to filtration in a moisture-saturated rock. In fine-grained rock, the infiltration rate is great at first, but as the pores become water-saturated it decreases until a constant value is reached, which can be determined by Darcy's law, i.e., infiltration becomes filtration. The zone of incomplete filling of the pores, the so-called "infiltration wedge," moves forward and if the water supply is cut off, the wedge expands backward and upward, due to continued infiltration from the water-saturated zone and to the tendency of water to spread uniformly throughout the moistened layer. In coarse-grained rock, the flow of water is of the turbulent type (following Smreker's law) rather than laminar. If an air seal appears below during the infiltration process, the air pressure in the rock pores will increase to a magnitude which will force the air through the water-filled pores and thus decelerate infiltration (Popov, 1950).

Ice, unlike other rocks, is profoundly affected by the infiltration of water, which changes the structure and water properties of ice, namely, its porosity, coefficient of filtration, capillarity, moisture capacity, etc. As a rule, a differentiation appears in the vertical profile of ice as it melts similar to the one observed in podsols. An eluvial-melt horizon appears at the top, where the melt water still has some heat and continues to melt the ice.[8] Farther down, in most cases, there is an equilibrium horizon with a neutral balance. Below this, there is an illuvial-freezing horizon, where the cold reserve is located and expended. This differentiation is barely perceptible during slight and brief melting, but the illuvial horizon keeps descending until it reaches a water-resistant ice layer or the bed underlying the ice rock.

Structural differences smooth out, ice crusts resorb, etc., in the eluvial horizon, while often a latent, thin, primary snow stratification appears in the illuvial horizon and then structural differentiation may occur because of the irregular freezing of the ice in rock sections of different density, cold reserve, thermal conductivity and water permeability.

The runoff of melt water, which leads to the reduction of the rock mass, does not occur until the ice stratum has melted through to the bed or to a water-resistant layer and a large enough hydraulic pressure head has formed to permit lateral filtration. Downslope, river-bed or underground runoff will occur, depending on conditions. No ice rock is lost until runoff begins; the process remains reversible and only structural changes occur after new freezing has taken place, namely, regelation perecrystallization of the ice rock (or the subsequent formation of congelation lake ice, in the case of complete melting).

Firnification

Regelation metamorphism of snow in its initial state is often observed while snow is falling from the atmosphere. If the air

---

[8] According to measurements made in the absence of direct sunlight, often the temperature of the upper, melting layer of snow is $+0.2-0.3°C$ (up to $0.5°C$). At the height of melting, S. I. Nebol'sin (1925) observed a snow temperature as high as $+4.1°C$ at the surface, $0.5-0.7°C$ at a depth of 5 cm, and only $0.0-0.1°C$ at 15 cm. Most researchers attribute this to the heating of the melt water (see, for example, Popov, 1948). However, this could also be explained by the heating of the air in the snow pores by scattered radiation that penetrates into these pores (V. M. Sokol'nikov, verbal communication).

temperature reaches the melting point or slightly exceeds it for a time during a snowfall, the peripheries of the snowflakes begin to melt. In the moist snow which forms, discrete droplets appear on the ends of the branches, corners and edges of the snowflakes, permitting them to coalesce into large clusters. After such snow freezes, its crystals become somewhat rounded, often fused into fairly strong intergrowths, but, in general, elements of the initial crystal form dominate in them. The snow does not lose these features of the original crystal form and become firn unless melting creates a continuous water film that envelops the snowflakes.

The first portions of melt water do not leave the melting layer, but are expended on the formation of a water film around the snowflakes and on capillary saturation of the pores. In this case the melt water exerts a strong influence on the snowflakes.

Regelation rounding, which occurs very rapidly during intense melting, is the basic process of the "warm" type of firnification. The projecting branches, corners and edges of the snowflakes have a somewhat lower melting point than do the central parts of the crystals and, what is most important, they have a larger specific surface and thus they melt first. The surface tension of the water film encasing the crystals has a compressive effect on the aggregate equal to $\dfrac{15.42}{r}$ mg/mm^2, where r is the radius of curvature in millimeters; consequently, water accumulates toward the central parts of the snowflakes. The only reason why freezing can occur in the concavities between the base of the branches while the projections are melting is that the melting point is not the same in all parts of the snowflake; the rounding can develop further during repeated melting and freezing. As a rule, regelation rounding, as opposed to sublimation rounding, immediately destroys all traces of idiomorphic or clastic texture and leads to the formation of almost spherical or secondary-subhedral crystals.

The snow settles intensively during rounding because the diameter of the particles becomes smaller and their centers converge and, in part, because the particles are no longer firmly bonded. The crystals which had frozen together, now, during melting, become separated by a liquid film and the wet snow becomes a very friable mass. The crystals can now turn and slip much more easily and the pores become constricted. While the surface is melting, the new snow at a depth of 20 cm settles at a rate of 80% of its initial thickness per day, or six times faster than "dry" snow; in this case, the density may increase from 0.15 to 0.25 g/cm^3 in 12 hours (Hughes and Seligman, 1939).

Collective regelation perecrystallization, which results in the growth of large grains and ordered crystallographic orientation, begins at the same time as rounding and settling. The mechanism of collective perecrystallization, like that of rounding, is based on the differences in the curvature and the size of the specific surface of the large and small grains. The less stable small grains gradually melt out, providing nourishment for the large grains. As Emden proved experimentally in 1890, this may occur even without perceptible temperature fluctuations, at a constant temperature of 0°C. He found that cryptocrystalline ice in a stationary, hermetically sealed vessel at a constant zero temperature first became a fine-grained aggregate and then, after several weeks, the grains became as large as hazel nuts.

The ordering of structure during collective regelation perecrystallization is a less comprehensible process and has been studied but little. On the basis of extensive measurements, Perutz and Seligman (1939) established that firn grains have regular crystallographic orientation with their main axes normal to the surface. Hughes *et al.* (1941) found the vertical orientation to be well defined in the upper firn layers and uniform to a depth of 14 m, where they observed a slight deviation. This orientation could not have been inherited from the snow, because it did not appear in the snow. Further, it could not have been produced during the movement of the glacier, because it was even better defined in the immobile firn fields and it could not have occurred during the settling process, because the firn grains were isometric. Perutz and Seligman associate it with the direction of the temperature gradient and assume that the development of this orientation is a function chiefly of the number of melting and freezing cycles experienced by the firn.

My investigations (see Fig. 83) have also substantiated the dominance of the vertical orientation of the main axes in regelation firn and the ice deriving from it (this orientation is much less clearly defined in regelation ice than in congelation ice). This phenomenon cannot be explained either by the orientation of the embryonic crystals or by geometric selection, since neither spontaneous crystallization nor mutually restricted crystal growth are observed during regelation perecrystallization. Only the melting out of some crystals and the isometric, nearly omnidirectional growth of others are observed. In this case, as in the case of orthotropic mutually restricted growth, perhaps those crystals survive whose main axes are oriented in the direction of the heat flux by anisotropic heat conductivity. However, it is by no means clear what role anisotropic heat conductivity might play in an irregular snow and firn lattice and how this could be reconciled with the persistence of the initially larger crystals. This subject requires further investigation.

As new water arrives during melting and as the pore sizes increase because of perecrystallization, the capillary water retention of the snow increases and the water begins to run slowly down into the next layer. Although water begins to leave the snow, at first the arrival of water from above is greater than the runoff and the amount of water in the given layer continues to increase until a certain maximum is reached. After the maximum water retention has been exceeded, the water in the given layer decreases because of continuing perecrystallization and the formation of percolation channels, even if water is being supplied steadily from above. This process of moistening, saturation, supersaturation and removal of water is repeated in turn in every layer and gradually extends downward.

The water retention of rock in general is inversely proportional to its water permeability and increases with decreasing crystal size, with increasing complexity of the crystal form and, to a certain extent, with increasing snow density. Snow retains water best at a density of 0.346–0.484 g/cm³, at an average of 0.415 g/cm³, which corresponds to a porosity of 55% (Church, 1942). Dense, fine-grained snow in thin layers can retain water amounting to more than 50% of the total weight of the rock (Bernard and Wilson, 1941), fresh snow with a density of 0.18–0.21 g/cm³ can accommodate 35–50% water, fine grained and medium-grained snow with a density of 0.25–0.32 g/cm³ can accommodate 25–35% water and coarse-grained snow with a density of 0.39–0.43 g/cm³ can accommodate 15–25% water (Kuz'min, 1948). On an average, snow retaining the largest amount of water it can by capillary forces has a density of 0.48 g/cm³, with observed variations of 0.35–0.60 g/cm³ (Oiia, 1949; Church, 1942).

After freezing through, young firn has a density of 0.35–0.60 g/cm³, which corresponds to its density as a water-saturated mixture.

The described scheme of melt water infiltration is complicated by the occurrence of negative temperatures in the underlying layer of snow. When melt water penetrates to this subzero layer of snow, the snow is heated by the freezing of the first portions of water and the release of the latent heat of crystallization. The freezing of 1 gram of water releases enough heat to warm 157.6 grams of ice 1°C; consequently, snow is heated incomparably faster in the presence of melt water than in the absence of it and only a relatively small amount of water is required. Nevertheless, when the temperatures are low and the snow is dense enough, and thus is an adequate heat conductor, the freezing water may form impermeable ice layers that will prevent infiltration. This is particularly frequent on wind crusts. Further percolation requires a sufficient rate of influx of water that has some reserve of heat which will melt the ice crust.

A thin, somewhat moist firn or ice crust forms beneath the surface of slightly melting snow with a low enough temperature in its lower parts, while above the crust there is a dark 1–2 cm interlayer of snow saturated with gravitational water. With further melting and influx of water, the entire system moves slowly downward, while a layer with a quite well defined columnar structure remains above: the ice grains are arranged in vertical columns separated by infiltration channels of melt water. Thus, after freezing there is some differentiation of the snow layer into less dense porous horizons of infiltration loss and illuvial horizons of denser firn and ice interlayers. In regions where thaws are frequent during the snow accumulation period, the snow cover has several firnified columnar horizons separated by firn-ice crusts, especially in the lower autumnal layers which acquire a characteristic stratified structure. Subsequently, the porous horizons of infiltration loss can easily become sand-snow layers.

With more intense melting, the differentiation extends to a thicker layer in the vertical profile of the snow cover. A horizon of infiltration loss forms above, where the water, heated somewhat above 0°C, melts out infiltration channels and can resorb ice interlayers up to 10 cm thick. Below, there is a layer of wet snow, in which the temperature of all three phases is 0°C, and an illuvial horizon, where the water freezes and the ice is warmed. At first, collective pere-crystallization and settling occur slowly in the middle, equilibrium zone before the minute grains melt out, but the illuvial horizon is especially active with respect to the ice formation processes. The active horizon keeps shifting upward and downward because of the "cold influx" from below (due to the cold reserves of winter freezing) and the differences in the intensity of melting. During this shifting, the density and size of the firn grains increase, eventually resulting in ice formation. Freezing from above plays a smaller role in the ice formation processes.

Strictly speaking, the regelation firn structures should be classified as anatectic; however, this would require the creation of a new terminology, since injection metamorphism deep within the earth's crust occurs under completely different conditions and forms rocks (migmatites) that have nothing in common with regelation firn, as far as structure is concerned.

Rocks which develop during "warm" ice formation differ from congelation ice only in the following: during the formation of "warm" rocks, the freezing of water depends on ready centers of crystallization, in this case the rock grains. The textures which appear under these circumstances are similar to those of congelation ice and may be characterized by corresponding terms.

Young *regelation firn* has *porous oriented allotriomorphic-granular texture* with isometric grains 0.3 mm and more in diameter, and a fairly well defined orientation of the main crystallographic axes normal to the surface of the layers. Here and there one finds sections with *hypidio-morphic-granular* texture, nearly straight boundaries at the crystal contacts and a dominance of angles close to 120°. In most cases, young firn has a density of 0.45–0.50 g/cm³, but it may vary between 0.35 and 0.60 g/cm³, depending on the density of the initial material, the cold reserve and the cold flux into the rock during surface melting. Some of the firn pores are closed by the frozen water. The newly formed hypogenous air inclusions have a characteristically intersertal arrangement and are spherical, elongated or irregular with traces of previous branchings. Usually, only very small spherical autogenous air bubbles appear within the crystals. The volume of the air bubbles reaches 5–10% of the total volume of the rock and the air pressure is close to atmospheric pressure.

The firn is stratified, often with various secondary modifications which develop while the profile is being differentiated by the formation of columnar horizons of infiltration loss, percolation channels and partial ice formation simultaneous with firnification.

Ice Formation

Regelation firn may become ice in two ways:

(1) by settling and paratectonic perecrystallization of the firn, and
(2) by infiltration and freezing of the melt water.

Under various conditions, one or the other of the processes dominates almost to the complete elimination of the other. As we shall show, the governing factor in this case is the relationship between the intensity of summer melting and winter freezing and the amount of solid precipitation deposited.

If the summer thaw can melt a considerable part of the annual snow layer and the winter freezing creates low enough temperatures in the ice layer so that the melt water will refreeze, ice formation will occur almost exclusively by infiltration and freezing, while firnification will be only a brief transitory stage and the whole ice formation process may end in a single season. However, if the melting or freezing is not intensive enough, after firnification the infiltration process will increase the firn density only slightly. Firn densification by settling goes on continuously and during subsequent melt seasons is accompanied by infiltration densification. However, even this joint action may not be effective enough and then ice formation will end with settling in a deeper zone, where percolation water from above does not freeze. If the infiltration densification does not penetrate deeper because of insufficient melting, ice formation will end at negative temperatures, in the cold firn. However, if infiltration densification ceases because the freezing has not been intensive enough, ice formation by settling will end at the melting point, in "warm" firn, through which water percolates and runs off along the channels and cracks below the ice. Ice formation is slow in both cases and decreases as the participation of infiltration and the freezing of melt water decreases.

Settling and paratectonic perecrystallization of firn. After the first rapid settling, which is linked with rounding of the snowflakes, settling in the regelation firn may continue in the "warm," wet melted state and in the cold, frozen state. The settling process in the cold, frozen state, i.e., in winter and spring in the zone of annual temperature fluctuations and below it in regions with a cold regime, does not differ in the slightest from the settling of unmelted firn. There can be a substantial difference only in regions of "warm" ice formation, where shear stress and downslope movement usually occur in the firn, in addition to compression. Then, when densification occurs and the structural freedom of the crystals is reduced, the processes of deformation and paratectonic recrystallization of the firn take on the same character as those of ice.

Settling and movement of melting firn have much in common with these same processes in snow and differ completely from the movement of dense frozen firn and ice. The grains have great structural freedom even when the firn is quite dense, because of the water film which separates the grains. Therefore, in firn both settling and downhill creep are caused by the independent movement (slipping and rotation) of the grains and of whole groups of grains with respect to each other. This was proved by observation of rows and grids of stakes inserted in the firn, which revealed a random backward and forward motion after just 4 days (Hughes *et al.*, 1941).

In the Alps, wet firn of density 0.4 g/cm³ at a depth of 2 m below the surface settled at an average rate of 0.23% of the initial thickness per day, thus 20 times faster than in Greenland in dry snow of the same density and under the same load. In summer (100 days) the densification amounted to 0.12 g/cm³, i.e., the density rose from 0.40 to 0.52 g/cm³. The rock settles considerably more slowly when infiltration ice, which is practically uncompressed, accumulates in the firn layer. The rate of settling at depths of 1 m to 7 m in the

West Ice (Vestfonna) of North East Land (Nordaustlandet), in a firn layer of the same density as above but with many layers of ice, varied from 0.002 to 0.004% of the initial layer thickness per day, i.e., at a rate several times slower than even that of "dry" snow of the same density.

The rate of differential movement in melting firn (measured by the displacement of the stakes) near the surface down a 35° slope was 1 mm/day per 1 m taken normal to the surface (the upper layers moved faster than the lower layers), with a general rate of movement of 5 cm/day on the glacier surface (Perutz and Seligman, 1939). On a slope with an 8° dip, the rate of differential movement in the firn amounted to 0.35 mm per day per 1 m of depth, with a general rate of movement of 7 cm/day on the surface.

Paratectonic perecrystallization does not promote the growth of some grains at the expense of others, because the movement of the grains of wet firn is differential and during this movement the stresses in the neighboring grains change in favor of one or another crystal. This also applies to "cold" firn, but, as far as we can judge from the available data, only as long as the "cold" firn settles without experiencing shear deformation, while in wet firn it is equally applicable to flow downslope. Therefore, the lack of grain growth is a characteristic feature of the densification of firn by settling; grain growth takes place exclusively as a result of the infiltration and freezing of melt water.

The differential movements of the individual firn grains also disrupt the primary ordered crystallographic orientation. The principal axes of the grains of young firn near the surface are oriented primarily normal to the surface; there is some departure from the vertical position at a depth of 14 m, while at a depth of 23 m, before the firn becomes ice, the main axes of the crystals run in almost all possible directions (Hughes *et al.*, 1941).

Before becoming ice, "warm" firn experiences the following basic structural changes: its crystallographic orientation changes from ordered to random owing to differential movement, it becomes denser and its grains become larger owing to the infiltration and freezing of melt water.

The infiltration and freezing of melt water. The rate of infiltration ice formation depends on the saturability of the freezing rock, i.e., on the relationship between the rate of arrival of water and the presence of a cold reserve or the rate of influx of cold into the rock.

If the temperature is low and the melting beneath the melt layer is brief, the water in the pores will freeze quickly, clog the pores partially or completely and form a layer of firn or ice, i.e., a melt crust.

"Ice glands" with snowflakes welded to them may be found in the friable snow beneath the melt crust. These ice glands are frozen drops and whole streamlets of water which had fallen or drained through openings in the crust into the snow to a depth of several tens of centimeters. The formation of ice crusts on the snow surface, caused by the freezing of supercooled droplets of low clouds or fog, is a phenomenon similar to the rapid formation of ice by a large cold reserve. Apparently this is the way in which interlayers of ice form in snow when melting is impossible, e.g., the layers of ice amid the winter layers of snow in Antarctica (Wade, 1945).

However, in most cases the rock's own cold reserve is not sufficient to change it rapidly into ice. After the rock has been heated to the melting point, ice can accrue only by the influx of cold from other layers of the rock. If water infiltrates into the deeper layers, there will be no temperature gradient and the cold will not be able to enter either from above or from below. Therefore, the descending water can form ice only before the rock is heated through, by using its own supply of cold. Densification of the rock by means of its own cold reserve can be represented as follows:

$$\Delta\delta = \frac{\delta ct}{L},$$

where δ is the initial density of the rock; c is the specific heat of the ice (about 0.5 cal/g°C), t is the negative temperature of the rock in °C; and L is the latent heat of fusion (about 80 cal/g).

Thus, firn of density 0.500 g/cm³ with a temperature of -10°C reaches a density of 0.531 g/cm³ when heated to 0°C by the melt water.

Further densification of the rock cannot occur until the downward movement of the melt water is halted by a cold flux from below or above, but then ice accretion is limited by the presence of water in the rock, and this is a function of the water retention of the rock.

By the water retention of a rock one usually understands its capacity to retain a certain amount of the so-called "suspended" water, i.e., the water maintained in capillaries with a hydraulic gradient close to unity; in other words, the water can descend vertically. The amount of "suspended" water which the melting snow can hold determines the density of the young firn, which varies from 0.35–0.60 g/cm³.

The water retention of a rock depends on the size and total volume of its pores. During firnification and ice formation, as the crystals become larger and the density increases, the pore size increases but the porosity of the rock decreases, therefore the water retention decreases rapidly. In firn with rounded grains, after the grain diameter exceeds 2–2.5 mm, the "suspended" capillary water can no longer fill the pores entirely and remains almost exclusively in the beaded and discrete states on the walls of pores and on the grain contacts. Therefore, after melting and infiltration have ceased, freezing of the firn does not increase its density to any great extent. whether the freezing comes from below or from above. Densification accompanied by the growth of the firn grains takes place basically when the firn is heated by melt water in summer, not during the subsequent winter freezing. For example, in the firn of the Isachsen Plateau (Isachsenfonna) on Spitsbergen, 13.9 g of water froze per 1 cm^2 per year during the summer warming, while only 2.2 g froze during the winter freezing (Sverdrup, 1935).

Repeated annual melting and freezing (which is much more frequent in the thin upper layer, because of the diurnal and aperiodic temperature fluctuations in summer) leads to the gradual growth of the firn grains and to its densification. Since the greatest freezing is observed in the layers close to the surface, grain growth and densification are most rapid there; grain growth and infiltration densification of the firn decelerate with depth in the less intensely freezing deep layers.

The thickness of the active layer (i.e., the zone in which the melt water freezes) and its relationship to the thickness of the annual firn layer, as well as the magnitude of freezing, are very important factors in the rate of gradual infiltration ice formation. The annual firn increment in the upper reaches of the Great Aletsch glacier in the Swiss Alps is 3–5 m and the cold wave penetrates 15 m; thus the firn remains in the active zone 4–5 years and experiences a corresponding number of melting and freezing cycles (Hughes and Seligman, 1939). The annual firn increment on the Isachsen Plateau, Spitsbergen, is 40 cm and the depth of penetration of the cold wave about 10 m; therefore, the firn passes through 25 cycles of melting and freezing and experiences considerably greater infiltration densification and grain growth. If the annual firn increment under these conditions decreases to 15 cm, the transformation from firn to ice will be complete at a depth of 5 m owing to infiltration alone (Sverdrup, 1935).

Firn grains grow very slowly in the Alps, because of the relatively slight freezing and the brief period during which the firn remains in the active zone: at the end of the first season the grains reach an average size of 0.5–1.0 mm, after 4–5 years, only 1–2 mm (Hughes *et al.*, 1941; Streiff-Becker, 1936).

In regions of cold climate, where the snow cover freezes at temperatures as low as $-30°$ and $-35°C$ and where the intensive cold flux from below continues all summer, the firn grains often reach a size of 5–6 mm in a single, brief melt season, and if the firn becomes ice, the grains become still larger.

Thus, grain growth and gradual infiltration densification, which is fairly uniform throughout the mass, are caused by the freezing of descending melt water during the warming of the firn. The gradual nature of the process and its uniformity are associated with the small cold reserve of the rock and the slight water retention of the firn.

However, the water retention increases sharply when the hydraulic gradient decreases considerably. When the gradient is zero, i.e., when drainage is impossible, all the water remains in the rock until melting is complete. The change in the density of the mixture and the change in the amount of water in snow which had an initial density of 0.10 g/cm³ at 0°C with the arrival of heat is depicted in Fig. 79.

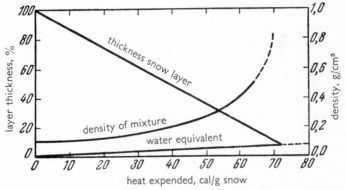

FIG. 79. Diagram of the change of the phase composition and density of snow with an initial density of 0.10 g/cm³ as melting increases, without runoff. (After W. T. Wilson, 1941.)

If the snow or firn is underlain by a more or less horizontal water-impermeable layer for a considerable distance, the level of the melt water will rise as melting increases, until the water finds a drainage route along the snow surface. Cases have been recorded (Lütschg, 1926, p. 171) where a layer of snow 2.5–3 m thick, situated on a plain, was saturated with water to a depth of 2.4 m; only a layer of granular snow about 20 cm thick rose above the water level and the channel of a powerful stream of melt water had cut through this layer. The temperature of the stream of melt water was $+1.2°C$, its rate of flow 1 m/sec and its volume of flow 175 l/sec. Such snow and firn swamps with lakes and streams of melt water form every summer on the level, crack-free parts of glacier surfaces. The crystals lose all cohesion and a foot traveler, sometimes even a skier, sinks deep into this water-ice slush. Snow swamps are found in all latitudes, including the high polar regions, but reach their highest development on tropical glaciers.

On gentle slopes, after a sufficient amount of water has collected, runoff begins beneath the firn along the surface of the water-resistant layer. At first the water filters evenly over the entire surface, at a rate on the order of several centimeters an hour, then a complex network of fine channels and stream beds develops beneath the firn and the rate of runoff increases to several meters per hour and more. On the steeper slopes, during the intensive melting of the snow and firn layer, water often accumulates in such quantities that when it breaks through it forms snow and firn "flash floods" similar to mudflows in dry mountain regions after a rain. The formation of water-bearing layers within the snow layer above the soil or above the wind crust on the slopes causes wet-snow avalanches.

Above the gently sloping water-resistant layers, the snow and firn may retain so much water that the mixture will reach a density of 0.90 g/cm^3. The firn pores in the water-bearing layers are almost completely filled with water that has a very large number of entrapped air bubbles. Ice forms immediately when such a mixture freezes.

The initial differences in the density and water permeability of the various layers of snow tend to increase in the illuvial horizon. Even the compact layers, which are semipermeable for water, become denser more rapidly when heated by melt water, because they have a greater thermal capacity per unit volume and are less porous, while the wind and melt crusts are water impermeable layers from the very beginning. Water-saturated snow or firn becomes ice after the melting ceases and new freezing from above begins.

Most often ice freezes above the ice crust, at the boundary of the snow cover and last year's firn, but thinner layers of ice may also form within the annual layer of snow which has become firn. Since the snow stratification is irregular and the properties of the snow differ even within a single layer, ice freezes unevenly in the firn layer and this irregularity increases with time. The ice layers rarely extend over great distances, but usually are lenticular with irregular lower and, especially, upper surfaces. The configuration of the lower surface depends solely on the attitude of the water-impermeable crust and thus is quite even and the upper surface usually has a number of projections and depressions (up to several tens of centimeters high), caused by the irregular freezing of the ice. In places the ice layers break off and become dense firn with isolated bodies of ice. Such areas of dense firn and ice abut the ice layers from above and below. In places the horizontal ice lenses are connected by vertical ice columns, while in other places amid the firn there are quite irregular ice bodies that enter the densified firn. On the other hand, small channels and cavities washed out by the streams of melt water appear above the ice layers and within the firn. Thus, the firn layer as a whole has stratified structure.

Most of the melt water freezes annually on the upper water-resistant layer, while a progressively smaller amount freezes in each layer moving downward, because the water retention, the freezing and the amount of melt water decrease with depth. Thus, the infiltration densification of the firn is most uniform and the ice formation in individual layers is most rapid in the upper part of the profile and decreases with depth. However, the lower layers experience a greater number of melting and freezing cycles so that the firn layer becomes denser and the ice layers thicker with depth, while the firn intervals between the ice layers become thinner. In regions of intensive infiltration ice formation with a quite thick active zone, the ice layers fuse at a certain depth and ice formation is completed essentially by infiltration. However, as a rule, individual firn lenses remain in the ice in this case. They are protected against the influx of melt water from above by the impermeable layers of ice. At a greater depth these firn lenses become ice by means of settling and paratectonic perecrystallization.

The situation is different in regions of weak infiltration ice formation. In moving firn, differential movement of firn grains and their intergrowths occurs simultaneously with the growth of layers of infiltration ice. These movements also involve crystals separated by water films and belonging to thin layers of ice which may subsequently be resorbed and degraded into porous firn. The results of this process are evident in the firn layer below the active zone, where infiltration ice formation ceases. There the number of ice layers decreases with depth and only the thicker layers remain.

As infiltration ice formation increases, more and more snow at the base of the annual layer and above the crusts becomes ice during the first year and a smaller and smaller amount remains as firn until the subsequent infiltration seasons. In the final analysis, under certain conditions all the snow may become ice in a single season by the infiltration and freezing of melt water in the pores. However, this type of ice formation is widely distributed only in a cold regime.

This can be explained by the fact that the heat capacity and thermal conductivity of the layer increase as the amount of ice in the cross section increases and its water-permeability decreases. In this connection, the freezing of infiltration ice is concentrated more and more in the upper layers of the profile, basically at the boundary between the snow cover and the first ice layer. The warm summer temperature wave can no longer be propagated downward by the infiltration of melt water and the release of the latent heat of crystallization, but is transmitted by ordinary conductive heat transfer, as is the winter cold wave. If a continuous, solid layer of ice had formed in the preceding year, all the melt water will gather above it, permeating last year's firn residue and the snow layer, and lateral runoff of the melt water must begin.

Under conditions of a warm regime, where the winter cold wave is damped by the summer warm wave, the freezing of new ice onto the surface of last year's ice due to the cold flux from below, will continue but a short time at the beginning of the melt season and will be compensated for by subsequent melting; however, so much time passes before autumn freezing begins that the melt water manages to drain off. In other words, under conditions of a warm regime the horizon of infiltration loss reaches the surface of last year's ice during the summer. Therefore, new ice cannot freeze onto the old by the influx of cold from below. Only in years with a cold summer can a layer of new ice freeze onto the surface of the old peripherally melted ice below the firn zone. Such phenomena have been observed on the temperate glaciers of Norway (Ahlmann and Tveten, 1923).

However, in a cold regime low temperatures persist all summer slightly below the ice surface, thus during periods of slight melting, infiltration ice forms in the lower part of the melting snow cover because of the cold flux from below. The snow melts from above, melt water accumulates on the surface of the layer of cold year-old ice and freezes there and only part of the melt water manages to run off during the periods of intensified melting. Melting causes the snow surface to subside, but the surface of the infiltration ice rises because of the freezing of the water-firn gruel from below. In colder years, thin patches of coarse-grained firn remain above the ice, while in warmer years the melting surface of the snow and the growing surface of the ice meet toward the end of the season. The snow disappears and the exposed, newly formed ice melts during the remainder of the summer. However, since the cold flux from below continues, some of the melt water which runs off along the surface refreezes, but now as extruded congelation ice. A thinner and more distinct stratification is obtained under these conditions than in firn with ice layers.

Structure of the firn and ice. Thus, under various conditions, the processes of "warm" metamorphic ice formation lead to the formation of layers of ice rock of quite diverse structure. The main differences lie in the composition of the layers of the two main types of ice, infiltration-recrystallization and infiltration ice. These layers differ in thickness and alternate with one another in various percentage relationships.

We shall apply the term *infiltration-recrystallization* to ice which has formed from regelation firn by two alternating processes: first by gradual infiltration densification of the firn, accompanied by grain growth, and second by settling and paratectonic perecrystallization, or by the joint and simultaneous influence of both these processes, with prevalence of the second. Paratectonic perecrystallization may include both recrystallization in cold firn and regelation recrystallization in "warm" firn, but the structural differences resulting from the two processes are so insignificant, insofar as we know at present, that they need not be classified separately.

Infiltration ice is ice formed from regelation firn by accelerated infiltration ice formation without substantial settling and paratectonic perecrystallization, i.e., by the filling of firn pores with melt water above water-resistant areas and by freezing of the water. In a vertical profile, infiltration ice may alternate with extruded congelation ice and with one more type, which we shall call *infiltration congelation ice*. This is the product of the freezing of water above an impermeable area, in the water-bearing layers of the eluvial horizon, where the firn was subjected to intense melting and thus where the orthotropic growth of crystals, so characteristic of congelation ice, occurs.

We shall use the term *infiltration firn* to designate the old firn which, after regelation rounding and collective perecrystallization, experienced infiltration densification, grain growth and differential movements of the grains during settling and flow.

In contrast to young regelation firn, *infiltration firn* has random, *porous allotriomorphic-granular texture* with grains larger than those of young firn, namely, grains up to 8–10 mm in diameter. Its density varies from approximately 0.40–0.60 to 0.83–0.86 g/cm^3. There is no definite line of demarcation between young regelation firn and old infiltration firn and thus this subdivision is somewhat arbitrary.

Infiltration-recrystallization ice has *random allotriomorphic-granular texture*. Strictly speaking, one should distinguish between the allotriomorphic-granular texture of infiltration-regelation ice and the granoblastic texture of infiltration-recrystallization ice, but as far as we can tell at present, there is no practical way to distinguish between them.

Infiltration-recrystallization ice is comparatively fine-grained, with crystals approximately 4–10 mm in diameter. This type of ice has a density of 0.82–0.84 g/cm³, which corresponds to a volume of 8.4–10.5% air in the enclosed air bubbles. The complex, branching air bubbles, which are isolated remnants of firn pores (Fig. 80) are the most characteristic feature of infiltration-recrystallization ice.

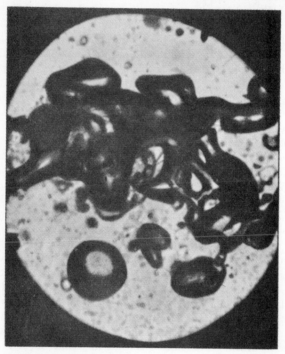

FIG. 80. Shape of air bubbles that are remnants of firn pores in infiltration-recrystallization ice. × 15. Photographed by B. I. Vtiurin.)

The bubbles of infiltration-recrystallization ice are wider than those of similarly branching bubbles of primary-recrystallization ice and become wider as the grains grow. As the firn skeletal structure of the firn becomes coarser and larger-grained, the pores in it and the hypogenous bubbles deriving from these pores become larger. In addition to the branching inclusions, there are also very fine, spherical, elongated and irregular bubbles, some of which are of hypogenous origin and some of autogenous origin (released from the melt water during freezing). Branching and other hypogenous air inclusions in infiltration-recrystallization ice are always arranged intersertally, while minute autogenous bubbles are found within the crystals (the poikilitic intergrowth type). The air pressure in the bubbles is somewhat higher than atmospheric pressure at a given height above sea level, because of the compression of the bubbles enclosed by the crystals.

Infiltration ice has *oriented allotriomorphic-granular texture* (Figs. 81 and 82). All its characteristics are associated with ice formation by the freezing of water which has filled the pores of the crystalline

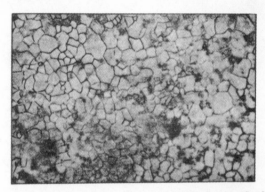

Fig. 81. Allotriomorphic-granular texture of infiltration ice. Surface of the layer. Actual size. (Photograph by N. V. Cherepanov.)

skeletal structure of the firn. Spontaneous crystallization does not occur, but there is no characteristic forced crystallization of orthotropic growth either, since the existing firn grains act as centers of crystallization. Therefore, the size of the infiltration ice crystals is determined by the size and closeness of packing of the firn grains (or of the snow, from which the firn is formed), while the irregular isometric shape of the crystals is determined by their arrangement with respect to each other. Fine-grained ice develops during the freezing of fine-grained snow drenched with melt water. The coarser-grained the firn from which the infiltration ice forms, the larger will be the infiltration ice crystals formed from it. Grains may also grow in the ice itself by collective regelation perecrystallization, if the given layer appears alternately in the melting eluvial horizon and in the freezing illuvial horizon. The maximum observed diameter of infiltration ice grains is 2–2.5 cm, the minimum, 0.5–1.0 mm. Owing to the difference in crystal sizes, infiltration ice is stratified and often this stratification is of the annual type and sometimes even thinner.

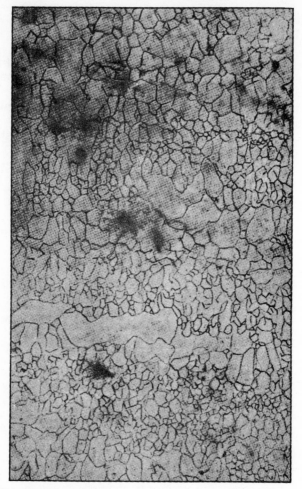

FIG. 82. Allotriomorphic-granular texture of infiltration ice. Vertical section.
Actual size. (Photograph by N. V. Cherepanov.)

Hughes *et al.* (1941) showed that infiltration ice has a crystallographic orientation in which the main axes are always normal to the
surface of the layers. Actually, however, a greater scatter of directions of the main axes is observed, including a position parallel to the
plane of the layers. This is associated with the corresponding crystallographic orientation of the firn grains, which acted as centers of
crystallization. Further, there is a clearly defined, dominant
orientation of the axes normal to the layers (Fig. 83).

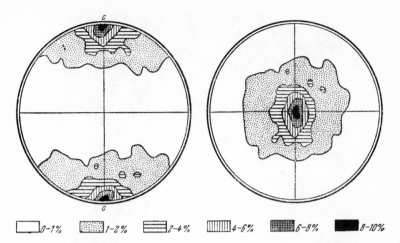

$\square$ *0–1%* $\boxed{\vdots}$ *1–2%* $\boxed{\equiv}$ *2–4%* $\boxed{\parallel}$ *4–6%* $\boxed{\boxplus}$ *6–8%* $\blacksquare$ *8–10%*

FIG. 83. Stereogram of the crystallographic orientation of infiltration ice (100 crystals).

Infiltration ice contains autogenous air inclusions of the oriented and poikilitic intergrowth types and also large spherical, irregular or flat horizontal intersertal inclusions. Bubbles of the oriented intergrowth type are not always found (only during rapid freezing), but they have such a peculiar shape that a find of such bubbles can be used as a definite criterion for identifying ice of infiltration origin. Infiltration ice always freezes normal to the surface and the freezing is directed either upward or downward. However, firn grains are the centers of crystallization; hence, if freezing is rapid and the water-drenched pores are wide enough, thin tubular or filamental bubbles will first grow radially in all directions from the center and then all of them will turn either upward or downward for a certain distance, depending on the general direction of freezing. Characteristic clusters of curved filamental bubbles will form, as if growing from a single root and adapted to a single monocrystal.

The large spherical and irregular intersertal inclusions are air bubbles trapped in the firn pores which formed during infiltration (hypogenous) or during freezing (autogenous). In continuous layers of infiltration ice, which accrue from year to year without firn interlayers, freezing occurs basically from below, but often simultaneously from above as well. The air separated out from the solution strives to float upward in the pores. Some of the bubbles are trapped at various levels, but most of them are stopped by the ice crust which has frozen only from above, and beneath which there is a horizon replete with

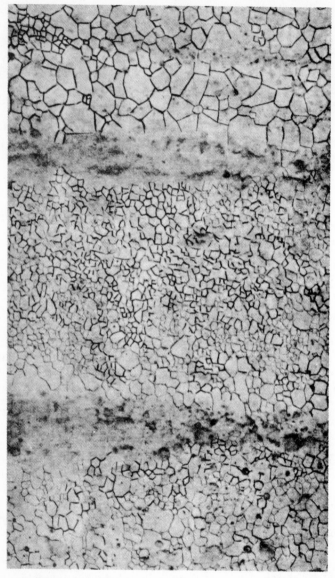

Fig. 84. Texture of infiltration ice (vertical section). The bubble layers form the boundaries of the annual layers of ice. Actual size. (Photograph by N. V. Cherepanov.)

large bubbles. Sometimes the large bubbles in the largest pores and melt cavities are flattened horizontally by hydrostatic pressure. Layers of this type may form within the annual layers, at the temporary water level of the pores in one of the stages of melting that has been cut short by chilling, but as a rule the most distinct and largest "bubble" layers are adapted to the tops of the annual layers of ice (Fig. 84). Bubble layers at the boundaries of the annual layers may also be caused by the melt cavities and channels which have been rinsed by the runoff water and then are saved from complete drenching by the melt crust of ice which forms above them. Thus, the ice has distinct stratification caused by the difference in grain sizes.

The transformation of snow into ice during a single melt season has often been observed in the Alps and the Pyrenees (Devaux, 1927; Bossolasco, 1930), and the density of the infiltration ice in these regions is usually about 0.89 g/cm³. Our observations show that the density of infiltration ice may differ with the degree of filling of the pores with water. The filling of the pores increases as the temperature of the melt water increases and the firn remelts in part, as freezing becomes slower and air can escape upward (provided freezing takes place exclusively from below). Most often the density of infiltration ice is 0.880–0.890 g/cm³, the volume of air inclusions 3–4%, and the observed extremes are 0.860 and 0.905 g/cm³, which corresponds to a volume of air inclusions of 1.3–6.2%. The air pressure in infiltration

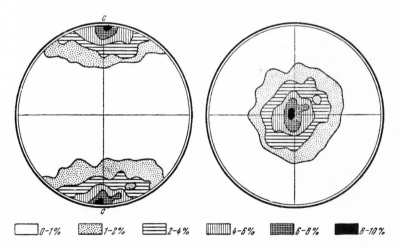

$\boxed{}$ *0-1%* $\boxed{}$ *1-2%* $\boxed{}$ *2-4%* $\boxed{}$ *4-6%* $\boxed{}$ *6-8%* $\boxed{}$ *8-10%*

FIG. 85. Stereogram of the crystallographic orientation of infiltration congelation ice (57 crystals).

ice is close to the atmospheric pressure at the given hypsometric level.

The *infiltration congelation ice* mentioned above is the densest variety of infiltration ice and has the least volume of air inclusions (density 0.900–0.905 g/cm^3).

If, during the period of intensive melting, the eluvial horizon should reach the water-impermeable layer above which melt water with excess heat circulates for a time, the firn in this horizon will melt through. When a water-drenched melt horizon of this type freezes from below, only forced crystallization from the firn grains will occur in it, but the laws of oriented orthotropic crystal growth will also become partially operative due to the considerable intervals between the firn grains. Orthotropic growth has practically no effect on the degree of ordering of the crystallographic orientation, because geometric selection cannot proceed far. Therefore, infiltration congelation ice has approximately the same type of orientation as infiltration ice (Fig. 85). However, the results of orthotropic growth are manifested fairly distinctly in the shape of the crystals, which become appreciably elongated in the direction of growth. Consequently, infiltration congelation ice has approximately columnar *hypidiomorphic-granular* texture, similar to the texture of rapidly crystallized congelation ice, but in this case the crystals may become large (Figs. 86 and 87).

Owing to uneven melting along the layers, hypidiomorphic-granular texture may alternate with allotriomorphic-granular texture and large crystals may alternate with small ones (Fig. 88), so that infiltration congelation ice is merely a local variant of infiltration ice. The columnar crystals in layers of infiltration congelation ice, which form from snow during a single melt season, may become 7 cm long (see Fig. 86), and the isometric crystals may become 4.5 cm in diameter (see Fig. 88).

Ice which forms from the "warm" type of ice metamorphism is stratified, with an alternation of structurally and texturally different layers of infiltration-recrystallization, infiltration and infiltration congelation ice, sometimes with extruded congelation ice as well. As the role of infiltration increases in the ice formation processes and the role of settling decreases, the ice stratification becomes thinner and more distinct, density increases and the number of air inclusions decreases.

The concentration of solid mineral and organic impurities at the boundary layers (which had acted as melt surfaces) is one of the secondary reasons why the products of the "warm" type of ice formation have more distinct stratification. The melting snow and firn

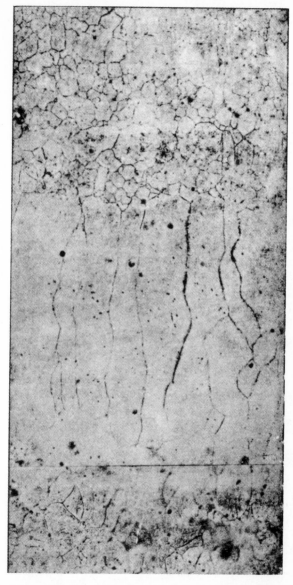

Fɪɢ. 86. Layer of columnar infiltration congelation ice in a layer of infiltration ice (section in the direction of freezing). Actual size. (Photograph by N. V. Cherepanov.)

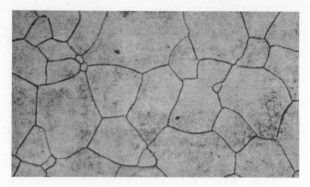

FIG. 87. Texture of the same layer of infiltration congelation ice as in Fig. 86, in a section perpendicular to the direction of freezing. Actual size. (Photograph by N. V. Cherepanov.)

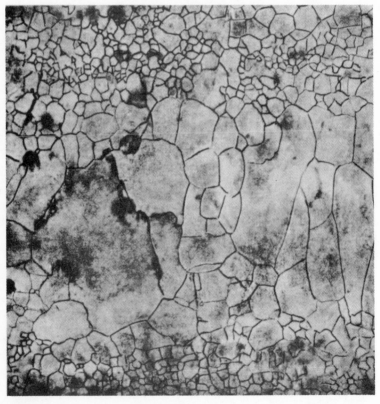

FIG. 88. Pockets of infiltration congelation ice amid the infiltration ice. Actual size. (Photograph by N. V. Cherepanov.)

act as a kind of filter which retains even the fine suspensions in the melt water of the surface layer and thus create these concentrations of impurities.

Infiltration and infiltration congelation ice play a substantial role in the structure not only of glaciers but also of hydroeffusives and the ice covers of water basins, where they form because of the saturation of the snow cover by underground, river, lake and even sea water which discharges onto the surface (Molchanov, 1925).

CHAPTER XIV

THE DYNAMIC METAMORPHISM OF ICE

The processes of ice metamorphism, i.e., the metamorphism of ice in the petrographic sense (a rock without pores), are almost exclusively dynamometamorphic. In order to examine the processes of the dynamic metamorphism of ice and their influence on structure, first one must know the sources, spatial distribution and nature of the deformations experienced by natural ice bodies.

STRESSES AND MOVEMENT IN NATURAL ICE BODIES

The stresses experienced by ice rock under natural conditions are caused, basically, by three factors:

(1) external dynamic influences;

(2) temperature fluctuations;

(3) the weight of the ice itself (and of the rocks overlying it).

Under specific conditions, each of these factors creates stresses sufficient to metamorphose ice. The magnitude, rate of increase and type of load determines whether the deformations will be elastoplastic or brittle. The elastoplastic deformations do not disrupt the continuity of the rock and, besides creating particular tectonic structures, lead to paratectonic perecrystallization of the ice.[1]

Brittle deformations, which disturb the continuity of the rock, are classified among the processes of dislocation metamorphism. In the case of strong plastic deformations, they correspond to the phenomena of regelation dynamic metamorphism, which are also

---

[1] Static stresses without deformation cannot cause appreciable rearrangement of structure, since perecrystallization soon leads to relaxation of stresses and the point of application of force must be shifted in order to renew the stresses and continue the process, i.e., there must be movement, deformation. This remark is certainly appropriate, in view of the tendency of geologists to examine the processes of perecrystallization of rock within the earth's crust (and thus inaccessible to direct observation) separately from the movement of masses in the earth's crust, which is the other aftereffect of directed pressure.

accompanied by a temporary disturbance of the continuity of the solid phase as it transforms into the liquid phase.

External dynamic influences do not play a leading role in the processes of dynamic metamorphism unless the ice rock is in a mobile medium, viz., the ice cover of water. Wind, agitation and flow (and, in the case of sea ice, tidal phenomena as well) are the main external influences on the ice of the hydrosphere. In ice that is initially immobile, these influences give rise to tensile and bending stresses and to tangential compression. In floating, drifting ice the tangential compression is increased substantially by the kinetic energy of the ice floes, which accumulates the energy of the external force in the time period required to attain the corresponding rate of motion. Furthermore, as the drifting ice is compressed, the load slowly changes from a nearly static one to a rapidly increasing dynamic load.

The various types of dislocation metamorphism are the main product of the external dynamic influences, but small plastic deformations, viz., the formation of gentle folds, can also occur in the case of tangential compression with a slowly increasing load. Intensive folding in the absence of hydrostatic pressure always leads to fracturing. Crack formation, which is the usual reaction of ice to tension, fracturing, crushing and hummocking under tangential compression are widespread phenomena of dislocation metamorphism.

Temperature fluctuations. Temperature fluctuations cause volumetric contraction and expansion of rocks, leading to complex, intense tensile stresses combined with slight flexure and cleavage. As a rule, compressive stresses do not stem directly from a thermal change of volume, but are always associated with the freezing of water in the rock.

The stresses resulting directly from expansion or contraction are adapted to the layer of temperature fluctuations, to a depth of 10–20 m below the diurnal surface, and they decrease abruptly in the first few meters. Stresses, particularly tensile stresses, appear in this layer every time the cold temperature wave penetrates deep into the rock. They lead to the formation of frost cracks in the ice cover of water, in glaciers and in frozen rock (ground).

When the warm wave propagates, the cracks usually close again and no perceptible pressure is created. The situation is different when the open cracks fill with water before closing and become ice veins. Then, during the subsequent expansion, the veins act as wedges and a tangential stress, which may become quite strong, appears in the rock. Such stresses appear during the spring expansion of the ice cover of water and during the summer warming of glaciers and frozen rock (ground). In glaciers, these stresses provide an additional impetus for movement and do not act independently, but in plastic, fine-grained frozen rock, in which perennial veins develop, tangential pressure exerts a considerable influence on both the enclosing rock (ground) and the ice.

When water freezes in a closed system, the external ice shell experiences considerable tensile, bending and cleavage stresses, which lead to swelling and fracture. The ice and the air included in the ice of a central nucleus are under great pressure; consequently, ice extracted from the central nucleus is weak and crumbles under slight pressure, but no traces of deformation and optic anomalies can be detected, because the pressure has been hydrostatic.

The natural weight of the ice. When lateral expansion is impossible, the natural weight of the ice will merely compress the ice, but in an unbalanced system it may lead to a complex combination of stresses and corresponding deformations.

The vertical pressure p, created by the weight of the ice at depth z below the surface, is

$$p = \delta z$$

where δ is the density of the ice.

If the relationship between pressure and deformation is assumed to be linear, the coefficient of lateral pressure will be

$$\epsilon = \frac{\sigma}{1 - \sigma}$$

The Poisson coefficient σ for glacier ice is 0.361 (Brockamp and Mothes, 1930), and $\epsilon = 0.565$. Consequently, according to the above assumption, 56.5% of the vertical pressure in the ice would be transmitted horizontally and the lateral pressure p_1 at depth z would be

$$p_1 = 0.565\delta z.$$

Actually, when the pressure increases, the deformation of ice does not increase linearly but with increasing velocity; therefore, at a certain depth the pressure in the ice will be transmitted hydrostatically. As yet, the change in the coefficient of lateral pressure in ice with depth has not been investigated quantitatively. Observations of the deformation of a tunnel in glacier ice which is at the melting point show that hydrostatic pressure is attained, in practice, at a depth of just 35 m below the surface, but apparently the ice at this site had been subjected to a pressure that exceeded the vertical pressure, since it was in a zone of longitudinal compression (Haefeli, 1951).

At temperatures of 0° to −1°C, hydrostatic pressure results in an average ice compression of

$$\Delta V = 34 \times 10^{-6} \, pV \, \text{cm}^3,$$

where p is the pressure in kg/cm² and V is the initial volume.

In contrast to snow and firn, in which most of the air is forced out during compression, the air in bubbles under pressure in ice is compressed according to the Boyle-Mariotte law, i.e., incomparably more than the ice itself.

The pressure and viscosity of ice. To understand the processes of ice movement, it is important to note that hydrostatic pressure does not affect the viscosity coefficient of ice. The opposite opinion is widely held, but usually its proponents do not distinguish carefully enough between the quite different principles involved in the increase of ice plasticity under hydrostatic pressure, namely: (1) the smaller chance of brittle deformation, because of the opposition to lateral expansion and (2) the attendant extension of the range of plastic deformations to higher pressures at the expense of brittle deformations; and (3) the magnitude of the oriented pressure required to attain a given rate of plastic deformation. As the hydrostatic pressure increases, brittle deformations generally do not appear until the ice actually melts, but this does not mean that plastic deformation under the influence of oriented pressure would take place more easily under these conditions than in the absence of hydrostatic pressure.

In unbalanced systems, plastic deformations of ice increase with depth below the surface; however, this does not occur because the viscosity of ice decreases under hydrostatic pressure, but simply because the directed pressures exerted on it by the weight of the overlying layer increase. The viscosity coefficient of ice that has been subjected to very large hydrostatic pressure does not decrease in the least; in fact, Bridgman's measurements show that it even increases slightly.

Viscosity can decrease under pressure only in "warm" ice, because of its "adiabatic" water content; 86% of the reduction of volume of "warm" ice under pressure is due to the compression of the ice itself and only 14% ($4.51 \times 10^{-6} \, pV$) is due to melting. On this basis, Hess (1937) held that the "adiabatic" water does not even compensate for the influence of densification. However, a contrary opinion holds that liquid water, even when present in only small quantities, exerts a considerable influence on the viscosity of ice. According to Haefeli (1946, 1948), the main role of water is to transfer hydrostatic pressure. However, it is difficult to say to what extent this factor could reduce the viscosity of ice that has a maximum water content of a few percent at depths of hundreds of meters, where the coefficient of lateral pressure even without this factor is close to unity. Evidently, water can play a larger role as a lubricant during differential movements in the ice. For example, there can be no doubt that the viscosity of ice decreases as temperature increases (this is particularly intense near the melting point), because it promotes internal gliding along the basal planes of the crystals. However, in this case the important thing is the actual possibility of the appearance of water between the friction surfaces, not the quantity of water at the crystal boundaries, since structural data indicate that the basis for movement of "warm" ice is internal gliding along the basal planes of the crystals and not intergranular adaptation and movement. Therefore, in emphasizing the difference between the viscosity of "cold" and "warm" ice, one may speak of the rigid crust of "cold" ice floating on a plastic core of "warm" ice, but one can scarcely attribute such a differentiation to the "warm" ice itself. At any rate, no special significance can be attributed to this factor until a quantitative study has been made of the influence of pressure on the viscosity of warm ice.

Unbalanced systems. In nature, the accumulation or loss of ice results in unbalanced systems, i.e., systems in which the pressure of the weight of the ice is not balanced on all sides by a corresponding resistance and, consequently, systems in which the ice is subjected to unilateral stresses. In underground ice, these systems sometimes form during the irregular melting of large masses of ice; however, the ledges formed by the outcroppings of underground ice usually do not creep. In the ice cover of water, disruption of equilibrium by changes in the ice thickness is easily eliminated by isostatic compensation accompanied by only slight flexures, which are unimportant for the dynamic metamorphism of ice against a background of powerful external forces. Further, in ice of sedimentary origin, the stresses which occur during the accumulation of ice on a solid surface lead to movements which completely change the structure of the rock, to say nothing of other very important consequences.

A layer of ice rock that is considerably longer and wider than it is thick and that has frozen to a uniformly inclined bed is the simplest example of an unbalanced system. A shearing stress τ parallel to the bed will be operative in this ice at depth z below the surface:

$$\tau = z\delta \sin \alpha$$

where α is the slope angle.

The layer will remain immobile until the shear stress τ exceeds the elastic limit of the ice rock to the very bed, but when the layer thickness or the slope of the bed increases, the elastic limit near the bed will be reached and downhill creep will begin. However, if the stress exceeds the shear strength of the rock as the layer thickness continues to increase or the rock strength decreases, cleavage and rapid sliding of the rock mass downslope will occur instead of slow flow without disruption of cohesion. During flow, practically all the work of the force of gravity is expended on overcoming the forces of internal friction and the rate of movement remains very slow, but after cleavage the resistance decreases sharply and energy is expended on imparting acceleration to the rock masses.

Rapid sliding, i.e., the descent of avalanches, plays a large role in the removal of snow from slopes. The snow loses equilibrium owing to the increased thickness of the snow layer caused by snowfalls (dry-snow avalanches), by the weakening of the individual horizons of the snow cover during the development toward looseness (wind-slab avalanches) or by the infiltration of melt water (wet-snow avalanches). The first rupture of the snow, after which rapid sliding begins, is caused not only by the shear stress parallel to the bed, but often by compression perpendicular to the bed (the previously discussed rapid settling of the snow with destruction of its structure) and by faulting perpendicular to the bed in the regions of "anchoring" at the upper part of slopes that are subject to tension (Bucher, 1948). These faults also cause the ice avalanches which often break off the hanging ends of glaciers. Ice avalanches create ice breccia and conglomerates, which play a role in the formation of regenerated glaciers.

Glacier movement. Only glaciers and the seasonal snow cover of slopes flow. Thus, glaciers are the only group of natural ice bodies in which ice is subjected to prolonged and uniformly directed para-tectonic perecrystallization, in addition to the influences of dislocation metamorphism.

The movement of glaciers, which is their distinctive feature among the natural ice types, is the main concern of glaciology in the narrow sense of the word, i.e., the science of glaciers. The rate of movement of glaciers was first measured in 1760, while the first ideas on the nature of their movement were expressed as early as 1705 (the "dilatation theory"). The most important steps in the study of glacier movement have been: (1) the accurate measurement of the distribution of velocities in a glacier (1830–1856), (2) the prolonged measurements of the rate of movement of the Rhone glacier, the Vernagtferner and Hintereisferner, made over a period of decades and accompanied in part by deep borings, and (3) since the 1920's, the use of photogrammetry, seismic measurements of ice thickness and ice meters ("ice clocks"), which make continuous recordings of

the nature of the movement. As the measuring method was being
refined, measurements were made of the movements of the most
diverse glacier types (except for the continental ice sheets) throughout the world. An enormous quantity of data was accumulated,
giving a quite complete picture of the geometry of glacier movement.
We shall give just a brief outline of the main conclusions drawn
from these data.

The rate of surface movement of a glacier increases more or less
smoothly from the margins toward the center of the glacier, corresponding approximately to the changes in the profile of the bed: the
rate of flow increases with the depth of the bed. In a vertical profile,
the rate of flow increases parabolically or elliptically from the bed
toward the surface, i.e., it is most intense near the bed and decreases

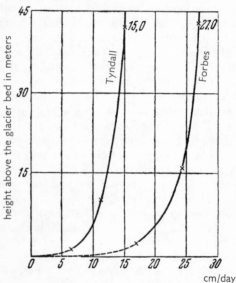

FIG. 89.   Curve of the rate of flow of ice in a vertical profile of the Mer de Glace
glacier along the front wall, according to measurements by Forbes in 1846,
and along the side wall, according to measurements by Tyndall in 1857.

Rate of flow at the bed (Accd. to E. G. Stevens)

Accd. to Forbes:	Accd. to Tyndall:
≃ 6.25 cm/day	≃ 4.17 cm/day
≃ 1/4 the rate of surface flow	≃ 1/4 the rate of surface flow

toward the surface (Fig. 89). Thus, the differential movements of
neighboring layers of ice in the vertical profile are maximum at the
bed and decrease to zero at the surface, in agreement with the change
of load. In the longitudinal direction, the rate of surface movement

gradually increases from the marginal crevasse (bergschrund) in the upper firn belt to the point of greatest ice thickness in the region of the firn line or below it and then decreases toward the end of the glacier tongue. If the ice thickness is uniform, the rate of flow will increase as the slope angle increases. If the cross section of the glacier becomes smaller, the rate of flow will increase and if the cross section becomes larger the rate of flow will decrease. The line of maximum rate of surface movement bends more than the geometric axis of the glacier, deviating from it toward the outside of the turn. When glaciers fuse, the rate of flow of the fusing edges increases rapidly, soon reaching that of the central parts.

The Streiff-Becker hypothesis stands aloof from these thoroughly reliable data. According to Streiff-Becker (1938), the bottom layers of the firn basin and also the depressions between the riegels (steps) in the glacier move at a greater rate than the surface, because of extrusion of ice from beneath the surface layers. Agassiz (1847) and later Tarr in 1910 and Hollingworth in 1931 also pointed out the possibility of this phenomenon.

Streiff-Becker's opinion was based on 21-year measurements of the firn increment and the rate of surface movement of the firn cap of the Claridenfirn in Switzerland. The Claridenfirn is one of the few Scandinavian-type firn caps in Switzerland and has drainage in all directions. Streiff-Becker calculates that if the annual firn increment is 3.2 m and the surface rate of movement 14 m/year, the total firn accumulation will be 3,500,000 m^3/year and the ablation 1,000,000 m^3/year. Since the elevation of the surface remained the same for 21 years, he concluded that the rate of movement was greater deep within the glacier than at the surface.

This cannot be regarded as a reliable conclusion, since Streiff-Becker apparently did not consider the densification of the firn and, what is more, he judged the rate of surface movement from measurements made at one point only on just one of the tributaries of the Claridenfirn, not along the entire cross section of the tributary, to say nothing of several tributaries. All the other facts which Streiff-Becker used to support his opinion can be explained without his hypothesis, while his concepts and Haefeli's supporting opinion that the viscosity of ice decreases with depth cannot be considered well founded.

Recently, the distribution of the rate of movement along a vertical profile in the firn regions of alpine glaciers was measured directly (Perutz, 1949, 1950). In June 1948, a vertical boring, which reached the bed of the glacier at a depth of 136 m, was sunk at the lower edge of the firn basin of the Great Aletsch glacier below the Jungfraujoch pass, where one would most expect "extrusion flow," according to

the adherents of the Streiff-Becker hypothesis. A pipe was inserted
into the bore hole and an electric inclinometer was lowered into the
pipe, permitting accurate measurement of the inclination of the pipe
at any point of the vertical profile. The first series of measurements
was made on 15 August, 1948, and a third series on 10 October,
1949 (Fig. 90). The rate of movement was greatest at the surface;
no differential movement was observed in the upper 50 m of the
profile and farther down the bore hole became elliptical with the
greatest curvature near the bed. Thus, there were no indications of
"extrusion flow."[2]

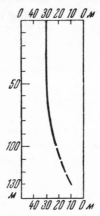

FIG. 90.   Movement in the vertical profile of the Jungfraufirn over a period of
14 months. (After M. Perutz, 1950.)

Glacier movement is slow; the greatest known rate of movement
is 38 m/day and about 7,500 m/year (Greenland); usually, however,
it is of the order of centimeters per day and tens of meters, or a
maximum of hundreds of meters, per year.

The kinematic theory of [glacier] flow. Knowledge of the kinematics of
glacier movement was synthesized in the *theory of flow* formulated at
the end of the last century and then expanded and supplemented by
approximations of the real conditions of a moving glacier (Reid,
1896; Finsterwalder, 1897, 1904; Bluemcke and Hess, 1899;
Mercanton, 1916; Hess, 1924).

The theory of flow states that glacier movement is geometrically
similar to the laminar flow of a fluid. Every glacier is, as it were, part

---

[2] For the results of subsequent measurements of the distribution of rate of
movement along a vertical glacier profile in Alaska and in the Alps see the works
of Sharp'(1953) and of Gerrard, Perutz and Roch (1952).

of a channel of arbitrary form, limited by a free upper surface. The firn line separates this free surface into an upper part, an accumulation region where material arrives on the glacier in the form of snow, and a lower part, an ablation region, where the material leaves the glacier in the form of water and water vapor. For every point on the glacier surface in the accumulation region there is a corresponding point in the ablation region. They are connected by a flow line which is the path of particles of material through the glacier. The flow lines never intersect; in the accumulation region they are submerged deep in the glacier, reaching their greatest depth below the firn line, and they approach the surface again in the ablation region. The entire glacier may be divided into elementary flow tubes along the lines of flow. A steady state will occur if an identical amount of ice passes through every cross section of a given flow tube in the same amount of time; for the surface, this can be expressed by the equation:

$$AdF = adf,$$

where

$$A = V \sin \Phi \quad \text{and} \quad a = v \sin \phi$$

Here, A is the annual increment in the accumulation region, a is the annual loss in the ablation region; dF and df are the area cross sections of a flow tube on the glacier surface in the accumulation and ablation areas, respectively; V and v are the corresponding rates of movement and Φ and ϕ are the angles between the flow lines and the glacier surface in the accumulation and ablation areas, respectively.

For the inner part of the glacier, the steady-state condition will be inversely proportional to the area cross section dF of the rate of movement v at every point of extension of the flow tube:

$$dF_1 : dF_2 = v_2 : v_1.$$

Proceeding from the simplest ideal case of steady flow, with the aid of additional assumptions that bring the flow model closer to reality, the flow theory explains the most diverse phenomena connected with glacier movement: the changes in the surface form of the glacier as a function of the rate of movement and melting, the distribution of moraines, the sensitivity of glaciers to fluctuations of climate. Further, it allows one to reconstruct, approximately, the shape of the glacier bed and to formulate mathematically the Forel-Richter theory of glacier oscillations.

With all this, the theory remains purely kinematic, since it treats only the geometry of motion.

The hydrodynamic theory of [*glacier*] *flow.* The similarity between the movement of glaciers and the flow of a viscous fluid has also inspired attempts to formulate hydrodynamic theories of glacier flow which would provide a quantitative association between movement, the physical properties of ice and the forces acting on the ice. These attempts came simultaneously with the efforts to formulate a kinematic theory, and even somewhat earlier (1888). The Russian physicist B. P. Veinberg established the modern hydrodynamic theories of glacier flow. In 1906 he proved that the laws of flow in a tube, produced when a mirror image of a channel is applied to the free surface of the channel, are applicable to the fluid flow along a channel in a glacier. All hydrodynamic theories derive from the Navier-Stokes equations, which express the basic principle of Newton's hydrodynamics, namely, that acceleration corresponds to the motive force, which is the resultant of gravity, the pressure gradient and friction. However, the integration of the Navier-Stokes equations required to devise a law of the movement of viscous fluids is beyond the limits of current mathematical analysis and most attempts made thus far have been limited to simplified ideal conditions.

Somigliana (1921), following Veinberg, examined the steady state of flow of a glacier in a cylindrical channel with a uniform slope and straight flow lines on the assumption of no accumulation or ablation. In developing the Veinberg-Somigliana theory, Lagally (1930, 1934) derived a simple formula for the relationship between the rate of movement u and the depth below the surface z for the longitudinal axis of a glacier with a flat upper surface, a semielliptical bed much wider than it is thick and, finally, a uniform and identical longitudinal slope angle of the surface and of the bed (α):

$$u = u_0 - \frac{\rho g}{2\mu} z^2 \sin \alpha$$

where u_0 is the rate of surface movement; ρ is the density of the ice; g is the acceleration of gravity and μ is the viscosity coefficient of the ice.

Lagally believes this formula can be applied to the sections of large glaciers where the rate of surface movement is constant, assuming that the bed is a plane parallel to the surface. Then the glacier thickness at any point of this section will be

$$z \sqrt{\frac{2\mu u_0}{\delta \sin \alpha}}$$

where $\delta = \rho g$ is the density of the ice.

Employing this formula under favorable conditions on glaciers of known thickness, Lagally obtained a mean viscosity coefficient of

1.0×10^{14} poise for alpine glaciers (0.92×10^{14} poise for the Hintereisferner and 1.07×10^{14} for Pasterze). After computing μ for the Hintereisferner, Lagally calculated the thickness of the Pasterze glacier as 300 m, and seismic determinations showed the glacier at that point to be 250–270 m thick.

The unsatisfactory aspects of the theory of viscous flow. Lagally's success proved that the theory of the viscous flow of glaciers is fundamentally sound. Nevertheless, facts which disprove the similarity of glacier movement and the flow of viscous fluids have long been accumulating simultaneously with the data which confirm the similarity. Just at the moment of the apparent triumph of the theory of viscous flow, some facts appeared which forced some of the founders and proponents of the theory to admit its inapplicability to at least some glaciers; others sought a way out by assuming that the viscosity differs considerably in different parts of a glacier; and still others assumed a special type of movement, i.e., *block slipping*, along with normal flow, and thus resurrected the views of the eighteenth-century scientists.

First, the theory of viscous flow cannot explain the fact of glacier erosion and polishing, which indicates that *ice slips along the bed*. Lagally (1934) admitted that this contradicts the theory that a glacier is similar to a viscous fluid, but he gets around the contradiction by remarking that the velocity of slipping along the bed is barely measurable and is a function of local conditions. Further, on the basis of measurements of the position of boring rods left in the Hintereisferner glacier in 1901 and discovered in 1931, Hess (1939) concluded that the rate of movement at the bottom of the glacier was 90.2% of that at the top (the top of the glacier had moved 940 m in 29 years, the bottom 840 m). Other researchers estimated the rate of slipping along the bed to be from 16% to 69% of the mean rate of surface movement (Deeley and Parr, 1914). Our measurements of movement in glacier cliffs which were partly in water and partly on land indicated that the rate of movement at the bed was 90–95% of that at the surface, thanks to which the glaciers had "ploughed out" the bottom deposits and amassed ridges up to 25 m high before the glacier front. Penetrating along cracks to the bed of the Upper Grindelwald glacier, Carol (1945, 1947) made direct measurements of the bottom rate of movement of the glacier and estimated it to be 36.8 cm/day or 134 m/year. Further, the familiar lifting of moraine material along thrust planes from the bottom of a glacier far within it is possible only because of movement along the bed. According to Wegener (Koch and Wegener, 1930), the displacement along major thrusts in the Storström glacier in Greenland may reach values of several kilometers. Not everyone agrees with this, but undoubtedly displacements of tens of meters do occur in many glaciers.

Another factor which contradicts the theory of viscous flow is the relatively very great rate of movement of many glaciers, which cannot be attributed solely to viscous flow. The clearest example of this is the Storström tributary of the Greenland ice sheet. This tributary moves at a velocity of 1700 m/year and is about 250 m thick. The differential movement, i.e., the greater rate of movement of the upper as opposed to the lower parts of the glacier, amounts to only 0.8 mm/m/year in the upper 6.5-m layer of ice over a period of $3\frac{1}{2}$ months. By linear extrapolation, we find that this represents a 20-cm decrease in the rate of movement at the bed, i.e., the viscous flow component of velocity is about 0.01%, that of slipping along the bed, 99.99%. Quadratic extrapolation, based on the assumption that velocity is distributed parabolically in the vertical profile, does not change the result much. To attain a velocity of 1700 m/year due to viscous flow, the viscosity coefficient of ice need be only 1.5×10^{11} poise, or several times less than that in temperate alpine glaciers, while actually it is greater owing to the low temperature of ice.

The number of recorded cases of this type has increased greatly in recent years. In addition to earlier data on the glaciers of the western coast of Greenland (Drygalski, 1897) which have been confirmed by new measurements, analogous results have been obtained in various places: on the tongue of the Notgemeinschaft glacier in the Pamir, in the Himalayas, the Karakorum, the Andes, on Spitsbergen and also in the northern glaciers of the Soviet Union. A review of the earlier material shows that block slipping was also the mode of movement of the Vernagtferner in the Alps during its advance in 1845, when the rate of movement reached 11 m/day (during the periods of retreat, 5 cm/day).

From these facts, R. Finsterwalder (1937, 1950) concludes that there are two types of movement: in slowly moving glaciers it is flow, as in viscous fluids, while in rapidly moving glaciers it is block slipping with unusual phenomena. Finsterwalder classifies glaciers in which the ratio of the annual rate of movement v to the width b or the depth is from 1:6 to 2:3 as rapidly moving glaciers, and those in which the $v:b$ ratio is much less as slowly moving glaciers. The Pasterze glacier, with a ratio of 1:20, and the Fedchenko glacier, with a ratio of 1:14, are examples of slowly moving glaciers. Zones of increased mobility along the margins and bottom of the glaciers are typical of rapidly moving glaciers. The rate of movement increases sharply in these zones, while the central part moves at an approximately uniform speed, as a solid mass with a slight relative displacement of the individual blocks into which this mass is divided by the irregularities of the bed.

There are also transitional, or rather, combined types of movement, where one part of the glacier moves as a stream and the other as a solid block. Time-dependent transitions from one type of movement to the other have also been observed.

The third group of phenomena which refute the viscous flow premise is associated with the possible transmission of directed pressure in ice. It has long been known that glaciers can surmount horizontal obstacles and even surmount sections with a reverse inclination of the bed, not as a fluid by raising the level and by draining across the threshold, but by the pressure of the higher-lying masses, because of which the glacier slides upward over the riegel, even assuming the backward tilt of the surface.

Prolonged measurements of the rate of movement have also revealed the special nature of glacier oscillations. An increase in the accumulation on a glacier does not cause an immediate increase in the rate of glacier movement, as it does in the case of a fluid. First, a fairly large mass of ice accrues in the accumulation zone and the surface swells, but a rapid acceleration of movement does not begin until the pressure of the ice in the upper reaches of the glacier becomes large enough to overcome the resistance of the slowly moving tongue. Quite characteristically, the wave of increased rate of movement and the resultant lifting of the glacier surface travel from the source to the terminus of the glacier at a considerably faster rate than the rate of movement of the glacier itself. Thus, this wave does not represent a transfer of material, as does the flash flood of a river, but results from the transfer of directed pressure within the ice.

This feature of ice flow was noted by Hess, who tried to construct a quantitative flow theory which would take into account the transfer of longitudinal pressure (Hess, 1931, 1935). Hess divides glaciers longitudinally into zones of movement (*Schubgebiete*), where kinetic energy accumulates, and zones of deceleration (*Bremsgebiete*), where the ice uses the energy imparted to it from the zones of movement. He does not accept Lagally's calculations of the rate of movement of the tongue of the Pasterze glacier, because his own data show that the weight of the ice in this sector could not overcome the bottom friction, and movement could be due only to the expenditure of energy transmitted from the firn region; in this case the longitudinal pressure induced by movement (which Lagally did not consider, having neglected the bottom rate of movement) is added to the shear component of vertical pressure.

Unfortunately, Hess's theory is far from perfect. He does not consider the energy exchange between the "partial glaciers," which correspond to the large flow tubes of the kinematic theory of flow. Further, according to Perutz (1947), the integration of several dependent variables, which at present cannot be estimated without making doubtful assumptions, leads to highly improbable conclusions about the distribution of stresses in glaciers. Nevertheless, in principle, the Hess approach to the solution of the problem of glacier movement is more correct than that of the proponents of the dynamic theory of viscous flow in its pure form.

The occurrence of a pulsating, spasmodic movement is another important fact which challenges the viscous flow theory and which is closely connected with the previously discussed nature of the long-range glacier oscillations. In addition to the frequently observed diurnal and longer fluctuations of the rate of movement, there are also briefer pulsations which cannot be caused by changes in the external conditions. In formulating his theory of flow based on observations of the Vernagtferner glacier, Finsterwalder (1912) concluded that the movement of the bottom layers of a glacier is due to individual spasms. Washburn and Goldthwait (1937) on the South Crillon glacier established the presence of velocity pulsations at 20-minute intervals. From the frequent periodic cracking sound in the Storström glacier, Koch and Wegener (1930) concluded that at least part of the movement is not continuous but derives from the accumulation of stresses and a subsequent spasm. I have definitely observed this phenomenon at the termini of glaciers that descend into water, where perhaps the pulsations are intensified by the resistance of the ice cover of the body of water. The crashing and grinding of hummock ridges amassed before the glacier front recurred at time intervals of 3 to 20 minutes.

The automatic recordings of movement along a thrust plane of the Brenva glacier in the Alps (R. T. Chamberlin, 1928) are even more convincing. They reveal an alternation of periods of no movement, slow steady shear and brief, rapid sliding of the upper part along the lower part. The recordings of the movement of the surface of the Scheibreen on Spitsbergen together with the crags rising amidst this glacier provide further evidence of this (Fig. 91, after Tollner, 1938). The objection by von Engeln (1934, 1935) that one cannot infer the processes which occur in the plastic inner core from the behavior of the rigid outer crust is not well founded, because the outer crust is at the melting point in both cases.

The plastic deformation of polycrystalline bodies is generally discontinuous. This was confirmed recently with respect to ice by the experiments of K. E. Ivanov and V. V. Lavrov (1950). The curve

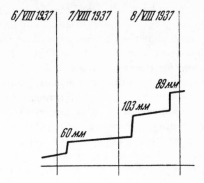

Fig. 91. Part of an automatic recording of the surface movement of the Scheibreen (Spitsbergen) 200 m from the glacier terminus. (After H. Tollner, 1938.)

of the deformation of polycrystalline ice under a steady load was step-like with 0.05–1.0-mm discontinuities repeated at intervals of several tens of seconds to 3 minutes. Characteristically, in the case of repeated loading, the deformation begins smoothly and does not become intermittent until some time has elapsed.

Thus, the pulsating movement of glaciers is due to the properties of the ice itself and is associated with the periodic accumulation and removal of elastic stress in the polycrystalline aggregate.

Finally, the temporally and spatially intermittent movement along the internal fault and thrust planes is an argument against viscous flow; however, we shall not dwell on that subject here, as it will be treated later. For a long time, a strange battle raged between the adherents of viscous flow and the adherents of sliding along thrusts, in which the proponents of viscous flow ignored thrust and the proponents of sliding attempted to prove its wide distribution. Now, apparently, the struggle has ended in a compromise, formulated in the works of Visser (Visser, 1938, *et al.*). The proponents of sliding along thrusts have ceased to deny the participation of plastic flow, which is confirmed, if by nothing else, by fold formation in the ice and without which the sheets of ice moving along the thrusts could not adapt to the form of the valley and the bed of the glacier. On the other hand, the proponents of viscous flow have been forced to admit movement along thrusts and have noted in passing that the results, in general, differ little from those of flow: instead of movement along an infinite number of glide planes in the ice, movement concentrates in a limited number of these planes, but the general picture of the distribution of velocities remains the same.

Plastic flow and the system of stresses. Thus, it is evident that glacier movement is considerably more complex than anticipated by the existing theories and that the development of a quantitative theory which would describe this movement accurately is a matter for the future. The reasons for the inadequacy of the theory of viscous flow are clear; ice is not a viscous fluid but a plastic body. Rheologically, friable snow corresponds to a viscous compressible fluid, which obeys Newton's law of the linear relationship between the rate of deformation (changes of strain) and stress; but ice flow does not obey this law. If one ignores the region of very slow deformations, actually the flow of ice begins after the load has reached the elastic limit, which is a function of the temperature and structure of the ice. When the load increases, the flow is accelerated very rapidly and, finally, following flow there may be some elastic aftereffect. The coefficient of viscosity is not a constant that characterizes the flow of ice, but varies greatly with changes of load. Thus, the flow of ice is not viscous, but elastoplastic and cannot be defined quantitatively until its individual characteristics have been investigated carefully.

Until a satisfactory general theory has been developed, the easiest method of approaching an understanding of the nature of stresses and movement in a glacier is the one indicated by Orowan (1949), whereby the simplest cases of gravity-induced plastic deformation are analyzed and the results are applied to the movement of glaciers.

The shear stress must reach the elastic limit λ before a uniform layer of ice h high can move slowly downhill:

$$\lambda = h\delta \sin \alpha$$

Therefore, for every slope angle there is a specific thickness at which a uniform layer of ice will be in "plastic equilibrium." An increase in the arrival of material from the atmosphere and an increase in thickness will cause a corresponding acceleration of movement. The elastic limit of glacier ice in shear[3] at 0°C does not exceed 0.1 kg/cm², while perceptible flow begins after a stress of about 1 kg/cm² has been reached. Consequently, on a 45° slope, slight movement begins when the ice is 1.54 m thick, and noticeable movement begins at an ice thickness of about 15.4 m. For a 10° slope, the corresponding figures are 6.28 m and 62.8 m, and for a 1° slope, 62.5 m and 625.1 m.

However, the slope of the glacier bed varies in longitudinal

---

[3] [I have used Shumskii's term "elastic limit in shear" here rather than Orowan's "yield stress in shear," as Shumskii has modified Orowan's presentation somewhat and apparently wishes to specify "elastic limit," rather than translating literally "yield stress." – D.K.]

profile, while the ice thickness cannot change immediately so as to satisfy the condition of "plastic equilibrium." The parts of the glacier which are thicker than required by this condition will exert pressure or tension on the parts which are not sufficiently thick. Longitudinal pressure and tension will develop and will vary along the longitudinal profile of the glacier, keeping the different parts of the glacier in simultaneous motion.

The longitudinal compressive force F, acting in the cross section of the glacier (assuming the usual case where the slope angle of the glacier surface changes more smoothly than that of the bed) can be determined approximately by the equation:

$$ F = \int_0^x h \, \delta \sin \alpha \, dx - \lambda x $$

where x is the distance of the section from the top of the glacier. The first term in the right side of the equation is the longitudinal force which would be produced by the frictionless motion of the glacier, the second term is the resistance of the internal friction of ice, which can be determined by the elastic limit.

If a long section with a small slope follows a steep gradient of the bed, the longitudinal pressure required to force the glacier over the section with the slight slope may exceed the elastic limit of the ice in compression. Then longitudinal compression of the glacier with increasing thickness will continue until the area cross section becomes large enough to transmit the increasing longitudinal pressure. In this case, the ice often crumples into folds of extremely diverse size, from very large to minute contortions (Figs. 92 and 93). On the other hand, the gently sloping section behind the steep part of the glacier is subjected to tensile stress, which is manifested in elongation and reduction of the cross section and in the formation of transverse fissures, after the elastic limit has been exceeded. This is the essential difference between the effect of tensile and compressive stresses, which understandably do not lead to extrusion.

Thus, glacier movement, examined in a vertical longitudinal section alone, is caused by shear stress due to the weight of the higher layers at every given point and by the stresses of longitudinal pressure or tension directed along the line of movement and coming from neighboring, more rapidly moving parts of the glacier which push the slower moving parts ahead or drag them behind.

The system of stresses and the nature of the movement are further complicated by the interaction of the parts of the glacier in the

Fig. 92.   Folding in a glacier cliff. (Photograph by N. V. Cherepanov.)

Fig. 93.   Anticlinal fold, complicated in the curve of the fold [in the vicinity
of the axial plane] by fine plication with rupture and drag along the upper limb.
Scale 1 cm ≈ 5 m. (Photograph by N. V. Cherepanov.)

transverse profile. The margins of a glacier are not thick enough to
move independently, but the intermediate glacier regions can move,
though not as fast as the center of the glacier. The longitudinal force
cannot compensate for this deficiency. Flow at the margins is caused

by shear stresses transmitted from the central parts of the glacier across the longitudinal vertical planes. In other words, the thick central parts draw the marginal parts of the glacier along with them. Consequently, the shear component with a horizontal axis, caused by the weight of the ice in a given vertical column, decreases from the center of the glacier toward the margins, but the shear component, which has a vertical axis derived from the kinetic energy of the central parts of the glacier, increases. In the center, the shear velocity around the vertical axis is zero, but increases toward the edges. This also explains the characteristic convex-downward shape assumed by the initially straight lines on the glacier surface. Hence, the shape of the velocity lines on a glacier surface is not always an indication of viscous flow.

Finally, various additional stresses and deformations appear while the glacier is adapting to changes in the direction of inclination of the bed and to the constriction and expansion of the drainage channels, etc.[4]

Block slipping. Thus, a very complex system of stresses and strains is created in a moving glacier. One of the main factors is plastic shear deformation, which has a horizontal axis and is parallel to the bed. It is maximum at the bed and decreases toward the surface, corresponding to the reduction of the vertical load. However, with all the changes in form and slope of the bed, the ice cannot adapt itself to the new conditions quickly, as a fluid can by changing its rate of flow, surface slope and size of cross section, i.e., depth of stream. The non-hydrostatic, directed transfer of rather small stresses is the basic reason why ice cannot adapt quickly. The elastic limit of ice in compression and tension is double that in shear. Therefore, changes in the flow conditions and the ensuing longitudinal compression and tension cause only a partial change in the ice thickness and a corresponding increase or decrease of the rate of flow, as in the case of a fluid. The degree of change in this case is a function of the extent to which the elastic limit of a given type of deformation is exceeded. The rest of the longitudinal stress is transmitted linearly, as in the case of a solid, so that each given section of the glacier pushes ahead or drags behind sections of the glacier situated ahead of it or behind it, respectively, which have a different rate of plastic flow.

However, only part of this type of additional impetus toward movement, which is external for a given part of the glacier, can be

---

[4] The theory of plastic flow of glaciers was developed further in the works of J. F. Nye (Nye, 1951, p. 554; 1952, pp. 82, 103).

expended on accelerating the laminar flow. Basically, it is expended on *block slipping along the bed*. Each change of inclination of the bed or width of the valley and area cross section of the glacier produces the same result, in part, as the extrusion of ice through an opening, namely: passive movement of the ice mass ejected by the active ice at the point where the cross section narrows, accompanied by complex additional deformations resulting from the adjustment of the stream at that point. Consequently, every change in the conditions of glacier flow results in a partial transformation of plastic flow into block slipping, which does not change the independent flow of a given section of the glacier, but is superposed on it. Therefore, the rate of block slipping resulting from every change in flow conditions is additive and increases toward the glacier terminus. The role of block slipping at the glacier terminus increases with increasing variability of the longitudinal slope and transverse profile of the glacier and with decreasing plasticity of the ice, i.e., with decreasing temperature of the ice. Block slipping increases especially in the lower part of glaciers which enter the water, because the resistance of the frictional forces of the forward part of the glacier decreases as the terminus is approached and, consequently, there is less danger that the elastic limit in compression will be exceeded because of longitudinal pressure.

The considerable increase of stresses at the contacts between the sliding blocks, on the one hand, and the glacier bed and margins, on the other, are particularly conducive to fault and thrust formation and the concentration of faults and thrusts in these parts of the glacier create zones of increased mobility, which separate the slowly flowing glacier margins from the central blocks. Therefore, not all block slipping takes place along the bed, but some of it occurs along the internal fault planes. When the pressure in the ice becomes large enough, it is transmitted in the direction of least resistance; therefore, the movement acquires a vertically upward component in sections where the bed is less inclined and in the thinner parts of the glacier or at points where the moraine content is higher (i.e., under steep ledges and at the glacier terminus). A considerable portion of this movement, directed obliquely upward, passes along the thrust planes, often entraining moraine material from the floor of the glacier (Fig. 94).

Thus, *plastic flow* is the main primary mechanism of glacier movement, but not the sole mechanism, except at the sources of a glacier. The imperfect nature of ice fluidity, which distinguishes it from the fluidity of liquids, creates movement of a new type in the flow process, namely, *block slipping along the bed*, which, owing to the weakness of ice, is transformed in part into the movement of a series of ice slabs along the *internal fault planes*. All three mechanisms of movement exist simultaneously and side by side in a glacier, but the relative role of each varies with the part of the glacier: the relative role of plastic flow decreases and the role of slipping along the bed and internal faults increases as the conditions of glacier flow become more variable and the distance from the sources of nourishment increases. The role of slipping along the bed increases and the development of internal faults and thrusts decreases with decreasing resistance of the forward part of the glacier, the irregularities of the bed and the moraine-ladened bottom layers to block slipping.

Fig. 94. Series of thrusts with a moraine at the glacier terminus. (Photograph by N. V. Cherepanov.)

Very rapid flow is indicative of major block slipping. The greatest rate of flow is observed in the tributaries of the ice sheets, because conditions are particularly favorable for the development of block slipping in places where the ice stream is forced from the broad ice accumulation region into a narrow valley and where a two-stage change of the longitudinal slope takes place, viz., from an upland plateau to a steep slope and then to a piedmont plain. Under the most favorable conditions the rate of block slipping may be hundreds and thousands of times greater than that of plastic flow, as in the case of the Storström glacier. A less intense, but similar change in flow conditions is observed in many valley glaciers, on passing from the broad firn fields to a narrow valley.

The erosional activity of glaciers is connected with slipping along the bed, therefore it is very slight in ice caps and firn basins, where plastic flow predominates, and increases sharply in valley glacier streams. This explains, for the most part, the frequently observed disappearance of traces of ancient glaciation at points where narrow valleys emerge onto plateaus and broad watershed areas.

Movement in ice sheets. Thus far we have examined ice movement caused by the slope of the surface on which the ice is bedded. Conditions are entirely different in a mass of ice that accumulates on a horizontal bed or on an uneven bed and where the ice is much thicker than the irregularities of the bed. In this case, the direction of flow is determined by the slope of the ice surface, independently of the slope of the bed. The liquid [precipitation] drains away in all directions from the point of deposition and does not enter a state of equilibrium until it reaches a horizontal surface; however, the more viscous the liquid is, the slower it will flow.

Since ice is a plastic rather than a viscous body, it will attain equilibrium on a convex surface with greater curvature at the edges than in the middle, rather than on a horizontal surface. Ice domes and sheets are similar to this and the magnitude of their surface curvature is inversely proportionate to their size. At elevations of more than 800 m, in places where the contour of the bed does not exert an influence, the Greenland ice sheet is shaped like the arc of an ellipse (in vertical profile) with a horizontal long axis (Meinardus, 1926, 1932, *et al.*). The equilibrium state of the ice sheet is continually disturbed by the deposition of snow in the central portions and by melting, evaporation and the calving of icebergs along the periphery. Simultaneously, the glacier strives toward a state of equilibrium by the flow of ice from the central portions toward the periphery. Evidently, this type of equilibrium also takes the shape of the arc of an ellipse in vertical profile, but it is flatter than that of an unbalanced, moving ice sheet.

It has long been thought that there must be an essential difference between the mechanisms of glacier and ice-sheet movement. This is evidenced by the different appearance of mountain glaciers and ice sheets and by the very slow movement of ice domes. P. A. Kropotkin (1876) provided the basis for a qualitative theory of ice sheet movement, which may be summarized as follows: ice flows very slowly from the center of an ice sheet toward its periphery in the direction of decreasing ice-sheet thickness. The Kropotkin theory was supplemented slightly by later investigators (W. Thomson, 1888; Nansen,

1892; and others). Drygalski's views differ most from those of Kropotkin, but, as we shall demonstrate later, they are erroneous. Drygalski (1897) held that the periphery of an ice sheet swells because of partial melting of ice in the center of the sheet, lateral extrusion of water in the bottom layers and refreezing of this water due to the reduction of pressure.

Thus far, Hess (1933) has made the only attempt to formulate a quantitative theory of the ice-sheet movement, with reference to the Greenland ice sheet. Hess proceeds on the assumption that the movement of ice in an ice sheet is determined not by the slope of the bed but by the propagation of initially vertical pressure and that the ice and water at the grain boundaries in the lower zone of "warm" ice are squeezed out in the direction of least resistance, i.e., parallel to the bed. The upper "cold" ice forms a rigid cover about 450 m thick on the lower, plastic ice, which moves from the center of the sheet toward the periphery at a still unknown velocity. The greatest rate of movement should be at the lower boundary of the rigid cold ice and should decrease downward because of friction against the bed. The cold ice cover is dissected by transverse cracks caused by the tension created by the flow of "warm" ice out from under the cold ice. Further, the rigid cover in the central cold part of the glacier settles as a whole as the "warm" ice spreads and melts. The behavior of the lines of motion on the surface of an ice sheet is still an unknown factor. According to Hess, the pressure p in the direction of movement is determined by the formula

$$p = \int_0^x \epsilon \delta \, (1 - f) \tan \alpha \, dx,$$

where ϵ is the coefficient of lateral pressure; f is the coefficient of friction against the bed; α is the slope angle of the ice surface and x is the distance from the center of the ice sheet. On the assumption that $\epsilon = 1$ and $f = 0.066$ for the lower "warm" ice, Hess found:

$$p = 855 \int_0^x \tan \alpha \, dx,$$

from which he established that the moving pressure increases from 0 at the center of the ice sheet to 270 kg/cm² at the edge, a distance of 400 km.

Demorest (1941, 1943, etc.) has made the most recent attempt to devise a theory of ice-sheet movement. He gives a general classification of the types of movement of glacier formations, or, to be more exact, the types of flow, since he regards movement along the fault planes as a variant of flow and does not mention block slipping. Demorest distinguishes two basic types of flow, extrusion and gravity, and two transitional types, "obstructed" extrusion flow and "obstructed" gravity flow. Both kinds of extrusion flow comprise a type of pressure-controlled movement which depends on the surface slope, while both kinds of gravity flow comprise a type of drainage-controlled movement which depends on the slope of the bed. Thus, he arrives at the following system:

Pressure-controlled (dependent on slope of glacier surface)	EXTRUSION FLOW OBSTRUCTED EXTRUSION FLOW	Shear stresses due to differential pressure and differential plasticity
Drainage-controlled (dependent on shape of glacier floor)	OBSTRUCTED GRAVITY FLOW GRAVITY FLOW	Shear stresses due to components of gravity

According to both Demorest and Streiff-Becker, the main feature of extrusion flow is its greater velocity within the glacier than at the surface. In the pure forms of extrusion and gravity flow, the movement is parallel to the bed, while in the "obstructed" variants it has an upward component resulting from obstruction by the thinner and more slowly moving ice before it. In defining the enumerated types of movement, Demorest also examines the mechanism of the adjustment of glacier movement to changes in the rate of accumulation and ablation.

Demorest's views soon became widely known and were accepted uncritically by many glaciologists, because of the precise classification, apt terminology and simple, purely qualitative approach to the problems of glacier movement. However, without belittling his achievements, it must be admitted that Demorest contributed nothing new to the problems of glacier movement, except for some erroneous assumptions. We shall not dwell here on Demorest's analysis of gravity flow, which is a popular account of what can be deduced directly from the kinematic and hydrodynamic theories of flow. His concept of "extrusion flow" as a mechanism of ice-sheet movement is the chief point of interest.

Demorest assumes that "extrusion flow" occurs because of the difference in the weight of the ice columns in the various parts of the transverse vertical section of the ice sheet, caused by the slope of the surface. Naturally, when the surface slope is small—and it should be less than 1–2° or "obstructed" extrusion flow will occur, the pressure difference on both sides is small. This difference is identical throughout the vertical profile from top to bottom and is not great enough to induce surface movement. If the plasticity of the ice were identical throughout the profile, movement could not occur in general, but according to Demorest, ice plasticity increases downward; thus movement occurs according to the curve in Fig. 95. There is no movement at the top, because of the small plasticity of the ice, and there is none below because of friction against the bed. The viscosity of the ice

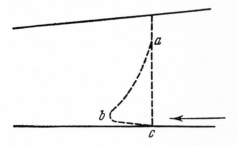

Fig. 95. Curve of the rate of "extrusion flow." (After M. Demorest, 1943.)

decreases downward because both the temperature and pressure increase. Thus, because of the differential viscosity (which definitely exists only in the cold upper layer due to the temperature increase) a slight differential pressure is sufficient to produce movement in the thick layer of ice.

In actually determining the cause of the movement, Demorest allowed an inaccuracy pardonable only for a purely qualitative theory. Clearly, it is not a matter of the pressure of narrow columns of ice adjoining a given section of the profile, but of the general distribution of pressure throughout the ice sheet. Movement in ice sheets is directed toward the least resistance to pressure, which is transmitted hydrostatically at a certain depth, while the magnitude of the moving pressure is a function not only of the slope angle of the surface and the thickness of the ice sheet at a given point, but also of the spatial variation of these values, which determines the horizontal dimensions of the sheet.

A tall, thin column of ice would actually be extruded laterally, because of the possibility of lateral expansion, as soon as the weight of the higher-lying ice reached the elastic limit of ice in compression, i.e., beginning at a depth on the order of 20 m. However, if the horizontal dimensions of this ice body were close to or larger than its vertical dimensions, extrusion of the bottom layer would be impeded by the shear stresses acting between the bottom layer and the bed and between the bottom layer and the higher layer of ice, in which the pressure had not yet reached the elastic limit in compression. The pressure must be very great to overcome these obstacles. As Orowan (1949) remarked, simple calculation shows that extrusion of the bottom layer becomes quite impossible if the ice body is hundreds of times wider than it is high, as in the case of continental ice sheets. In such cases, plastic flow should encompass practically the entire volume of ice, i.e., the ice should spread out, not be extruded. Kropotkin understood this very well when he spoke of the spread and creep of ice-sheet ice, not of extrusion. Kropotkin (1876, p. 471) wrote, "If, for some reason, they [the upper layers of ice – Shumskii] did not have a natural tendency to spread, they would be augmented by those lower layers in which pressure causes the particles to creep. Thus, all layers of the mass would participate, little by little, in the general movement from the center toward the periphery."

His deduction is confirmed by the formation of crevasses beneath the surface in the central parts of ice caps, even at their very summits, and these are not thermal cracks, but are definitely of dynamic origin and gradually expand with time (see, for example, Moss, 1938). Evidently, crevasses also exist in the center of the continental ice sheets, but they do not appear at the surface, because the rate of firn accretion is greater than the rate of crevasse formation and the firn layers cover the crevasses in thick bridges. One can get an idea of such crevasses from Fig. 96.

Thus it can be stated that we still do not have a satisfactory theory of the distribution of stresses and movement in ice sheets. Orowan (1949) merely calculates now high the central part of an ice mass should be before the entire mass of the ice can flow. The condition for the initiation of flow is:

$$1/2 \ \delta \ h^2 = \lambda r$$

where h is the height of the ice in the center of the sheet, λ is the elastic limit of the ice in shear [the "yield stress in shear," in Orowan's equation – D.K.] and r is the radius of the sheet [or half the width of the ice ridge, in the case examined by Orowan – D.K.].

If the surface of the bed of the ice sheet rises, gravitational flow must be added to the omnidirectional flow. Gravitational flow and omnidirectional flow do not differ in principle, because

Fig. 96. Crevasse at the edge of the ice cap. (Photograph by the Expedition to North East Land, 1935–1936.)

omnidirectional flow may be regarded as the movement of ice along the glide planes which lie within the ice mass.[5]

---

[5] At present, J. F. Nye is doing further work on developing the theory of ice-sheet movement (Nye, 1951, p. 554; 1952b, p. 529).

Types of dynamic metamorphism. Now let us examine the micro-mechanism of the deformation of ice bodies caused by stresses within these bodies and let us examine the effect of such deformations on ice structure. First, let us treat the group of dislocation metamorphism processes, whose petrographic results have already been examined, particularly the formation of tension cracks.

The formation of tension cracks under the influence of external dynamic forces and temperature variations, and during ice flow, is a widespread characteristic of all natural ice bodies, with the exception of segregation ice deep within the earth's crust. Crack formation reaches especially large proportions in glaciers, where it is con-current with flow and slipping along the bed and results from these processes, but does not play an essential role in the mechanism of movement. From the petrographic point of view, crack formation is interesting only as an indication of the presence of ice veins. The small slipping motions along the planes of glacier cracks (crevasses) and the partial melting of crack walls that come into contact with each other as a result of this slipping are far less important factors in the formation of ice structures. In temperate glaciers,[6] usually the partial melting of the crack walls takes the place of ice vein formation.

The other dynamometamorphic processes important for ice rock formation can be divided into three main groups, according to the forces which invoke them:

(1) metamorphism induced by flow,
(2) metamorphism induced by pressure,
(3) metamorphism induced by friction.

METAMORPHISM INDUCED BY FLOW

By flow metamorphism we understand the changes experienced by ice in the process of plastic shear deformation. This is the most widely distributed type of metamorphism in ice of sedimentary origin, connected with the basic mechanism of the movement of mountain glaciers and ice sheets, i.e., plastic flow. As a rule, flow metamorphism embraces the entire mass of the glacier, except for the passively transported upper layer of the ice 15–20 m thick, where the weight of the higher ice is not great enough to cause flow. The bottom layers experience the greatest metamorphism; however, the intensity of the flow processes gradually decreases upward corresponding to

---

[6] For an account of the theory of crack formation, see standard courses on general glaciology and also specialized works, for example, those of Lagally (1929, 1934).

the reduction of stresses. We shall call ice which has perecrystallized in the flow process, *secondary-recrystallization ice.*

The character of this type of metamorphism is determined by the micromechanism of the ice flow. The plastic properties of mono-crystals and polycrystalline assemblages of many substances, particularly of metals, have already been determined on the basis of internal slipping and the mechanical twinning of crystals. In this case, the mutual displacements of the crystals play a secondary, subordinate role, and melting and solidification generally do not occur. However, many researchers claim that the mutual displacements of ice crystals play the leading role in the mechanism of glacier flow. This viewpoint is inherited in part from the days when brittle and plastic bodies were sharply differentiated and is based in part on the proximity of the melting point and the ease of phase transitions in ice.

Tyndall was the first (1857) to express the view that glacier flow results from the mutual displacement of the sections of ice that have been fragmented by cracks and have frozen together, i.e., he suggested "regelation." Subsequently, Tyndall recognized glacier strains as the main units of displacement and this view was supported by Helmholtz in 1865. A. Heim (1885) also held to this opinion in general.

After the plasticity of ice crystals themselves had been demonstrated (McConnel, 1890, 1891; Mügge, 1895, 1899, 1900), the mutual displacement of grains began to be associated with the melting of the projecting points of the grains, which are subjected to higher pressure, and generally with the presence of a film of liquid water between the crystals. Drygalski (1897, p. 487) was an extreme proponent of motion caused exclusively by regelation processes. Essentially, Drygalski recognized only motion in the liquid phase. Some investigators (T. Chamberlin, 1904; R. Chamberlin, 1936) continued to adhere to the principle of rigidity and brittleness of ice crystals and developed a hypothesis of the "solid flow" of glaciers, considering it to be completely bound to the partial melting of the projections and the movements of the grains before closer packing. Other investigators (Hamberg, 1895, 1932; Tarr and von Engeln, 1915; von Engeln, 1934) recognized that plastic deformation of the crystals also plays a certain secondary role, but they assigned the main role to mutual displacements of the grains, which became possible because of the presence of a liquid film of salt solution and the regelation process. Finally, others (e.g., Hess, 1933) ascribed approximately equal roles to the plasticity of the grains and to their displacements.

The opinion that glacier movement results from displacements of the grains was supported by calculations which showed that the observed velocity of glacier movement could be produced by the sum of very slight movements of each individual crystal. For example, T. Chamberlin (1904) calculated that each crystal in a glacier 6 miles long would have to move only 1/10,000 of its diameter per day, with respect to its neighboring crystal, or the distance of its own diameter in 30 years to produce a total velocity of movement of 3 ft/day at the glacier terminus. Using this as an example, Hamberg (1932) made calculations for the Mikkaglaciär in Swedish Lapland, which showed that a crystal need rotate only 0.1° per day, or one revolution in 10 years, to impart a velocity of movement of 30 m/year to ice 100 m thick.

These views were criticized quite justly by Hawkes (1930). The mutual movements of crystals caused by partial melting should result in the melting away of the projections in the direction of the pressure and in the movement of the grains flush against the grains lying ahead of them. However, if this were the case, the individual movements could not accumulate at the glacier terminus, but only at the upper end, so that a glacier 6 miles long would have an immobile terminus, while its upper part would move at a rate of 3 ft/day, becoming shorter in the process of moving. After complete mutual adaptation of the grains, further movement could occur only by flattening and elongation of the crystals in a plane perpendicular to the direction of the pressure, which is not observed in practice. At any rate, the movements of the grains cannot explain the actual complex picture of velocity distribution in a glacier body.

The fundamental objection to the hypothesis of differential movement of the grains is that there can be no relative displacements of the grains, because the grains are very irregular in shape and form intergrowths (Hagenbach-Bischoff, 1889). This objection is even more serious, since our observations show that if an irregular combined form of crystals does develop, it develops during the flow process. At first crystals of infiltration-recrystallization ice and infiltration ice are usually rounded and isometric, but after flow begins often complex intergrown forms appear, which are flattened or elongated in the direction of movement (Fig. 97). This fact also refutes the hypothesis (Deeley and Fletcher, 1895) that, owing to perecrystallization, glacier grains may change shape rapidly under the slightest stress, so that they can slide along each other without breaking. Those who have studied the structure of secondary-recrystallization ice can scarcely doubt that if mutual slipping or rotation of the crystals actually does take place, it is merely a secondary non-essential factor of ice flow.

Opposing views, which consider the plastic deformation of the crystals themselves to be the basis of ice fluidity, were first expressed by Hagenbach-Bischoff (1889) and Emden (1890) and later were developed by Mügge (1899) and Tammann (1922).

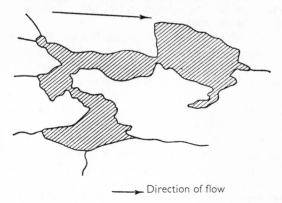

Direction of flow

FIG. 97. Vertical section of a glacier-ice crystal formed during the flow process. (Microscope sketch. × 5.)

The deformation of the air inclusions within crystals, observed in Greenland (Drygalski, 1897), in the Alps (Perutz and Seligman, 1939) and by the present author in "cold" glaciers, affords direct evidence that ice flow is caused by the slipping of layers along the basal planes in each crystal. In the process of flow, the air bubbles are elongated and flattened in the direction of internal slipping, i.e., in the basal plane of the crystals. Furthermore, the insertion of small screws into the ice did not reveal differential movements, as in firn, but gave a picture of uniform shear deformation of the upper layers with respect to the lower. In the Eiger glacier, the average shear velocity for 14 days was 0.78 mm/m/day (Perutz and Seligman, 1939).

The only qualitative differences between the flow processes in "cold" glaciers and in "warm" ice are in the details of the behavior of the inclusions, which we shall treat below. Further, experiments with a mass consisting of wood and ice showed that the deformation mechanism remains unchanged even at a temperature of $-25°C$, when there can be no melting under excess pressure (Perutz, 1948).

A question arises which the opponents of plastic flow (Deeley and Fletcher, 1895; von Engeln, 1934) have used as an objection to the possibility of deformation of the grains: how can the plasticity of each individual crystal in one plane only be used for movement, if the orientation of the glide plane varies in each crystal and if the shear is retarded by neighboring crystals which are rigid in the given direction? Actually, unobstructed slipping along the basal planes could occur only if the basal planes of all the crystals were oriented in the shear plane, and as a matter of fact, this is just the orientation that develops during flow.

For reasons which we shall examine below, the orientation is rarely completely ordered and the ordering which becomes visible in polarized light can be detected only when the traces of the optic axes on the stereogram become sufficiently concentrated; generally speaking, zonal orientation can be revealed only by statistical methods. Therefore, it is not surprising that most investigators have been unable to detect ordered orientation visually in glacier ice. However, many have observed a special orientation where the main axes are perpendicular to the movement and to the bed. This has been observed in mountain glaciers (Bertin, 1866; Hagenbach-Bischoff, 1882; Sherzer, 1907; *et al.*), in the tributaries of the Greenland ice sheet and in Antarctic icebergs (Drygalski, 1897, 1921), which indicates that this phenomenon is quite widespread.

It has been established by statistical methods that ice which has experienced flow has regular orientation in both temperate glaciers (Perutz and Seligman, 1939; Demorest, 1941) and "cold" glaciers (Shumskii, 1947*a*, *b*). On a stereogram of the structure of secondary-recrystallization ice, the optic axes are sometimes grouped in bands, elongated in the direction of movement, generally retaining an orientation perpendicular to the direction of movement (Fig. 98). The large crystals usually have a more sharply defined uniform orientation than do the small crystals, which are more scattered (Fig. 99). In places, a structure with a semizonal orientation of the axes perpendicular to the direction of movement is observed, where the crystal axes deviate as much as $45°$ to both sides of the *c*-direction in the *bc*-plane (Figs. 100 and 101).[7]

In a polycrystalline aggregate with tightly packed grains, the grains not only do not have the structural freedom required for independent movement, but neighboring crystals even obstruct slipping of the layers along the basal planes within the grains, while plastic flow becomes increasingly more difficult as the grains become smaller. Therefore, flow, i.e., the shear deformation of polycrystalline ice, takes place in such a way that crystals whose basal planes are

---

[7] For additional information on glacier ice structure, see H. Bader (1951), P. Rigsby (1951), W. Schwarzacher and N. Untersteiner (1953) and Chap. VIII of the present work.

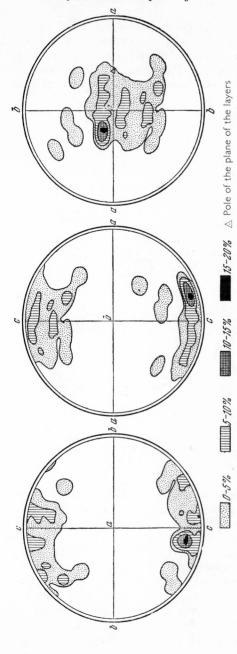

Fig. 98. Stereogram of the crystallographic orientation of "cold" secondary-recrystallization ice, whose texture is depicted in Fig. 24.

oriented in the shear plane deform plastically, while elastic bending of the elementary basal plates occurs in crystals with a different orientation, and crystals in an even less favorable position break, i.e., cataclasis occurs. The elastic bending of crystals leads to the appearance of optic anomalies, cloudy extinction and biaxiality,

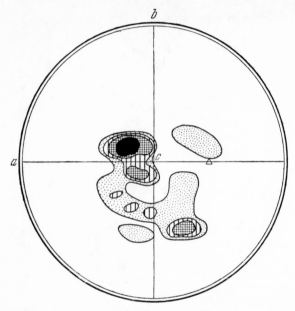

△ Pole of the plane of the layers

FIG. 99. Stereogram of the crystallographic orientation of the same sample of secondary-recrystallization ice as in Fig. 98, constructed for the large crystals only.

which are almost always observed in ice that has experienced flow. The described irregular, spasmodic nature of ice flow can be explained by the periodic accumulation and removal of elastic stresses in the crystals.

Grains which have experienced only plastic deformation have less internal free energy and during recrystallization or regelation perecrystallization grow at the expense of grains which were subjected to elastic deformation and which, therefore, have greater free energy. Consequently, it is not a matter of the larger crystals growing at the expense of the smaller crystals, but of crystals which are more favorably oriented with respect to the direction of movement in a

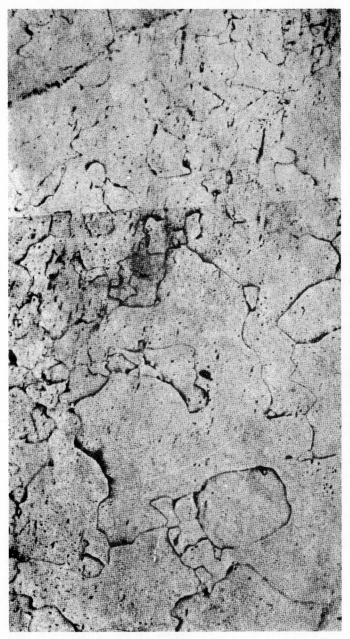

FIG. 100.   Structure of "cold" secondary-recrystallization ice with semizonal orientation. Actual size. (Photograph by N. V. Cherepanov.)

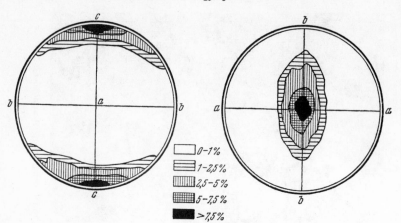

FIG. 101. Stereogram of the crystallographic orientation of the ice depicted in Fig. 100.

given section of the glacier growing at the expense of those less favorably oriented. The process of grain growth in a glacier, as well as the formation of ordered orientation, are very closely connected with the flow of ice.

During the flow process, the less favorably oriented crystals become smaller not only because of migratory perecrystallization which favors neighboring grains, but also because they disintegrate into smaller crystals of similar orientation which are better able to resist the stresses acting on them. The disintegration may result from polygonization or cataclasis, but the influence of these two can be distinguished only in the (apparently rare) cases where cataclasis leads to the formation of an open crack, into which air penetrates. Then, after regeneration, the plane of the former crack remains visible because of the thin network of minute air bubbles included in the ice (Figs. 102 and 103). The crystal boundaries which appear as a result of cataclasis and especially of polygonization differ from the ordinary recrystallization boundaries only in that they are straight.

The fracturing of the crystals removes the elastic barriers to movement. This explains phenomena such as the smooth progress of ice deformation under secondary loading and the fact that once ice flow has begun, it continues under a pressure considerably smaller than that required to initiate the flow (Tarr and von Engeln, 1915, p. 92).

The direction of flow in a glacier does not remain constant with respect to the orientation of the moving ice mass, but fluctuates somewhat. Furthermore, during flow, ice is also subjected to the

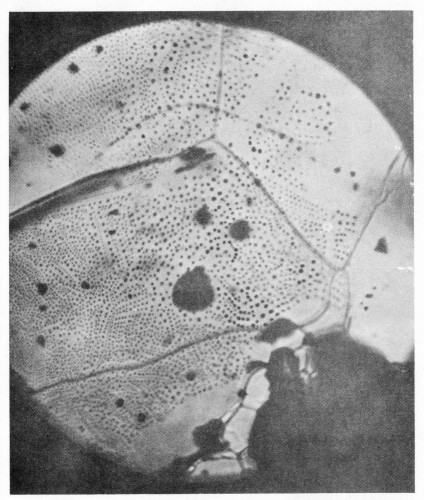

FIG. 102. Network of hypogenous air inclusions in the plane of a regenerated
crack in the ice. × 125. (Photograph by B. I. Vtiurin.)

complex system of stresses described in the preceding chapter. Therefore, in time polygonization and cataclasis may also affect grains
which have already grown out and have been oriented in a specific
direction of flow. In this case, it is very important that the stresses on
a crystal in the aggregate and the danger of fractionation of such a
crystal increase as the crystal becomes larger. Therefore, a grain
cannot grow indefinitely during flow, but is altered by crushing from

time to time after it has reached a certain size limit. This crushing usually occurs in the sections of the glacier where the ice is subject to the greatest stresses, e.g., in ice falls, in connection with which smaller grains are observed under ice falls. Tammann (1929) ex-

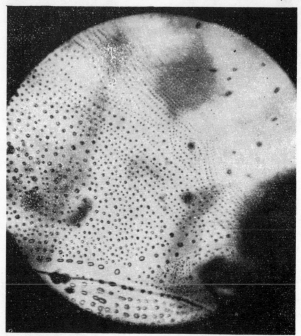

FIG. 103.   Network of hypogenous air inclusions in the plane of a regenerated crack in the ice. × 125. (Photograph by B. I. Vtiurin.)

pressed the idea that the antiquity of Antarctic glaciation requires that all of Antarctica be covered exclusively with monocrystalline ice, in which the semblance of separation into fine crystals is created merely by the saline interlayers which had been preserved around former grains. This does not comply with reality at all, and Tammann made this blunder specifically because he did not consider glacier movement and its dual effect on ice crystals.

Ice flow is a requisite for the growth of glacier grains (if we exclude growth by collective regelation perecrystallization, which will be discussed later). This is proved beyond a doubt by the regular crystallographic orientation of the secondary-recrystallization ice with respect to the direction of movement and by the lack of grain growth in the passively transported, *inactive* upper crust of a glacier.

However, only slow and smooth flow leads to grain growth, while any acceleration of deformations accompanied by increased stresses[8] causes crushing of the grains.

This, basically, explains the grain-size distribution in the moving ice of glaciers, clarified in particular by recent investigations in the Alps and Scandinavia (Seligman, 1949; Ahlmann and Droessler, 1949; Mercanton, 1950; *et al.*). Generally, the grain size at the surface of a glacier increases from the upper reaches toward the terminus of the glacier and the longer the glacier is, the larger the grains will be. The grains are smaller in steep glaciers and apparently this is due not only to the briefer process of paratectonic perecrystallization, but in part to the greater intensity of the stresses. For these same reasons, the grain size increases from the middle toward the edges of the glacier in the transverse profile.

According to earlier observations (Drygalski, 1897, p. 483), the grains in the Greenland glaciers scarcely reach the size of a walnut, and in a few exceptional cases, the size of a small pear. Since crystals 14 × 12 × 9 cm, weighing as much as 700 g (Hagenbach-Bischoff, 1882) were found in the active ice at the termini of alpine glaciers, A. B. Dobrowolski (1923, p. 653) hastily concluded that polar glaciers generally have finer-grained ice than do alpine glaciers, because the colder polar temperatures delay perecrystallization. The Antarctic researchers Wright and Priestley (1922, pp. 107 and 124) even thought this could be expressed as a direct relationship: the average grain size in glaciers decreases as the local average annual temperature. However, all this can be explained as follows: the deep ice layers subject to flow rarely emerge onto the surface because of the slight melting in polar glaciers. What is more, detailed study of Greenland glaciers has revealed ice with grains the size of "muskmelons" (Fig. 104). One may object that the deep layers of ice in Greenland are at the melting point, but my investigations of glaciers that were "cold" to the bottom, smaller than alpine glaciers and with an average ice temperature as low as −10°C below the surface crust, revealed crystals as large as 12–16 cm in diameter (Fig. 24), weighing 500–700 g. Crystals this size are rarely found in the Alps. The average grain diameter of the "warm" alpine glaciers does not exceed 2.5 cm anywhere, while in comparatively small "cold" glaciers it is often greater than 5 cm.

---

[8] We mention this because the process can follow another direction, which leads to the formation of the so-called "blue bands" (see this chapter, the section entitled "Regelation metamorphism," under the heading "Metamorphism induced by friction").

From this we can conclude that temperature does not have much of an effect on the rate of paratectonic perecrystallization within the range 0° to 10°C and that this effect is masked by other factors. It must be assumed that at temperatures of −5°C to −10°C migratory perecrystallization in ice of negligible salinity occurs basically by

Fig. 104.   Monocrystal of ice of the Grand Quarajaq [Store Isbrae] glacier in Greenland. (Photograph by I. Georgi.)

recrystallization in the solid phase, while at the melting point the grains are separated by a liquid film and regelation perecrystallization should play the main role.

Thus, the data given here on the grain sizes of "temperate" and "cold" glaciers indicate that recrystallization at the lower temperatures occurs in the solid phase at least at approximately the same speed as in the case of an intermediate transition across the liquid phase at the melting point. Perhaps this is connected with the more rapid accumulation of salts between the crystals of "warm" ice, and Tammann's observations indicate that salts retard perecrystallization.

The difference between the paratectonic perecrystallization processes in "cold" and "warm" ice is expressed most obviously in the behavior of the inclusions. The migratory recrystallization of ice in the solid phase does not exert any influence on the solid and gaseous inclusions, as already noted toward the end of the nineteenth century (Deeley and Fletcher, 1895). The moving boundary of the crystals passes around the inclusion on all sides and the inclusion gradually moves with respect to the crystals: it moves from one crystal to another, from the boundary inside the crystal, etc. Thus, solid salts in the hypoeutectic are not redistributed during recrystallization.

The liquid salt interlayers behave differently. During regelation perecrystallization, isolated salt inclusions previously situated within the grains get into the moving liquid film between the grains and, consequently, the film thickness increases at a given temperature. Very slow migration of the solution downward, its removal with the melt water along the drainage channels and cracks and the gradual removal of salt from the ice become possible after the salt films have reached a certain thickness at the melting point. On the basis of 50 electrometer determinations of the general mineralization of the ice of Swiss glaciers, it was established (Renaud, 1949) that both the central parts of the ice crystals and the liquid films between the crystals are less saline at the glacier termini than in the firn region.

The ice of cold glaciers, whose temperature is several degrees below zero, is not hypoeutectic, since the most widely distributed salts have a considerably lower eutectic temperature. However, because the liquid phase content in sedimentary ice at temperatures below $-1°$ to $-2°C$ becomes negligibly small, the salts probably do not form a continuous film, but only isolated inclusions between the crystals. In part, the crystals come into direct contact with each other and this permits recrystallization in the solid phase; then the isolated liquid inclusions, like the solid or gaseous inclusions, are surrounded by grain boundaries. Evidently, this also explains the relatively high rate of perecrystallization of "cold" ice which has experienced flow.

The form and mutual orientation of the air inclusions do not change during paratectonic perecrystallization, only the position of the inclusions with respect to the ice crystals changes. Furthermore, during the flow of the ice the air inclusions may deform together with the crystal which contains them, flattening in the direction of shear. Therefore, the stratification and other primary structural features resulting from the arrangement of the air inclusions are generally preserved in the secondary-recrystallization ice, but become less clearly defined and completely lose their affiliation with texture. The interlayers of bubble ice penetrate the individual parts of large monocrystals and pass into neighboring crystals, while the rest of the crystal remains completely transparent or contains a bubble of different form and genesis. This is responsible for a characteristic feature of secondary-recrystallization ice, namely: its air inclusions (e.g., the remnants of firn pores), which are typically intersertal, are situated within the crystals.

The air bubbles in secondary-recrystallization ice are not always flattened to a great extent, but even when they are completely flattened, one may distinguish between the basic types of bubbles, i.e., simple autogenous forms and branching hypogenous forms, because the hypogenous bubbles retain their narrow lateral spurs.

During flow, at first the ice slowly becomes submerged in the glacier in the accumulation region and then gradually melts onto the surface in the ablation region. In this process, at first the ice is subjected to ever increasing hydrostatic pressure (up to 100–150 atm in large glaciers and in ice sheets), then the pressure decreases. This entails some behavioral features of air inclusions in ice which may be regarded as indirect results of flow metamorphism, since flow is the basis of glacier movement.

As the ice becomes submerged in the accumulation region, the air bubbles become compressed by the ice, decrease in volume and the air pressure increases almost to the value of the external pressure. The reverse process takes place in the ablation region as the load decreases, i.e., the bubbles expand, but this process differs in "cold" and in "warm" ice.

In "cold" ice, the compression process with subsequent expansion of the air bubbles is not completely reversible, since only a negligible part of the work in it is expended on the elastic change of volume; most of it is expended on the plastic deformation of ice. For reverse expansion to occur, the air pressure on the walls of the small bubbles scattered throughout the ice mass must overcome the great resistance of internal friction that appears during the omni-directional expansion of ice. Therefore, in "cold" ice a large pressure excess remains in the bubbles after the external pressure has been removed. Koch and Wegener (1912) found a pressure of 8.4–10.0 atm in the ice of the Storström glacier. Shumskii obtained almost the same air pressure (up to 9 atm) with much greater measurement accuracy in the ice of the bottom layers of comparatively small cold glaciers. The large pressure variations in neighboring layers with bubbles of different size and number was an interesting feature in this case.

The air bubbles expand differently in "warm" ice (Bader, 1950). As the ice becomes submerged in the accumulation region, the water on the walls of the bubbles should freeze, since the pressure in them is less than the external pressure on the ice. Consequently, the "adiabatic" water in the submerging ice will not appear in the air bubbles, but at the boundaries between the crystals. Conversely, while the ice melts out onto the surface, the bubbles expand because of the melting of the surrounding ice and the volume decreases 9.08%. When the hydrostatic pressure decreases, the ice temperature increases because of the heat generated by the freezing "adiabatic" water, but at the same time the walls of the bubbles melt because of the excess air pressure and the air is enclosed in a water shell which contains part of the air in a dissolved state. Such "water bags" around the bubbles were described back in 1858 by Tyndall, who observed them in ice which had not been affected by solar radiation.

The air pressure p_1 in the bubbles with a "water bag" can be determined by puncturing the ice at the lower opening of the bag and by measuring the increase in the bubble diameter:

$$p_1 = p_{atm} \frac{d^3_{atm}}{d^3_1}$$

where p_{atm} is atmospheric pressure; d_1 is the initial diameter of the bubble and d_{atm} is the diameter of the bubble after the ice has been punctured.

As the ice melts and the "water bag" forms, the bubble expands, but an ever increasing amount of air passes into the solution. The initial air pressure before the melting of the bubble walls can be calculated by the ratio of the amount of air in the bubble to the water in its "water bag."[9]

In this connection, a small excess air pressure in the bubbles is a characteristic feature of "warm" ice that has melted out onto the glacier surface. In the ice of the Malaspina glacier, the air pressure varied between 1 and 2 atm (Bader, 1950), while in the ice of one of the alpine glaciers, the air pressure was only 0.5 atm (Mercanton, 1917). It is even more interesting that the initial air pressure, before the walls of the bubbles in the ice of the Malaspina glacier melted, was only 1.6–2.3 atm, although the ice was taken at the terminus of a very large glacier and, according to the investigator's estimate, the pressure on this ice in the glacier was of the order of 50 atm. However, apparently "warm" ice, like cold ice, is impermeable for air, which has no egress from the glacier, and the pressure is reduced by the unique mechanism of ice expansion.

The air bubbles of "warm" ice do not have a higher air pressure

---

[9] We have not given the measurement and computation method developed by H. Bader, because it is more complicated and less accurate than the method, described earlier, of freezing the sample and measuring the pressure.

and "water bags" unless they are situated within the crystals. When the crystal boundary, which moves during the perecrystallization processes, reaches the "water bag" the excess pressure of the bubble drives the water into the intergranular film, where its excess freezes on the walls of the crystals, separating them. Consequently, the air bubble is liberated from the "water bag" and expands. This is repeated every time the grain boundary passes through an air bubble. In melting out onto the surface, the bubble ice of the Malaspina glacier increased 2.5% in volume, in the manner described (Bader, 1950).

Secondary-recrystallization ice has *oriented crystalloblastic texture*, primarily granoblastic, but sometimes with the grains elongated and flattened in the shear plane, similar to lepidoblastic texture. The grains have an irregular, serrated form and are as much as 15 cm or even more in diameter; thus they are larger than the grains of primary-recrystallization ice and other primary types of sedimentary-metamorphic ice. The main axes are oriented primarily perpendicular to the direction of movement and the orientation varies from linear to semizonal. The ice always experiences a certain amount of cataclasis and is characterized by optic anomalies.

The texture and composition of secondary-recrystallization ice is generally relictal, primary, more or less darkened by deformations (flattening) of the air bubbles and also by changes in the shape of the air bubbles during the formation and destruction of the "water bags" in the "warm" ice. Texture is completely divorced from structure: the hypogenous inclusions lose their intersertal arrangement and penetrate into the crystals. Quantitatively, the material composition of the rock corresponds to the primary composition, except for some freshening of the "warm" ice. The pressure of the included air is higher: in "warm" ice it is negligible, in cold ice it is as much as 10 atm, depending on the depth to which the ice descends into the body of the glacier. The density of the rock at the moment it changes from firn to ice can be determined from the data on the pressure of the included air, which can be used to identify the primary structure of the ice.

METAMORPHISM INDUCED BY PRESSURE

Directed pressure on ice may produce completely different results, depending on the magnitude of the pressure and its rate of increase, on temperature and the possibility of lateral expansion of the ice. The main types of pressure metamorphism are cataclasis, extrusion flow and temporary melting—the regelation of ice.

Cataclasis of Ice Under Pressure

In petrography, cataclasis means the bending, cracking or complete crushing of some (and sometimes all) of the rock components by dynamic processes. Weak cataclasis in ice can be detected in cloudy extinction in polarized light with an analyzer and in optic biaxiality, which results from bending of the basal platelets of ice. Stronger cataclasis is expressed in the disintegration of large crystals into groups of smaller ones. A further intensification of directed pressure which is already increasing at a sufficient rate, with the possibility of unobstructed lateral expansion, results in fracturing, crushing and hummocking of the ice. On the other hand, when the directed pressure increases slowly or lateral expansion is impeded (in the case of hydrostatic pressure), the ice does not crush, but flows, and extrusion flow begins. However, as experiments have shown, even when the continuity of the ice mass is preserved, powerful deformations, in particular the extrusion of ice through openings, cause the large crystals to break up into groups of small crystals and this is sometimes accompanied by a considerable change in the crystallographic orientation (see, for example, Tarr and von Engeln, 1915, p. 90).

From what has been said, it can be seen that cataclasis without disruption of the continuity of the rock is an essential component of flow metamorphism produced either by shear deformation or by extrusion. It plays an independent role in the ice of some perennial veins. The lateral pressure in perennial ice veins, increasing slowly from year to year, cannot lead to fracture and crushing or to extrusion flow, because there is not much resistance to the expansion of ice perpendicular to the pressure, i.e., vertically. It is not the ice but the more plastic, i.e., the less viscous, enclosing frozen rock that is extruded. It crumples into folds in the process and often is split by cracks into a series of blocks, which are displaced with respect to each other (Fig. 105). Since extrusion may act only upward, the resistance of enclosing rock to extrusion increases downward, and the lateral pressure in the epigenetic perennial ice veins increases with depth. The lateral pressure in the "syngenetic" veins becomes great primarily in the sections which cut through the more rigid, sandy layers of enclosing rock. A considerable portion of the larger primary crystals in the sections of perennial ice veins which experience powerful lateral pressure disintegrate into groups of small crystals with similar crystallographic orientation and straight boundaries. As a result, *cataclastic* or *pseudoporphyritic texture* appears, in which the large primary crystals remaining among the fine crushed granules look like phenocrysts. A considerable portion of the crystals is

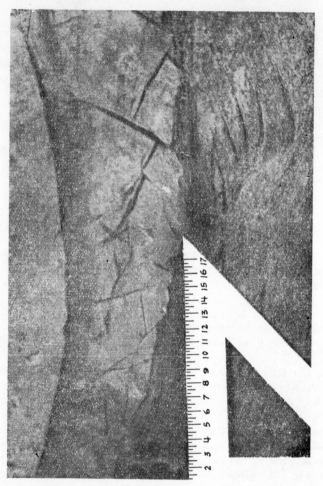

FIG. 105. Vertical section of the contact of a perennial ice vein with the enclosing frozen rock. The dark area represents the ice, the light area, the frozen rock. There is a series of diagonal faults between the main body of the vein and the apophysis. (Photograph by B. I. Vtiurin.)

optically biaxial; in some cases the average angle of the optic axes of all crystals is 10–12°, while in individual crystals it can reach 30–50°.

It is interesting to note that the exceptionally strong flexures of crystals of perennial vein ice do not result in the growth of some crystals at the expense of others.

Furthermore, the optic biaxiality does not show any tendency to decrease even after remaining in an unloaded state for a long period of time (up to 4 years). This is explained by the intensive polygonization of the curved crystals into a series of tiny blocks which have a very similar orientation and which are indistinguishable in polarized light, but which seem to be biaxial because they enter the field of view of the microscope simultaneously. Only this pseudo-biaxiality can persist for a long time. It is not associated with elastic stresses in the lattice, for these stresses had relaxed long before, during polygonization. Naturally, such processes do not lead to crystal growth, as in the case of ice which has been subjected to flow.

The secondary compression of air inclusions is a characteristic feature of perennial vein ice which has experienced lateral pressure that exceeded its elastic limit. The pressure of air enclosed in some sections of the perennial ice veins reaches 1.5–1.7 atm. This is accompanied by flattening of the air bubbles, which become disks oriented in the place of the vein, i.e., perpendicular to the direction of the pressure (Fig. 106).

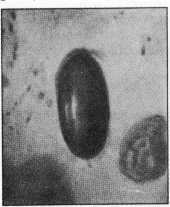

Fig. 106.   Discous bubble, flattened by lateral pressure, in the ice of a perennial ice vein. × 20. (Photograph by B. I. Vtiurin.)

A similar deformation of the air bubbles should occur in "warm ice," even under less pressure.

W. Thomson (1858) showed by theory and experiment that all the water cavities and air bubbles in the ice should flatten in the planes perpendicular to the direction of pressure, because the melting temperature decreases under pressure. This flattening is caused by local pressure differences created by the bubbles. If two bubbles are situated along the line of pressure, the pressure between them will

decrease and the pressure around them increase; however, if the
bubbles lie along a line perpendicular to the pressure, the partition
between them will be under higher pressure and the surrounding ice
under lower pressure. In both cases the bubbles flatten. In the first
case they are separated by a thicker freezing partition, in the second
case they grow toward each other. The same thing will happen when
the bubbles are situated obliquely. Thomson made the erroneous
assumption that the stratiform or banded structure of glacier ice
develops in this way, forgetting that only the deformation of the
bubbles was being considered, not their redistribution within the ice.
The abovementioned structural features of glacier ice are of either
sedimentary or tectonic origin and are associated with shear deformations, not with pressure.

The cataclasis of ice with destruction of the rock, i.e., fracturing,
crushing and hummocking due to tangential compression, takes
place exclusively in the ice covers of water, which are thinner than
the ice covers of land and thus are better able to bend and expand
laterally. Further, pressure produced by external dynamic forces
increases at a greater rate in the ice covers of water than in those of
land. The collision of floating glacier termini rarely results in
hummocking.

The slow lateral compression of an ice cover leads to the formation

Fig. 107.   Double brachyanticline of sea ice formed under the pressure of a
glacier projection. (Photograph by N. V. Cherepanov.)

of gentle folds, which break open in the curve of the fold in the vicinity of the axial plane after a certain critical limit has been passed (Fig. 107). Much larger ridges and swellings, which cause intensive cracking of the ice, are observed at points where glaciers meet or fuse at an angle, especially the thin glacier margins. Rows of large, gently sloping waves which stretch for hundreds of kilometers and which are caused by tangential pressure have been observed in the floating ice shelves of the Antarctic (Bucher, 1942).

The compression fracturing and hummocking of the ice covers of water often begin at the earliest stage of ice formation and recur periodically during the entire period of growth and existence of the ice. N. N. Zubov (1944) distinguishes three types of hummocking on the basis of the shape of the ice accumulations; the three types coexist in varying degree:

(1) the thrusting of flat floes, which is especially characteristic of young, thin ice and results in *rafted hummocks;*

(2) the breakup and extrusion of large floes to an inclined or vertical position, forming *broken hummocks;*

(3) the crushing of the edges of the floe into fine fragments and the amassing of ridges or banks, forming *fractured hummocks.*

On the sea, hummocks reach a height of 5–7 m, sometimes 13 m, above water level, while the ice accumulations on shoals, the "stamukhas," attain heights of 15–20 m and sometimes 40 m. Hummocks on lakes and rivers are not this high.

Sometimes enough time passes between the crushing of the ice floes and the amassing of the hummocks or the freezing together of the ice fragments to round out the moving and rotating pieces of ice. After freezing together, an ice cover of this type becomes tectonic breccia or conglomerate, cemented by the congelation ice of subsequent generations. Usually, fracturing and crushing are preceded or accompanied by mechanical damage to the crystals of different parts of the ice which retain their external appearance of continuity; therefore, the first generations of ice in a hummocked, highly compressed ice cover of water often have cataclastic or pseudoporphyritic texture. Optic biaxiality with optic axes up to 20° has been observed in sea-crystals (Golovkov, 1936).

Ice covers of this type may be regarded as a single type, viz., *compression-cataclastic ice.*

Extrusion Flow

Extrusion flow in ice takes place under the influence of directed pressure with the possibility of lateral expansion, when there is a pressure increase slow enough to avoid crumpling or when there is hydrostatic pressure which prevents crushing. In this case, the flow is perpendicular to the pressure. Extrusion flow occurs in individual sections of the glacier body where an excess unilateral pressure is created for some reason. Often it is accompanied by intensive folding and *macrofluvial, banded structure*, which usually can be detected only from the arrangement of the interlayers of mineral inclusions or air bubbles (Fig. 108).

Fig. 108.   Bottom part of a glacier with macrofluidal banded structure.
(Koch and Wegener, 1930.)

Most often extrusion flow and fold formation in the bottom layers of glaciers are caused by the resistance offered to normal flow by the projections of the bed and the accumulations of moraine material in the ice. Carol (1943, etc.) made direct observations of extrusion flow above a projection of a glacier bed. The general velocity of flow of the ice at the bed was 36.8 cm/day, but the 88-cm thick bottom layer of ice, which was compressed by a rock projection of the bed, extruded over the obstacle at a rate of 71.8 cm/day, i.e., at twice the normal velocity. Unfortunately, the author's description of the ice itself ("consistency, close to that of cheese") contributes little to an understanding of the changes experienced by the ice. What is important is that the water percolated down from the ice along innumerable capillaries (evidently, along the grain boundaries).

Regelation Metamorphism

If the directed pressure is sufficiently intense and increases rapidly enough, the individual sections of ice which had been rendered less plastic by an admixture of mineral inclusions cannot eliminate the excess pressure by extrusion flow, and melt. Evidently, this is a widely distributed phenomenon in the bottom layers of glaciers that have been overloaded with moraine and decelerated by projections of the bed. Owing to the pulsating nature of the ice movement in the bottom sections, which are more viscous because of the moraine admixture, the ice melts periodically, the excess stress is removed and new freezing occurs. Local pressure differences may amount to many atmospheres over a distance of only a fraction of a meter. It has been demonstrated that considerable portions of the ice in the bottom layers melt, not only in temperate glaciers but also in "cold" glaciers.

These processes are particularly interesting from the standpoint of the mechanism of glacier erosion, which should be greatly facilitated by frost weathering. The frost weathering is intensive because super-cooled melt water, which is released from under pressure and drains downward, freezes in the cracks in the bed. A large amount of thermal energy is expended on the melting of ice under excess pressure and this decreases the temperature of the bottom layer of the glacier and creates a temperature gradient and heat flux from the glacier down toward the bottom layer. The mechanism of glacier erosion is created in this manner and consumes not only the kinetic but also the thermal energy of the moving ice.

However, the melting of ice under excess pressure is also interesting from the standpoint of the petrology of ice, since this process leads to the formation of a special type of ice, which we shall call *compression regelation ice*. This is produced by the melting of sections of the ice in the body of the glacier under excess pressure and the subsequent freezing of the melt water after elimination of the pressure excess. Compression regelation ice lies inside or beneath masses of secondary-recrystallization ice in the form of fairly large *regelation lenses*. The author found groups of lenses in the morainic layers on the limbs of closed folds in the bottom horizons of cold glaciers at distances up to several meters from the bed (Fig. 109).

The lenses were as much as several meters long in the direction of the fold, 20–30 cm wide and several centimeters thick. Some of the lenses became hollow cavities with only a thin layer of regelation ice on the walls, because the supercooled water under pressure could flow out from them into the longitudinal cracks of the glacier and freeze there, forming ordinary veins. The ice which filled the other

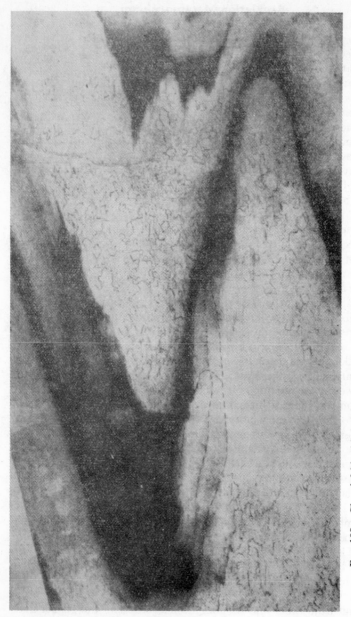

FIG. 109.   Closed fold with intensive plication in the curve of the fold [in the vicinity of the axial plane]. Section in the ac-plane. The dark area represents the interlayers of morainal material, folded like an accordion in the vicinity of the axial plane. The regelation lens is indicated by dashed lines. Half actual size. (Photograph by N. V. Cherepanov.)

FIG. 110. Section of the same fold as in Fig. 109, in the *ab*-plane. The end of the regelation lens can be seen in one of the limbs of the fold between the moraine interlayers; a small boulder can be seen on the other limb. Half actual size. (Photograph by N. V. Cherepanov.)

lenses had radial, columnar, hypidiomorphic-granular texture, close to that of rapidly crystallized congelation vein ice. The crystals grew from the walls of the lens toward the center, encountering each other along a sharply defined axial plane. Crystallization in the

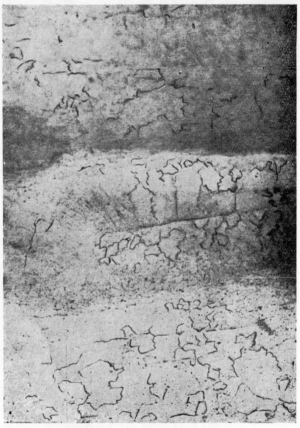

Fig. 111. Section of the middle part of the same regelation lens in the *ab*-plane. Actual size. (Photograph by N. V. Cherepanov.)

lenses began spontaneously for the most part, without any relationship to the structure of the enclosing ice. The ice was permeated by a myriad of tubular air bubbles of the oriented intergrowth type, indicating that they grew from the periphery toward the axial plane of the lenses. Some lenses had a complex structure, indicating twofold or more melting and freezing that encompassed ever smaller sections of the ice, as demonstrated by the superposition of one lens on another, partially remelted lens. Figures 109–111 are contact prints of two mutually perpendicular sections of part of a regelation lens that had experienced twofold melting, and Fig. 112 is a schematic diagram of its structural details under a microscope. *The air*

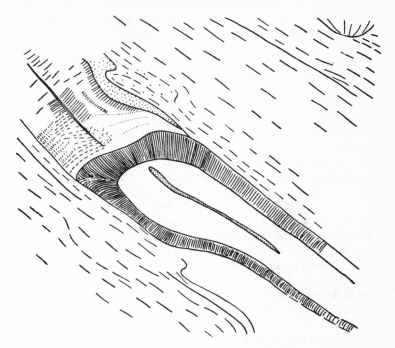

FIG. 112. Schematic diagram of the structural details of the same regelation lens, under the microscope.

pressure in the ice of regelation lenses is 3–5 atm higher than that of the *enclosing* secondary-recrystallization ice, which is a distinctive feature of compression regelation ice. The ice of the investigated regelation lenses melted at a temperature of less than −0.05°C under a pressure of at least 7 atm.

METAMORPHISM INDUCED BY FRICTION

Phenomena which are not characteristic of the entire mass of ice engaged in flow occur along the planes of motion as a consequence of a secondary effect of the plastic flow of glacier ice, namely, differential movement along the internal planes of the glacier. This movement, which does not destroy the continuity of the ice, may be concentrated along sharply defined fault planes or along fairly broad zones of higher plasticity. In the first case, when the processes develop along the lines of dislocation metamorphism, glide surfaces and sometimes friction breccia and mylonitized zones form. In the second case, the friction effect evidently is not so much mechanical as thermal, the processes develop along the lines of regelation metamorphism and result in the formation of layers of transparent blue ice, the so-called "blue bands" or ribbons. Thus far, not much study has been devoted to the question why friction metamorphism follows one or the other trend or to the details of the mechanism of "blue band" formation.

Some glaciologists still cling to L. Agassiz's view (Agassiz, 1847) that, basically, the "blue bands" of glaciers derive from the sedimentary stratification of firn. In 1844, J. D. Forbes stated that "blue bands" are metamorphic new formations, but his view has still not triumphed, despite such corroboration as the more clearly developed banded structure in the lower part of glaciers, the presence of several intersecting systems of "blue bands" and their occurrence in regenerated glaciers fed by ice falls and not associated with firn.

Actually, the proponents of the view that banded structure is of sedimentary origin could confront this evidence only with the argument that glacier movement should cause the firn layers to assume the same spoon shape as observed in the blue bands. This can be deduced from the kinematic theory of flow and has been proved by experiments on the flow of stratified wax models of a glacier (Hess, 1904, p. 170). Reid and Crammer claim to have traced the transitions from firn stratification to banded glacier ice in some glaciers. However, in cases where several intersecting systems of blue bands were observed directly, the proponents of the sedimentary origin hypothesis either denied the facts outright or assumed that part of the bands consisted of congelation veins deformed by flow or else were the seams of regenerated cracks.

The lengthy argument between these factions could only be solved by methods of structural glaciology, by which the origin of a particular structure can be determined in each individual case. The mode of occurrence of sedimentary stratification in glaciers is actually very close to that of banded structure and these types cannot always be differentiated by petrographic methods.

Dislocation Metamorphism

The investigations of H. Philipp (1920, 1932) are chiefly responsible for the recognition of the special mechanism of glacier flow along the internal glide planes. Even the adherents of the viscous flow theory of glaciers have been forced to recognize this mechanism. Philipp proved that fault planes occur extensively not only in arctic glaciers, but even in the painstakingly investigated alpine glaciers, where they had previously escaped attention.

The fault planes of glaciers are closed cracks or open cracks as much as 2 cm wide with completely smooth walls that intersect the ice crystals. Often they form a fairly regular system, penetrating the glacier tongue approximately along the planes of equal rates of movement, i.e., generally parallel to the bed. The fault planes rise in places where a junction forms because of the reduction of the slope of the bed or the ice thickness. This accounts for the spoon-shaped bedding of the planes with a reverse dip at the glacier termini and on the edges of the ice domes. When the inclination of the bed increases, sometimes two intersecting systems of faults develop, in which case the second is parallel to the steeper part of the bed. Individual, larger faults or series of imbricated thrusts develop in the bottom layers of the glaciers, sometimes cutting off the nearly stationary or moraine-ladened sections from the active upper part of the ice (see Fig. 94).

According to Philipp's data, the fault planes are closest together (0.25 m or less apart) in the zones of greatest deformation near the glacier bed and margins, farther on they are 0.5–2.0 m apart and toward the center of the glacier, as much as 3 m apart, while they do not occur at all in regions of block movement. The faults do not extend continuously for great distances, but consist of a series of individual parallel surfaces, which overlap each other echelon-fashion at the ends. The outcroppings of a series of such faults were several hundred meters long on the surface of the alpine glaciers studied by Philipp, while on the Gepatschferner they were as much as 2 km long.

There is much evidence that the upper parts of a glacier slip along the substratum, along the fault planes. This evidence includes: the displacement of structures intersected by faults, the overhang of the ice mass of hanging walls at the terminus and margin of a glacier, the lifting of moraine material along the fault planes from the floor high into the glacier and onto the surface and, finally, direct flow measurements. Displacements of structure and an ice overhang of as much as 0.5 m along the fault planes have been observed in alpine glaciers and as much as 1.5 m in the Gepatschferner, while an over-hang of several meters on each of two thrusts was observed on the face of one of the hanging glaciers of the Karakorum (Visser, 1938). Measurements made in 1905 show that the rate of flow along a thrust in the Victoria glacier of Canada was, on an average, 3 cm/day over a period of 7 days.

Friction breccia appears much less frequently along thrusts than do the narrow and clearly defined glide planes. Philipp (1932) observed friction breccia along the thrust planes in two alpine glaciers, one of them in winter. The ice in the brecciated zone was so crushed that a ski pole could be thrust almost half a meter into it. Apparently friction-breccia formation is somewhat more frequent in cold climates; it has been observed in the glaciers of East Greenland (Odell, 1937) and in Antarctica.

Crushing is more intense and widespread in the more mobile zones along the margins of glaciers which have very rapid block movement. A mylonitized zone 30 m wide was observed on the margin of the Rakhioto glacier in the Himalayas, where the rate of flow increased from 0 to 700 m/year. Apparently, there are similar zones in the rapidly moving tributaries of the Greenland ice sheet.

The phenomena of frictional dislocation metamorphism in pure form are unimportant for the formation of glacier ice, but they are of considerable interest in connection with the formation of the widely distributed ribboned and banded structures in glaciers.

Regelation Metamorphism

Bands of blue ice or ice contaminated with moraine material, as well as fault planes, i.e., thrusts, develop only in glaciers and therefore, undoubtedly, are genetically affiliated with the movement of ice. It is also characteristic that banded formations are not found in the passively transported upper crust of the glacier, which does not participate in the flow. The ribboned or banded structure of a glacier generally has the same kind of spoon-shaped bedding as do the thrust planes and the primary sedimentary stratification. The unequal melting of alternating layers of ice with different impurity contents, deriving both from sedimentary stratification and from banded structure, leads to the formation of long troughs and ridges on the surface of glaciers. These have been given various names, e.g., "furrowed ice," "rut ice," "Reid ridges," etc. In conformity with the spoon-shaped bedding of the layers and the bands, the troughs and ridges on the glacier margins extend parallel to the margin, while "ogives," i.e., arcs which are convex downward, usually form in the center of the glacier (H. and A. Schlagintweit, 1850).

In contrast to sedimentary stratification, which forms a single system, and glide planes, which form one system and occasionally two intersecting systems in places, tectonic ribbons or bands may form three or more intersecting systems of different ages. Further, the bands in each parallel system also differ in age, or at least they form alternately, in part. The bands of the different systems develop during the movement of glaciers which exhibit considerable differences in cross section or slope, causing affluence phenomena or acceleration of flow when an obstacle is encountered, and when glaciers fuse. In the glaciers of Alaska, Swedish Lapland and other regions, cases are known of a very complex and anomalous form of ogive that apparently develops because of some still unstudied anomalies of the flow and of the velocity distribution of the ice.

Sometimes the tectonic ribbons and bands in glaciers are widely spaced, but often they are almost flush against each other. The thickness of the bands varies from 1 mm to 2.5 m. The thinnest bands (1 mm) as well as bands up to 1.5–2.0 m thick have been found in Greenland. The thickest individual bands (up to 2.5 m thick) were found by the author on the thrust planes of small cold glaciers in the northern part of the Soviet Union. These bands are sometimes quite long and form a series of short lenses that overlap like tile.

These bands are either blue or "dirty" ("dirt bands," J. D. Forbes). The blue bands stand out from the general mass of enclosing glacier ice in that they consist of completely transparent ice, almost devoid of air, while the dirt bands contain varying amounts of moraine material. The ice of the blue bands is the purest of the natural ice types, has a density of 0.9166–0.9168 g/cm^3 and is highly transparent (Fig. 113). The "dirt" bands, on the contrary, are often saturated with rock fragments, and in the bottom layers they even contain large blocks of rock. However, it would be incorrect to contrast blue and dirt bands as different types, because transitions between them can often be observed in the direction of strike.

The lifting of moraine into the glacier and often the displacements of primary structures (see Fig. 114), which can amount to 1 m and more, indicate that the bands, like the fault planes, are elements along which differential ice movement occurs. It has been established that bands form between subsequent examinations of glaciers, which is a further indication that the bands are new formations which appear during glacier movement. For example, new bands appeared at the northern spur of the Quarajak Nunatak in Greenland [the Store Isbrae] over a period of one year (Drygalski, 1897, p. 242). While the displacement of a plumb line of screws in a grotto of the Eiger glacier in the Swiss Alps was being measured, it was discovered that a blue band, along which the upper mass of ice moved 3.5 mm, had formed in a period of 14 days (Perutz and Seligman, 1939).

The relationship of the distance between the bands which produce surficial ogives to the annual rate of flow of a glacier, discovered, for example, by Haefeli (1951) in the Swiss glacier Mt. Collon is another matter of great interest. This indicates a connection between band formation and the annual pressure waves beneath ice falls which

Fig. 113.   Slab of ice from a blue band 12 cm thick; on the left it becomes ordinary infiltration-recrystallization ice with air bubbles. The white flecks in the "crystal" ice were caused by a crack which formed while the sample was being taken from the glacier. (Photograph by N. V. Cherepanov.)

form because of the seasonal differences in the rate of flow of the glacier.

Various viewpoints have been expressed with respect to the actual mechanism of band formation. All researchers except those who confuse tectonic bands with sedimentary layers attribute band formation either to the pressure on the ice or to the friction during shear.

In 1866, Tyndall founded the first point of view. He considered the banded, or as he called it the "veined," structure to be pressure schistosity. In his opinion, the bands form in planes normal to the direction of greatest pressure as a result of the partial melting of ice and the release of air. However, Tyndall did not explain why only certain layers melt. The Klebelsberg view (von Klebelsberg, 1948, p. 60) that banding is the "result of strong compression, schistosity and pressure structure," is even less explicit. V. V. Piotrovich (1933) assumes that the walls of cracks which are being compressed should melt under pressure, because the rate of movement and the kinetic energy of the ice mass differ on the two sides of the crack.[10]

Consequently, the proponents of this point of view hold that the blue bands are of the same origin as the previously described lenses of compression regelation ice. However, Shumskii's measurements of the pressure of air included in the ice at the contacts of the blue bands exclude this possibility. He found that this pressure is exactly equal to the air pressure in the whole mass of enclosing ice and that it is insufficient to melt the ice in cold glaciers, where the bands are especially well developed. The structure of the blue bands is completely different from that of the compression regelation ice lenses. This means that blue-band formation cannot be attributed to melting or to shearing under excess pressure.

Forbes (1859, p. 255) considered that a "general bruise" in the direction of movement of one part of the ice with respect to another causes ribboned structure. However, since crushing alone obviously should lead to the formation of friction breccia and not blue bands, Philipp in 1914 and later others (Koch and Wegener, 1930; Hamberg, 1932) included melting of the ice in their explanation of the origin of blue bands. Movement along the fault planes in all rock is accompanied by intense friction and crushing, but only in ice is the heat produced by friction sufficient to cause temporary melting along the thrust plane.

The amount of kinetic energy converted into thermal energy by friction depends on the pressure between the rubbing surfaces; thus the movement along the faults near the glacier surface merely causes slipping or crushing, but deeper down under pressure it also melts the ice. The glide planes and the brecciated and mylonitized zones, on the one hand, and the blue bands, on the other, are merely different results of the intermittent movement caused by the pressure difference and, perhaps, the glide planes observed on the glacier surface become blue bands deeper within the glacier.

According to Philipp (1920), ordinary ice containing air inclusions crushes along the glide planes and melts simultaneously, the air is released from it and after heat is lost to the neighboring layers of ice, the water freezes, mending the plane of separation and forming

---

[10] G. Crammer expressed the idea that some of the bands are seams of regenerated cracks which had deformed during the flow process, but which had formed by the slipping of the crack walls along each other and not by pressure. This view was upheld by the Third International Glacier Conference in 1903 (see Kalesnik, 1939, p. 83). Undoubtedly, bands of such origin, as well as deformed congelation veins formed by the freezing of water in cracks, do exist in glaciers.

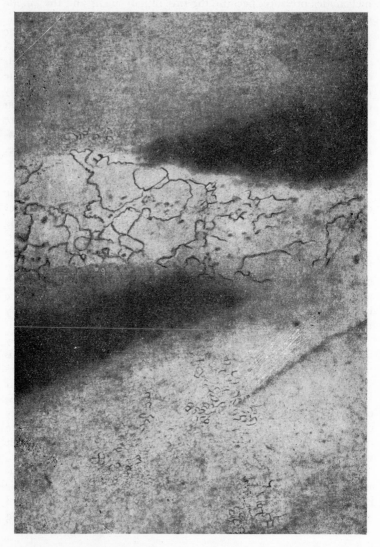

FIG. 114. Blue band intersecting a layer of moraine in fine-grained secondary-recrystallization ice. The ice of the band is relatively coarse-grained. In the band there is an axial zone of unaltered secondary-recrystallization ice. Actual size. (Photograph by N. V. Cherepanov.)

a thin blue band. The blue band becomes wider as the intensity of the crushing increases, i.e., as the hanging masses of ice become thicker and as the temperature decreases and the ice becomes harder and more brittle. According to Philipp, the separation of the bands into strips of different structure indicates that the motion is recurrent and spasmodic.

According to Perutz and Seligman (1939), neither crushing nor melting play a role in the formation of blue bands; instead the bands result from accelerated perecrystallization in specific layers of ice. However, this perecrystallization is not accompanied by a redistribution of the inclusions, whereas the blue bands form by the removal of impurities from the ice. In most cases, the air can be removed completely during band formation, but it has often been established (by the accumulations along the selvages) that air bubbles float upward, while the moraine material settles (Koch and Wegener, 1930, p. 258; Hamberg, 1932, p. 95; Perutz and Seligman, 1939, and also the author's observations).

It would be difficult to assume that this could occur without melting of the ice. The air cannot be removed completely from the ice unless melting takes place with subsequent very slow freezing. Probably this occurs during the formation of blue bands. Possibly the bands widen during the successive spasmodic motions which cause the melting of more and more layers of ice. In this case, sometimes interlayers unaffected by the regelation process remain between the remelted layers and retain the primary structure and the same type of air bubbles as in the ice which encloses the band. The axial section of the blue band in Fig. 114 shows an interlayer of this type which has not remelted.

Thus, blue bands represent ice which has formed by regelation in the presence of friction, i.e., it is *friction regelation ice.*

Although regelation quite certainly participates in the formation of blue bands, much remains to be learned about the details of the mechanism of their formation. Very little study has been devoted to the structure of the blue-band ice, but the data presently available show that it is highly diverse, which clearly indicates that the conditions and processes of blue-band formation are also highly diverse.

Blue bands are divided into two types, according to the size of their ice crystals, (1) crystals smaller than those of the enclosing ice and (2) crystals larger than those of the enclosing ice. Agassiz, Deeley and Fletcher, Meyer, Hamberg and Philipp observed bands of the first type, while Hagenbach-Bischoff and Perutz and Seligman observed bands of the second type.

My observations indicate that the blue bands in "cold" glaciers are generally of the second type (Figs. 114 and 115). The crystals in them are platy, are flattened in the plane of the bands and sometimes become as much as 22 cm in diameter in that direction. In both temperate glaciers (Perutz and Seligman, 1939) and cold glaciers, this type of band has the main axes oriented normal to the plane of

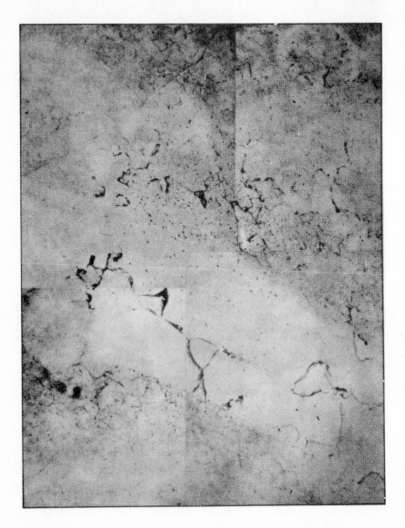

FIG. 115. Blue band with large crystals. (Photograph by N. V. Cherepanov.)

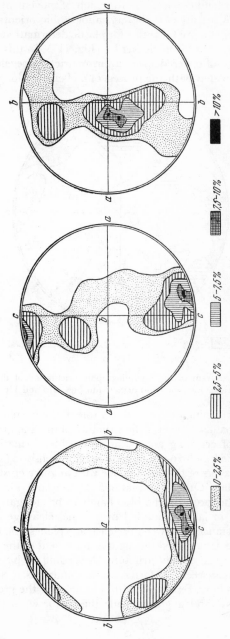

FIG. 116. Stereogram of the crystallographic orientation of the blue-band ice depicted in Fig. 115.

the band, sometimes with a tendency toward a zonal arrangement
of the axes perpendicular to the direction of movement (Fig. 116).
However, even in this case the crystallographic orientation of the
band ice is always more favorable for plastic deformation in the plane
of the bands than in the enclosing ice (Fig. 117). In this connection,
the appearance of ordered orientation of friction regelation ice is
probably connected with the process of movement along the bands.

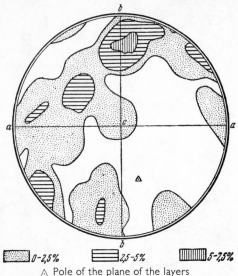

FIG. 117.   Stereogram of the crystallographic orientation of the ice which
encloses the blue band depicted in Figs. 115 and 116.

Evidently, crushing does not play a role in the formation of large-
grained blue bands. However the structure of the fine-grained bands
bears traces of crushing and cataclastic schist formation. Agassiz
(1847) described the structure of a blue band consisting of a series of
parallel interlayers of fine-grained ice with angular crystals, divided
by ice partitions. Other observations (Deeley and Fletcher, 1895)
have shown the grains in the blue bands to be elongated, flattened
and arranged in layers bounded by parallel cleavage planes. The
smaller the distance is between the cleavage planes, the finer will be
the grains that are crushed during the movement of the ice. Philipp
(1920) observed a similar structure. According to his description,
the ice of young, recently formed blue bands has a fine foliation
which can easily be separated with a knife, and the grains in each
ice leaf are fine and angular, while the ice between the bands is

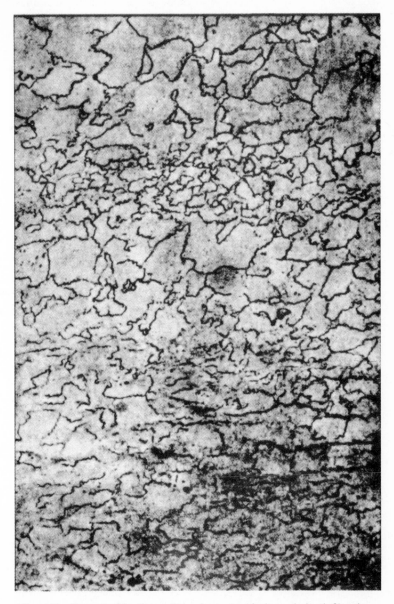

F IG. 118. Contact of the "crystal" ice (ABOVE) with the enclosing infiltration-recrystallization ice. (Photograph by N. V. Cherepanov.)

coarse-grained. One gets an impression of cataclastic separation, in which the grains were crushed by the bands, similar to the mylonitization zones of hard rocks. In other cases, the blue band had just one seam along which it could be separated.

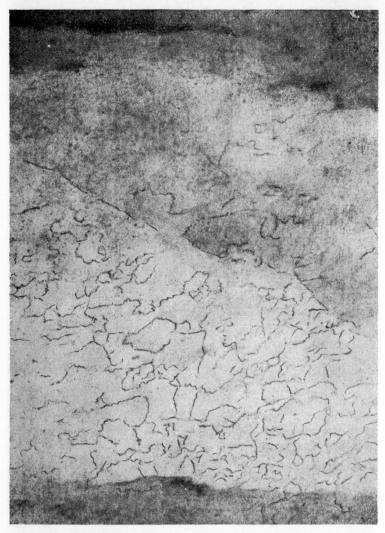

FIG. 119. Apophysis of a thick lens of "crystal" ice among perecrystallized infiltration-recrystallization ice with fluidal structure. Actual size. (Photograph by N. V. Cherepanov.)

According to Philipp, this structure is characteristic only of recently formed blue bands. With time, the ice of the bands becomes perecrystallized on participating in the flow of the ice mass, the band boundaries become undulating and indistinct and the grain boundaries no longer coincide with the band boundaries. The grains expand, regardless of the arrangement of the air bubbles, and assume an irregular, serrated and intergrown form. Apparently, the thick lenses and bands of "crystal" ice observed by Shumskii in cold glaciers are of this type (Figs. 113, 118 and 119).

According to Philipp, the possibility of longitudinal cleavage is an indication of recent band formation. The younger the band is which formed as a result of crushing, the more distinct will be its angular, fine-grained composition. Because of perecrystallization, the older blue bands can no longer be distinguished on the basis of grain boundaries and smaller grain size, but only on the basis of their color and small air content.

GRAVITATIONAL CRUSHING

To complete our review of the processes of dynamic metamorphism of ice, we should mention the gravitational crushing and rolling of ice fragments during ice avalanches.

Ice avalanches, which slide down from the termini of hanging glaciers, avoiding the steep part of the slope, become unique streams of ice fragments that gradually decelerate on the gentle slopes and floors of valleys. Friction causes a rotary motion in the streams of fragments and the fragments are rolled in the process. Since the ice becomes weak after flowing a distance of 2 km in a matter of a few minutes, the primary *ice breccia* becomes a *spherical conglomerate* or, to be more exact, an ice meal containing ice spheres up to 1 m and more in size (Heim, 1932, 1935). The result is like that of the break-up of river ice, except that it occurs considerably faster, over a course 5–10 times shorter.

Regenerated glaciers and the ephemeral avalanche cones at the foot of slopes consist of such ice breccia and flow conglomerates. The conglomerate structure of the regenerated St. Suphellebre and Böjumbre glaciers in Norway remained unchanged up to the very termini of these glaciers (Hamberg, 1932, p. 90). During flow, the fragments and blocks of ice cemented by the ice meal became flattened and elongated in the direction of movement, becoming lenses with a length-thickness ratio of 150 : 40 cm; 50 : 5 cm; 15 : 3 cm, etc. Thus, there was a semblance of schistose or parallel-fluidal structure.

Very little study has been devoted to the structure of snow-avalanche cones. In wet avalanches, usually the deposits are firmly cemented by regelation. Dry avalanche deposits consist of dense snow of fragmental, agglomerate structure. In the process of falling, wet snow is rolled and peripherally melted in the moving stream of snow and, consequently, the freshly deposited cones of the wet avalanches are accumulations of snow spheres, disks and cylinders primarily with horizontal axes of rotation perpendicular to the direction of flow, and from several centimeters to 3–4 meters in size.

CHAPTER XV

THE THERMAL METAMORPHISM
OF ICE

Collective regelation perecrystallization, the migration of inclusions caused by the temperature gradient and the partial destruction of ice are processes of the thermal metamorphism of ice.

Collective regelation perecrystallization is the only perecrystallization process which is not associated with movement and which continues to a vanishingly small velocity in medium-grained and even coarse-grained ice rocks. In contrast to paratectonic perecrystallization during which the danger of grain fractionation increases with increasing grain size, collective regelation perecrystallization does not encounter any oppositely directed processes, provided the melting is not intense. Consequently, the surface ice layers of the inactive parts of glaciers which have experienced regelation perecrystallization over a long period of time often consist of crystals larger than those of the neighboring active parts of the glaciers. The grains of dead glacier ice can be as large as 15–25 cm in diameter, i.e., they can be of the same order of magnitude as the crystals of the blue bands in glaciers (the zones of internal melting) and the slowly growing crystals of congelation ice (in the lower part of the ice cover of reservoirs, in hydrolaccoliths, etc.).

It has been noted that the grains of the surface crust of the ice tongues of the Alps are generally larger than those deeper down. In tunnels cut into two Swiss glaciers the mean grain diameter at the surface was 25–30% larger than at 8–15 m inside the glacier (Seligman, 1950). There are also cases where the grain size increased considerably (2–8fold) in ice tables (platforms) left among tunnels hewn in the glaciers. Evidently, this resulted from collective regelation perecrystallization and from the removal of load connected with the cessation of ice-flow cataclasis. In cold ice, where regelation perecrystallization cannot occur, the grains do not grow in the non-flowing ice.

The migration of inclusions. Liquid and gaseous inclusions in ice migrate toward the heat source under the influence of the temperature gradient, i.e., they follow a direction opposite that of the heat flux. In 1912, Koch and Wegener (see Koch and Wegener, 1930, p. 256) first established the inevitability of this process for gaseous inclusions and later Whitman (1926) proved it theoretically and experimentally for liquid salt inclusions. The saturated vapor pressure on the end of an air bubble facing a higher temperature is higher than on the opposite end of the bubble, which causes diffusion of the water vapor in the direction of thermal flux, volatilization of the ice at the warm end of the bubble and sublimation at the cold end. Consequently, the walls of the bubble and, of course, the air contained in it shift to the opposite end, toward the heat source. This process is slow, because it requires a large amount of heat and is accompanied by a change in the shape of the bubble during migration. The curvature of the bubble surface increases at the vaporizing end and decreases at the opposite end. As the bubble becomes longer, the temperature difference at the ends of the bubble increases and the process is accelerated, which causes the bubble to stretch. On the other hand, the reduction of the saturating vapor pressure with increasing curvature of the concave surface prevents extreme elongation. Therefore, the temperature gradient should cause the air bubbles to become cylindrical or slightly pear-shaped with the wide part at the cold end.

The same thing happens with the cells of salt solution in ice. The equilibrium concentration of salt is lower at the warm end of the cell than at the cold end, the salt ions diffuse in the direction of least concentration and the equilibrium concentration is disturbed: ice melts at the warm end of an inclusion and water freezes at the cold end. As a result, the salt solution cell becomes elongated and migrates toward the heat source.

In a sea ice cover with a large temperature gradient, salt migrates downward comparatively rapidly and in summer this is accelerated still more by the drainage of the heavier solution downward along the melt channels and by the replacement of this solution with atmospheric air. This freshens saline ice and the freshening process continues with time, particularly during the summer periods.

The migration of air inclusions is less important. The temperature gradient is too small within old, large ice massifs and it changes direction completely on a periodic basis in the surface layer, where it becomes quite large.

The partial destruction of ice. This phenomenon results from the irregular selective melting of ice, which is influenced by two factors:
   (1) radiant energy,
   (2) the irregular distribution of inclusions which have a higher coefficient of absorption of radiant energy than does the ice.

Selective melting can take place along the ice crystal boundaries with a very slow influx of heat by conductive heat transfer, because the thin intermediate layer at the crystal boundaries is less stable and the salt impurities which collect there depress the melting point. However, when the ice surface comes into contact with relatively warm air, as a rule the heat influx resulting from convection is too rapid to be expended on selective melting alone and the surface begins to melt away uniformly. Therefore, one may distinguish two different processes of ice melting:

(1) the thermal process, primarily convective surface melting;

(2) radiation "volume" melting.

Thermal melting, which may include the entire surface of an ice body in contact with air, water or other rocks, usually results in the leveling out of the melting surface. The thermal effect of flowing water is an exception; this leads to the formation of an irregular, dissected surface and internal channels and cavities in the ice. M. M. Ermolaev (1932a) applied the very apt term "thermokarst" to this group of formations. Closed melt depressions, which result from uneven radiational melting, are another element of thermo-karst topography.

The long-wave part of the radiation, which exerts the thermal influence, penetrates in ever decreasing force to a depth of several meters in a layer of transparent ice. However, after the surface layer begins to melt, it becomes much less permeable for radiant energy. Therefore, the radiational melting of ice never goes beyond a surface layer 1–2 m thick, and in snow, no deeper than 20–40 cm.

Radiational melting, which affects a relatively thick layer of ice rock, is always selective because of the uneven distribution of impurities, which are better absorbers of radiant energy than is ice. These impurities include salts and insoluble solid inclusions.

The salt inclusions lie primarily along the ice crystal boundaries. During radiational melting, a thin continuous film of liquid salt solution forms along the crystal boundaries and when this film becomes thicker it forms a network of thin channels and cells reminiscent of whitish foam (Fig. 20). Simultaneously, minute cavities saturated with water vapor appear in the melt channels and in the ice flowers, because the volume decreases during melting. As melting progresses, the water from the spaces between the crystals evaporates in part but mostly runs off and the ice separates into individual grains that are scarcely in contact with each other at some points. The melted layer becomes white and opaque, like snow, and concentrates the further radiational melting in a still thinner surface zone, This process has been called variously "sun weathering" of ice

(Buchanan, 1887, 1908), "radiational-thermal shielding" (Devaux, 1933), the formation of a "melt crust" (Konovalov, 1936), etc.

In many regions with large ice masses, radiational melting plays a clearly dominant role in the first half of the melt season, but convective-thermal melting prevails at the end of the season. In this case, the ice surface is first covered by a white "melt crust" and becomes similar to snow. In high latitudes, the cliffs and the entire surface of glaciers and icebergs are white at that time and this has even led to the erroneous idea that in high latitudes there are "underdeveloped" glaciers which never go beyond the firn stage. However, at the end of the summer, when selective radiational melting ceases, the "weathered crust" is destroyed by convective-thermal melting and a dense blue ice emerges onto the surface.

In a typical case, the radiational melt crust becomes brittle and friable, like snow, so that often one may push a ski pole half a meter or more into it. From time to time these crusts slide down the steep ice slopes and cliffs and accumulate at the foot in heaps of slightly melted ice crystals, which freeze together into sedimentary ice breccia. Generally, these formations are short-lived, because they are destroyed by forces which keep the ice cliffs vertical (melting, erosion or abrasion).

Selective melting caused by the presence of insoluble solid inclusions is of less general importance. This factor leads to the development of highly diverse, fairly large forms of surface relief of the melting ice, including ice ridges several tens of meters high, covered with a thick layer of moraine in the lower part of glaciers and corridors nearly as deep in places where the medial moraines have melted out onto the surface in the upper part of the ablation region of glaciers. These types of differential ablation have frequently been described and classified.

From the petrographic point of view, the negative microforms of selective melting are very interesting, viz: the cryoconite holes or dust wells, the glacier mills, honeycombs, etc., which form a layer of honeycomb or spongy structure corroded by melting. Usually, such a layer forms because of the irregular amount of dust or sand deposited in the melting layer. The radiational melt crust, which separates into individual crystals, is eroded still further by thin dust wells and becomes quite similar to porous firn, except that the crystals of this "secondary firn" are often considerably larger than those of ordinary firn. Another essential difference is that regressive destructive "firnification" embraces only the surface layer of ice, which is not more than a few tens of centimeters thick.

CHAPTER XVI

THE CYCLE OF SEDIMENTARY ICE METAMORPHISM

As our review of the processes of ice rock metamorphism has shown, ice of sedimentary origin is metamorphosed to a much greater extent than is congelation ice. The reasons for this are: (1) the skeletal growth forms of atmospheric ice crystals in a snow cover are thermodynamically unstable, and (2) only the sedimentary ice forms accumulate in masses large enough to experience the processes of flow and dynamic metamorphism under the influence of their own weight.

Although the processes of sedimentary ice metamorphism are highly diverse, one can detect some cyclic features in them or, to be more exact, a certain spirality. All the processes which act upon freshly fallen solid precipitation before it melts away at the terminus of a glacier or in an iceberg may be classified in two time periods, (1) from the deposition of the snow cover to the moment of ice formation and (2) from that moment until the ice melts away. The first half of the cycle, i.e., the surface processes of metamorphic ice formation, includes the stages of snow diagenesis, firnification and ice formation itself and these alternate regularly in time. The second half of the cycle includes the various deep processes of dynamic metamorphism which do not have any regular time sequence and which may alternate often as the dynamic and temperature conditions change, and it also includes the processes of thermal metamorphism of ice.

During the first half of the cycle, the random assemblage of barely contiguous ice crystals becomes a solid aggregate of ice crystals impermeable for water and air, as a rule considerably larger than the primary snow crystals. In this case, the rock density increases considerably and the porosity decreases, but the pores transform in part into closed air bubbles. Consequently, during the ice formation processes, air is either absorbed or assimilated by the ice, thanks to which the air is enclosed in individual cavities within the ice and is subjected to higher pressure and thus participates in the transfer of stresses in the rock. This assimilation of air by the ice and the presence of a system of communicating pores, which permits the migration of water and gases and the differential movements of entire ice crystals in the rock, are characteristic features of the first half of the metamorphic cycle of sedimentary ice.

The conditions and trend of the processes change essentially after the ice formation stage. In its "healthy" unmelted state the rock is impermeable for water and air. Differential movements can occur only by plastic deformation of the crystals or else along the fault planes and then only under the considerable pressure of higher masses of ice. Metamorphism leads to a further increase in the density of the rock, approaching the maximum density of pure ice. This occurs by reduction of the volume of air bubbles, in which case the air is compressed or else released and removed from the rock during temporary melting.

Thus, the composition of the final product of metamorphism approaches that of the initial material and is almost pure ice, while in the intermediate stage, during the transition from firn to ice, the composition of the rock differs most from that of the initial material because of the large quantity of enclosed air bubbles. This return to the initial stage constitutes the cyclic nature of the metamorphism of sedimentary ice. However, here, as in other cases of alleged closed "cycles" in nature, the processes actually follow a spiral,

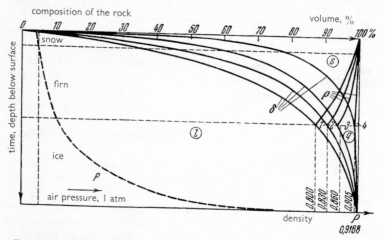

Fig. 120. Diagram of the cycles of sedimentary ice metamorphism. 1. recrystallization ice formation; 2. infiltration-recrystallization ice formation; 3. infiltration ice formation; 4. congelation ice formation; δ, density of the rock; ρ, density without the communicating pores; P, pressure of the included air; l, volume of the ice; S, volume of the pores; q, volume of enclosed bubbles.

since the initial material, i.e., the discrete ice particles, are quite different from the final product, a monolithic mass of ice.

Mechanical compression, i.e., the convergence of the crystals, the migration of material and the filling of pores in the liquid phase participate in the processes of ice formation. The metamorphic cycle differs according to the quantitative relationship of the roles of these processes in ice formation. As the role of compression increases, more air will be captured by the ice in the intermediate stage and, *vice versa*, as the role of melt water increases, the amount of air captured by the ice will decrease. If melting is complete and congelation ice forms, the density of the rock may be 0.914–0.905 g/cm^3, depending on the rate of freezing at the moment of ice formation; the density of infiltration ice varies from 0.905 to 0.860 g/cm^3; infiltration-recrystallization ice varies between 0.820 and 0.840 g/cm^3 and recrystallization ice has a density of about 0.800 g/cm^3. Figure 120 depicts these differences in the behavior of the processes of sedimentary ice metamorphism.

THE GENETIC CLASSIFICATION OF ICE ROCKS

Our genetic classification of ice, based on the processes of ice rock formation outlined above, is an attempt to extend A. B. Dobrowolski's petrographic classification of ice. Like any attempt of this type, to a certain extent it reflects current knowledge, and since our knowledge is being greatly enriched at present, undoubtedly the classification will soon have to be modified and supplemented.

We have subdivided the three basic groups of ice rocks, viz., congelation, sedimentary and metamorphic, into ten subgroups which include twenty-eight types of ice rock. Some parts of the classification could be given in further detail even now, but we have refrained from doing so in the interests of maintaining approximately equivalent systematic units. However, some of the less studied ice types, especially segregation, injection and friction regelation ice will be further subdivided once sufficient information about them has been accumulated. Only then will we be able to unify the principles of systematization which have not been full adhered to in the present classification (Table 4).

TABLE 4

GENETIC CLASSIFICATION OF FRESH ICE ROCK

Group of rocks	Subgroup	Rock	Processes and physical conditions of formation	Mode of occurrence
Congelation Ice (Analogues of Magmatic Rocks)	Ordinary congelation ice	Primary congelation ice	Protocrystallization of greatly supercooled water, especially fast moving; freezing of slush	The ice covers of moving water or its surface layers, the ice of streams, ice veins
		Selective congelation ice	Forced orthotropic crystallization with geometric selection or with participation of protocrystallization	The layers and ice covers of water, ice veins
		Orthotropic congelation ice	Forced orthotropic crystallization	The ice covers of calm water, layers in the ice covers of water, ice veins
		Rhythmic congelation ice	Omnidirectional freezing of water in a system closed by ice	The central nuclei of ice mounds and of omnidirectionally freezing masses of water on glaciers and in frozen rocks
	Repeated congelation ice	Extruded ice	Freezing of water draining along a solid surface	The layers in hydroeffusives and glaciers, the covers of the walls and floors of caverns, of cliffs and the walls of ice crevasses, columns, stalactites and stalagmites
		Perennial vein ice	Freezing of water in the frost cracks of plastic frozen rock	Polygonal network of perennial ice veins in frozen rocks
	Segregation congelation ice	Segregation ice	Slow freezing of fine-grained moist friable rocks in open systems with local redistribution of moisture	Lenticular schlieren in fine-grained frozen sedimentary rocks

Texture and Structure	Predominant orientation of the main axes	Composition	Characteristic air inclusions
Allotriomorphic - granular and platy hypidiomorphic-granular, fine-grained	None	$\delta \geq 0.8936$ $q \leq 26‰$ $p = p_{hydr}$	Autogenous and xenogenous intersertal
Columnar hypidiomorphic-granular	None or zonal, parallel to the surface of freezing and linear, parallel to the heat flux	$\delta = 0.905\text{--}0.914$ $q = 3\text{--}13‰$ $p = p_{hydr}$	Autogenous, of the oriented intergrowth type
Prismatic-granular	Parallel to the heat flux	$\delta = 0.905\text{--}0.916$ $q = 1\text{--}13‰$ $p = p_{hydr}$	Autogenous, of the oriented intergrowth type; xenogenous, of the intergrowth type
Radiolitic, allotriomorphic-granular rhythmic structure, concentric-conchoidal	Parallel to the heat flux or lacking	$\delta < 0.8936$ $q > 26‰$ $p > p_{hydr}$	Autogenous, along the basal planes
Hypidiomorphic - granular, allotriomorphic-granular, radiolitic, irregularly stratified structure	None or zonal, parallel to the surface of freezing and linear, parallel to the heat flux	$\delta = 0.8936\text{--}0.916$ $q = 1\text{--}26‰$ $p = p_{hydr}$	
Allotriomorphic - granular, platy hypidiomorphic-granular. Vertical, irregularly stratified structure	From parallel to the heat flux to random	$\delta = 0.880\text{--}0.908$ $q = 25\text{--}42‰$ $p = 1.0\text{--}1.7$ atm Mineral inclusions $2\text{--}10‰$ of the volume	Intersertal autogenous and xenogenous (up to 60%)
Prismatic-granular, hypidiomorphic - granular, allotriomorphic-granular	From normal to the surface of the schlieren to random	$\delta = 0.914\text{--}0.9168$ $q = 0\text{--}3‰$ $p = p_{hydr}$	Almost without inclusions

TABLE 4—continued

GENETIC CLASSIFICATION OF FRESH ICE ROCK

Group of rocks	Subgroup	Rock	Processes and physical conditions of formation	Mode of occurrence
Congelation Ice (Analogues of Magmatic Rocks)	Segregation congelation ice	Injection ice	Freezing of moistened friable rock in closed systems with migration and incorporation of exudable water	Laccoliths and intrusive layers in frozen sedimentary rocks
Sedimentary Ice (Snow)	Fresh snow (snow cover)	Fluffy snow	Non-eolian desposition of solid atmospheric precipitation at a negative temperature	Layer of the upper part of the snow cover
		Blown snow	Eolian deposition of solid atmospheric precipitation	Layers, lenses, snowbanks and dunes of the surface part of the snow cover
	Young snow (snow cover)	Fine-grained snow	Early diagenesis of snow: freezing together, sublimation rounding and settling	Layers, lenses, snowbanks and dunes of the snow cover
	Old snow (snow cover)	Granular snow	Epigenesis of snow: collective sublimation perecrystallization and settling	Layers and lenses of the snow cover
		Sand snow	Sublimation diaphthoresis: sublimation loss and the formation of depth hoar	Layers in the lower part of the snow cover
Metamorphic Ice	Firn	Recrystallization firn	Settling with crushing of loosened layers and recrystallization	Surface layers in the central portions of the accumulation regions of continental ice sheets; ditto, at very great elevations in mountains
		Regelation firn	Regelation rounding, collective perecrystallization and settling	Upper layers in accumulation regions of glaciers and in snowbank glaciers

Texture and structure	*Predominant orientation of the main axes*	*Composition*	*Characteristic air inclusions*
Allotriomorphic-granular	None	$\delta = 0.885{-}0.9168$ $q = 0{-}34\%_0$ $p \lesssim p_{hydr}$	—
Idiomorphic - crystalline, skeletal-crystalline porous agglomerate	None; rarely, normal to the surface of the layers	$\delta = 0.01{-}0.10$ $q = 0{-}1\%_0(?)$ $p < p_{atm}$	Hypergenous and autogenous
Clastic porous agglomerate with vestiges of skeletal	None; rarely, normal to the surface of the layers	$\delta \approx 0.10{-}0.50$ $q \approx 0{-}2\%_0(?)$ $p < p_{atm}$	Hypergenous and autogenous
Fine-grained porous agglomerate with vestiges of skeletal	None	$\delta \approx 0.10{-}0.50$ $q \approx 0.3\%_0(?)$ $p \leq p_{atm}$	Hypergenous, hypogenous and autogenous
Granular, porous agglomerate, from fine-grained to coarse-grained, in part secondary idiomorphic-crystalline	None	$\delta \approx 0.25{-}0.60$ $q \approx 2{-}7\%_0(?)$ $p = p_{atm}$	Hypergenous, hypogenous and autogenous
Coarse-grained and secondary idiomorphic-crystalline porous agglomerate	Depth hoar crystals, parallel to the heat flux	$\delta = 0.20{-}0.30$ $q = 2{-}7\%_0(?)$ $p = p_{atm}$	Hypergenous, hypogenous and autogenous
Porous granoblastic	None	$\delta \approx 0.49{-}0.80$ $p > p_{atm}$	Hypergenous and intersertal hypogenous
Porous allotriomorphic-granular, fine-grained	Parallel to the heat flux	$\delta \approx 0.35{-}0.60$ $q = 5{-}10\%_0$ $p = p_{atm}$	Hypergenous and intersertal hypogenous

TABLE 4—continued
GENETIC CLASSIFICATION OF FRESH ICE ROCK

Group of rocks	Subgroup	Rock	Processes and physical conditions of formation	Mode of occurrence
Metamorphic Ice	Firn	Infiltration firn	Infiltration densification and grain growth, settling and paratectonic perecrystallization	The deeper layers in the accumulation regions of glaciers and snowbank glaciers
	Primary sedimentary-metamorphic ice	Primary-recrystallization ice	Settling and collective recrystallization	Deep layers in the central accumulation regions of continental ice sheets
		Infiltration-recrystallization ice	Infiltration densification and grain growth, settling and paratectonic perecrystallization	Deep layers in the central accumulation regions of ice caps and snowbank glaciers
		Infiltration ice	Infiltration ice formation: filling of the firn pores with melt water and its freezing	Surface layers in the accumulation regions of glaciers and snowbank glaciers
		Infiltration congelation ice	Infiltration ice formation in melt horizons	Surface layers and lenses in accumulation regions of glaciers and snowbank glaciers
	Dynamo-metamorphic ice	Secondary-recrystallization ice	Friction-induced metamorphism: paratectonic perecrystallization and cataclasis. Extrusion flow	Main mass of moving glacier ice. Folded ice in the bottom zone of glaciers
		Friction regelation ice	Friction-induced regelation metamorphism: melting and freezing (in part, with crushing) along thrust zones	Blue and moraine-contaminated "ribbons" or "bands" in glaciers
		Compression regelation ice	Pressure-induced regelation metamorphism: melting and freezing in sections where there is a temporary pressure excess	Lenses in the bottom layers of glaciers

Texture and structure	Predominant orientation of the main axes	Composition	Characteristic air inclusions
Porous allotriomorphic-granular, coarse-grained	None	$\delta \approx 0.60\text{--}0.80$ $p > p_{atm}$	Hypergenous and intersertal hypogenous
Granoblastic	None	$\delta \geq 0.80$ $V = 125\text{--}130\%_0$ $p > p_{atm}$	Fine, branching intersertal hypogenous
Allotriomorphic-granular	None	$\delta \geq 0.82\text{--}0.84$ $V = 84\text{--}105\%_0$ $p > p_{atm}$	Coarse, branching intersertal hypogenous
Allotriomorphic-granular	Parallel to the heat flux	$\delta = 0.860\text{--}0.905$ $q = 13\text{--}62\%_0$ $p = p_{atm}$	Autogenous, of the oriented intergrowth type, arranged in clusters; layers of large intersertal inclusions
Hypidiomorphic-granular	Parallel to the heat flux	$\delta = 0.900\text{--}0.905$ $q = 13\text{--}18\%_0$ $p = p_{atm}$	Autogenous, of the oriented intergrowth type, arranged in clusters
Crystalloblastic, from granoblastic to lepidoblastic. Macrofluvial banded composition	Perpendicular to the shearing plane	$\delta > 0.80$ $0 \leq V \leq 125\%_0$ $p > p_{atm}$	Deformed (flattened) relictal hypogenous, having lost their intersertal arrangement
Allotriomorphic-granular (in part cataclastic)	Perpendicular to the plane of the bands	$\delta = 0.9160\text{--}0.9168$ $V = 0\text{--}1\%_0$ $p = p_{norm}$	None
Radial hypidiomorphic-granular	Parallel to the heat flux	$\delta > 0.80$ $0 \leq V \leq 125\%_0$ $p > p_{norm}$	Autogenous, of the oriented intergrowth type

TABLE 4—continued
GENETIC CLASSIFICATION OF FRESH ICE ROCK

Group of rocks	Subgroup	Rock	Processes and physical conditions of formation	Mode of occurrence
Metamorphic Ice	Dynamo-metamorphic ice	Friction - cataclastic ice (ice breccia resulting from friction, and mylonites)	Friction-induced crushing and abrasion in thrust zones	Glacier zones
		Compression-cataclastic ice (ice breccia and conglomerates)	Pressure-induced crushing and rolling, and the movement of fragments	Parts of the ice covers of moving water
		Clastic ice (ice breccia, conglomerates and mylonites)	Gravitational crushing and rolling during the flow of fragments	Ice-avalanche cones, the main mass of regenerated glaciers
	Thermal metamorphic ice	Regelation ice	Collective regelation perecrystallization	Surface layers of dead glacier ice
		Destruction ice	Selective radiational melting	The "melt crust" of the upper surface of ice bodies

NOTE:

δ, density of the rock in g/cm^3; q, volume of the closed air inclusions ‰; V, volume of included air under normal conditions in ‰ of the rock volume; p, pressure of the included air; p_{atm}, atmospheric pressure; p_{hydr}, hydrostatic pressure at a given level below the surface; p_{norm}, pressure of the air included in the enclosing ice.

Texture and structure	Predominant orientation of the main axes	Composition	Characteristic air inclusions
Cataclastic (breccia-like, mylonitic)	None	—	—
Cataclastic (breccia-like, mylonitic)	None	—	—
Agglomerate	None	—	—
Allotriomorphic - granular, coarse-grained	Relictal	—	—
Secondary-porous, honey-comb, spongy	Relictal	—	Secondary hypergenous

Part III

The Geography of Ice

CHAPTER XVII

THE NATURE OF THE ICE FORMATION PROCESSES

Now that we have become acquainted with the natural groups and varieties of ice rocks, we must examine the laws of their *geographic distribution* on the earth's surface.

An elementary knowledge of the properties of ice indicates that ice distribution and climate are related, and this can be fully verified empirically.

The temperature 0°C is the thermodynamic limit of the habitat of ordinary fresh ice and this limit changes but little within the range of pressures encountered in the cryosphere. However, even this outer limit of distribution of all ice rocks does not coincide with the zero isotherm of the ambient medium, because the phase equilibrium of the medium is dynamic, not static. In places where moisture is in short supply, ice undergoes volatilization and radiation melting within the range of negative temperatures, while in places where ice forms and arrives in abundant quantities, ice is preserved even when the temperature of the ambient medium is high, despite intensive melting. For example, the termini of some rapidly moving mountain glaciers penetrate into regions where ablation reaches 20–30 m/year. Furthermore, the position of the actual zero isotherm of the ambient medium is time-dependent. On the other hand, the position of the zero isotherm of the medium depends, to a considerable extent, on the climate-forming influence of the ice, which changes the radiational properties of the surface and requires the expenditure of large amounts of heat on phase transitions.

Thus, the relationship between the outer limits of ice distribution and the climate of the earth's surface is very complex, a point illustrated in part by the existence of a whole series of outer limits of natural ice distribution. Generally speaking, these outer limits are created by climate, but by no means coincide with the trend of the isotherms: the snow and firn limits, the limits of distribution of the stable seasonal snow cover and the seasonal freezing of reservoirs, the limits of distribution of floating ice and icebergs, the limits of permafrost and seasonal freezing of the soil, the limits of frosts and snowfalls which do not form stable ice and snow covers, etc. The internal boundaries between the regions of distribution of the various types of ice in the cryosphere present an equally complex picture.

The concepts of climatically-induced qualitative differences in the behavior of the ice formation processes were first based on a comparison of the size of glacier ice crystals in the polar regions and in the Alps. Many investigators (Tol', 1897; Wright and Priestley, 1922; Dobrowolski, 1923; *et al.*) thought that the ice of polar glaciers had smaller grains than the ice of temperate-zone glaciers because of the lower temperature. This has been proved incorrect, despite the apparent logic of the explanation. The principal defect of such a generalization is that it does not consider the difference between the deep and surface processes, which are caused by quite different factors.

These concepts were expressed more succinctly in Ahlmann's so-called "geophysical classification of glaciers" (Ahlmann, 1933, 1935, 1936), which has been the only attempt thus far to classify glaciers on the basis of the transformation of material in them. According to Ahlmann's classification, glaciers are divided into:

(1) *Temperate glaciers* with a thin layer of firn that rapidly re-crystallizes into ice at the melting point, and

(2) *Polar glaciers* with a thick layer of firn that slowly recrystal-lizes at constantly negative temperatures. In turn, he sub-divides polar glaciers into:

   (a) *High-polar glaciers* with firn at least 200 m thick and with no melt water whatsoever;

   (b) *Sub-polar glaciers* with firn 10–20 m thick and with melt water in summer.

Besides the obvious incongruities in Ahlmann's evaluation of the firn thickness of "temperate" glaciers [<10 m? (Shumskii's question)] and "high-polar" glaciers, his classification has other shortcomings which make it unacceptable on principle. Specifically, it does not consider the phenomena of vertical zonality and therefore simplifies the actual state of affairs considerably.

H. Sverdrup (1935, p. 390) made a more important and methodo-logically sound contribution to the explanation of the laws of the distribution of the ice formation processes. He established the exist-ence of a relationship between the magnitude of the annual firn increment and the rate of its conversion into ice, combining the problems of structural transformations with the material balance and the temperature regime.

A review of the processes of natural ice formation shows that some of these processes should be directly dependent on climate, while others can only be indirectly dependent. The first group includes the deposition of sedimentary ice, all the processes of congelation and metamorphic ice formation, and, finally, the processes of thermal metamorphism and destruction of the ice. In contrast, the processes of dynamic metamorphism of ice are indirectly dependent on climate, through intermediate factors, primarily the type, size and thickness of the ice bodies and the dynamic conditions and the temperature regime of the ice layer. Furthermore, every process in the first group is influenced to some extent by local factors that are not directly dependent on the macroclimate.

Thanks to local conditions, particularly orohydrographic conditions, the spatial distribution of the various ice rocks can be highly diverse. With all this complexity, however, certain regularities do appear in the distribution of the main types of congelation and sedimentary-metamorphic ice and reflect the latitudinal and vertical zonality of climate. A quite different type of regularity is observed in the distribution of dynamometamorphic ice types. Our first task is to examine the zonal distribution of congelation and sedimentary-metamorphic ice.

Practically speaking, there is only one natural process of ordinary ice crystal nucleation, namely, the freezing of liquid water on foreign nuclei of freezing. Ice crystals grow and form in two ways, by the freezing of water and by the sublimation of water vapor. The freezing of continuous water masses yields congelation ice; sublimation on a solid surface merely leads to the formation of individual layers of the snow cover. Most types of sedimentary ice form by the deposition of crystals of sublimation and congelation ice that had formed in the atmosphere from water vapor and droplets of supercooled water.

In the lower part of the cryosphere, where thermodynamic conditions are favorable only periodically, congelation and sedimentary ice exist during the cold season, while metamorphic ice formation processes do not play any essential role and, as a rule, the snow cover converts in part into ice only during the season of melt water runoff. Higher in the cryosphere, where ice can exist continuously, the snow cover eventually becomes ice. Three types of ice form there, (1) recrystallization, (2) infiltration and (3) congelation. There are also transitional, combined types. The regions in which one of the enumerated processes of ice formation dominates also occupy a regular position in space, which reflects climatic zonality.

The works of A. A. Grigor'ev demonstrate that the character of all the physicogeographic processes is determined chiefly by the *heat and moisture balance*[1] of the earth's surface. This is true of all the physicogeographic zones, but where the distribution of the ice formation processes is concerned, the heat and moisture balance is not merely important, it is all important. Although the heat and moisture balance exerts an indirect influence on most of the processes which play an evident role in the inner or lower geographic zones, the main processes of the cryosphere, namely, the formation and destruction of ice, are a direct expression of this balance.

To explain the mechanism of the relationship between the nature of ice formation and climate, one must study the relationship between the ice formation processes and the heat and moisture balance of the earth's surface. At present, there are still too few data to compare the total heat and moisture balance for even a few points. Nevertheless, to approach the problem properly, first one must get a picture of all the items in the material-energy balance of a surface in the cryosphere and then, by generalization, put it into a form by which the principal laws of the geographic distribution of ice rocks can be determined from the available data.

The heat balance and the temperature regime of a surface composed of any rock whose aggregate state has not undergone changes may be examined independently of the material balance, which usually is produced by mechanical processes alone or, more rarely, by chemical processes. However, the accumulation and ablation of an ice rock surface, i.e., the material balance, as well as the formation of structure and the temperature regime resulting from the energy balance are related and interrelated in a complex manner. Their interaction is depicted schematically in Fig. 121.

The amount of solid atmospheric precipitation deposited on the surface and the gain and loss of surface energy are the main factors, whose relationship determines the character of the ice formation processes. Liquid precipitation is a source of heat, but when the surface layer has a cold reserve, liquid precipitation, as well as solid precipitation, may be a source of ice. Owing to the enormous latent heat of vaporization, the vaporization-volatilization and condensation-sublimation processes exert a considerably greater influence as

---

[1] Here, the term "balance" is not used in the literal sense as equilibrium, but merely to express the laws of the conservation of energy and matter. The balance equation definitely does not require the preservation of equilibrium, i.e., the return to the initial state after some cycle of changes has been completed. This would exclude evolution. Therefore, in what follows, we shall also use the expressions "positive" and "negative" balance; in principle, the balance can be calculated for any time segment of interest to us, and the "heat balance," for instance, is defined as the change in the amount of heat.

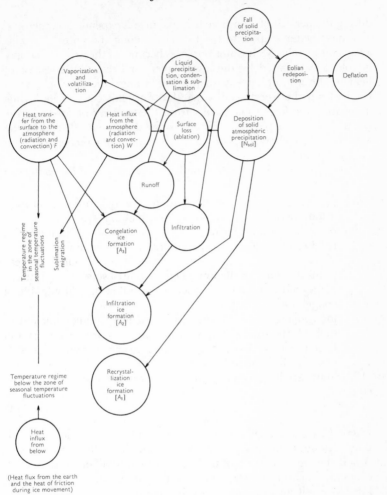

Fig. 121. The structure of the ice formation processes.

heat exchange factors than as factors of the gain and loss of surface material. Vaporization greatly reduces the rate of surface loss due to melting, while condensation increases it.

The irregular nature of the processes of heat exchange with the atmosphere, i.e., the alternation of the gain and loss of heat by the surface, causes the temperature of the surface layer to fluctuate and leads to the sublimation migration of ice in snow and firn. The excess heat which did not manage to penetrate deep into the rock during the periods of a positive heat balance is expended on melting. The melt water seeps into the firn layer along the pores or drains away completely. Melt water refreezes because of the previous supply of cold accumulated by the lower layers or because the release of heat to the atmosphere again prevails. Congelation ice formation results from the freezing of water that does not contain ice, while infiltration ice formation results from the freezing of water in the pores between ice particles. Finally, snow that is not affected by the action of the melt water, provides the material for recrystallization ice formation.

Thus, the following specific conditions are required for each type of ice formation:

(a) for recrystallization ice formation: the accumulation of solid atmospheric precipitation without melting;

(b) for infiltration ice formation: (1) the presence of an unmelted residue of atmospheric precipitation; (2) an influx of heat, causing the formation of melt water in an amount sufficient to fill the pores of the unmelted residue of solid precipitation; (3) a cold reserve in the rock or an influx of cold capable of congealing the melt water;

(c) for congelation ice formation: (1) a heat influx sufficient to melt all the solid precipitation or to cause melt water runoff from the ice surface; (2) a cold reserve or new cooling capable of congealing the melt water.

The moisture balance of a unit surface can be represented by the equation

$$N_{sol} + N_{liq} - M = A \qquad (1)$$

where N_{sol} is the algebraic sum of the solid atmospheric precipitation, its sublimation and volatilization into the atmosphere; N_{liq} is the algebraic sum of the liquid atmospheric precipitation, its condensation and vaporization; M is the runoff; and A is the gain or loss of ice (all measurements in water equivalent).

The ice formation processes are adapted to the fairly thick layer of rock next to the surface rather than to the surface itself. When undertaking a detailed study of these processes, one should make separate calculations of the heat balance of the thin surface layer which participates in the convective heat exchange with the atmosphere, the layer underlying it which still receives radiant energy, and the layers in which heat is transferred by different means, with and without infiltration. Since we do not yet have sufficient data for these separate computations, we must limit ourselves to an examination of the total heat balance of the entire layer whose regime determines the nature of the ice formation processes. The layer of seasonal temperature fluctuations is such a layer. If ice formation does not end in this "active layer," only recrystallization ice can form below it and the behavior of the recrystallization process will be only indirectly dependent on the surface regime, through the intensity of alimentation and the temperature level.

The irregularity of the processes of heat exchange between the surface and the atmosphere is responsible for the temperature fluctuations of the active layer. The surface temperature fluctuations are transmitted downward by the laws of heat transfer. In dry and impermeable rocks, the surface temperature fluctuations, which can be determined by harmonic analysis, recur in depth with a lag and with decreasing amplitude. In ice rocks, this picture is complicated considerably by the deposition of new layers of snow and by the deep penetration of short-wave solar radiation, while the natural long-wave radiation is from the surface only. In firn, in addition, the propagation of the heat wave is accelerated by infiltration during the melt periods and by the subsequent delay of complete freezing of the moist rock with absorption of latent heat.

The amplitude of temperature fluctuations at depth z below the surface is

$$A_z = A_0 \, e^{-2\pi\frac{z}{b}}$$

where e is the base of natural logarithms, b is the wave-length and A_0 is the amplitude of the surface fluctuations. The wave-length b is a function of the period of the fluctuations τ and the properties of the rock, i.e.,

$$b = 2\sqrt{\pi\tau a}$$

where a is the thermal diffusivity or the ratio of the thermal conductivity k to the thermal capacity per unit volume:

$$a = \frac{k}{c\delta}$$

where c is the specific heat per unit mass and δ is the density.

For pure ice, the diurnal fluctuations have a wave-length of about 1.1 m, for the longer aperiodic fluctuations due to advection the wave-length is somewhat longer, while for the annual variations it amounts to 21–22 m. In firn of density (δ) 0.4, the whole-year wave (b) is 14.8 m long. At the depth of the half-year wave, where the phase of the fluctuations is exactly opposite to that of the initial phase (with a six-month lag), the amplitude of the fluctuations decreases to 1/23 of the surface amplitude, while at the depth of a single whole-year wave it decreases to 1/535 of the surface amplitude, i.e., the temperature is practically constant at that depth. Twenty meters can be taken as the critical thickness of the active layer. However, if the propagation of heat in the firn during the warm season is accelerated by infiltration, the active layer may become 10 m thick or less, chiefly because the cold wave is propagated over a shorter period of time, namely, 10–8 months instead of a year, after which the infiltration warming overtakes and extinguishes the cold wave. Thus, the active layer, whose regime determines which ice formation process will occur, is about 15 m thick, on an average, with variations from approximately 10 m to 20 m.

The heat balance of the active layer (or the change of its heat supply ΔW) may be determined as the algebraic sum of the heat fluxes that pass through its bounding surfaces over a given time interval. One may neglect the internal sources of heat generated by the conversion of mechanical energy and also the heat expended on most of the internal physicochemical processes (except for phase transitions), since they are negligibly small for a layer of this thickness.

If we consider only the fluxes which are propagated in the form of radiant energy by conductive heat transfer and diffusion-sublimation (or distillation) and convective transfer, the heat balance formula for the active layer will be:

$$\Delta W = W_{\mathrm{r}} + W_{\mathrm{c}} + W_{\mathrm{vs+vc}} + W_{\mathrm{int}} \tag{2}$$

where W_{r} is the radiation balance of the surface; W_{c} is the convective heat exchange with the atmosphere; $W_{\mathrm{vs+vc}}$ is the exchange of heat with the atmosphere by the volatilization-sublimation and vaporization-condensation processes and $W_{\mathrm{int}} = k\dfrac{dt}{dz}$ is the heat flux through the lower boundary of the active layer caused by the temperature gradient dt/dz, where z is the depth below the surface. Consequently, the temperature gradient is positive when the temperature increases with depth (k is the coefficient of thermal conductivity of the rock).

Generally, every acquisition of heat by the active layer is indicated by a plus sign and every loss of heat by a minus sign.

All items in the heat balance can be determined experimentally. We cannot go into detail here on the methods used to calculate each one of them; this has already been done for the heat balance of the snow cover by H. V. Sverdrup (1936), P. P. Kuz'min (1947, 1948), E. G. Popov (1948), and others.

However, a heat balance calculated in this way is incomplete, because considerable amounts of heat are also transported by material across the boundaries of the active layer during precipitation and runoff. The heat content of the falling precipitation and the runoff water must be determined if these heat factors are to be considered.

For calculating the heat balance of a snow cover, Eckel and Thams (1939) proposed that the amount of heat per unit mass of water at 0°C should be taken as zero. Then, 1 g of ice at 0°C would have a cold reserve L of approximately 80 cal, while at subzero temperatures $-t°$, it would be $-L + ct$, where c is the specific heat of ice.

This concept of a cold reserve of the snow cover, which has already been used in cryopedology, would be very valuable for glaciology. Nevertheless, in calculating the heat balance one may not assume that the amount of heat in water or ice at 0°C will be zero, since the loss of heat during the runoff of melt water, which is an important item in the heat balance of water, and the addition of heat by solid precipitation having a temperature of 0°C, which is an important item in the heat balance of ice, are not considered. The only solution to the problem is to calculate temperature from absolute zero, where the thermal energy is actually zero, i.e., the heat content (enthalpy) of the incoming or outgoing material must be taken into consideration.

Then the complete formula of the heat balance will be:

$$\Delta W = W_r + W_c + W_{vs+vc} + m_{vs}(72 + ct_{vs}) + 152m_{vc} +$$
$$+ h\delta_{sn}(72 + ct_{sol}) + m_{liq}(152 + t_{liq}) + W_{int} - 152m_{water} \quad (3)$$

where $m_{vs}(72 + ct_{vs})$ is the algebraic sum of the gain and loss of heat due to volatilization and sublimation; $152m_{vc}$ is the algebraic sum of the gain and loss of heat due to vaporization and condensation, which are not considered in the existing formulas for calculating W_{vs+vc} and are due to a change m_{vs} in the mass of the snow cover caused by volatilization-sublimation at temperature t_{vs} and a change m_{vc} in the mass of the snow cover caused by vaporization and condensation; $h\delta_{sn}(72 + ct_{sol})$ is the heat content of the deposited solid precipitation at temperature t_{sol} which formed a snow cover h thick with density δ_{sn}; $m_{liq}(152 + t_{liq})$ is the heat content of the liquid precipitation which fell in an amount m_{liq} at a temperature t_{liq}; $152m_{water}$ is the heat supply of water which has run off in the amount m_{water}, considering that the temperature of the escaping melt water is usually close to 0°C.

Each term of the formula is understood to be the integral sum of the heat introduced into the active layer by the given process for any time interval of interest to us and may be found by integrating all the variables that enter into the given term with respect to time.

When the process is stationary,[2] the heat balance is constant, i.e., it is the heat content of the accumulating or ablating layer, by whose thickness h_a the lower boundary of the active layer should be displaced:

$$W_r + W_c + W_{vs+vc} + m_{vs} (72 + ct_{vs}) + 152m_{vc} +$$
$$h\delta_{sn} (72 + ct_{sol}) + m_{liq} (152 + t_{liq}) + W_{int} - 152m_{water} =$$
$$h_a\delta (1 - \alpha) (72 + ct) + 152h_a\delta\alpha \qquad (4)$$

where δ is the density of the accumulating (or ablating) layer with an average temperature $\bar{t}$, and α is the liquid water content of this layer (in practice, this will appear only if the layer temperature remains at the melting point).

The heat content thus obtained per unit mass at the limit of penetration of the seasonal temperature fluctuations also determines the layer temperature $\bar{t}$.

To clarify the role of this complex combination of heat exchange factors in the ice formation processes, let us move all the terms of the equation to one side and group them as follows.

Each term of the equation which indicates a heat flux not associated with the movement of material may designate a heat gain or loss by the active layer and all these processes, except for the flux $W_{int} = k\dfrac{dt}{dz}$, which is constant with respect to the magnitude and direction of the flux, show an alternation of heat gain and loss for different time intervals and this alternation results in a corresponding temperature increase or decrease (or a corresponding change in the aggregate state) of the active layer. The situation is somewhat different for heat fluxes associated with the movement of material. Although every addition of material corresponds to an energy gain, the average heat

---

[2] In this case, the stationary state may be attained only at the summit of an ice cap under conditions of a constant climate. In all other sections of the surface, when the material balance is positive, the given section will inevitably be displaced: upward, if the relief of the bed of the ice mass remains immobile (merely settles, in the so-called snowbank glaciers), or a horizontal component of motion will appear if the accumulation is balanced to a greater or lesser extent by the ablation of ice (glaciers). Consequently, the surface moves in time because of other conditions, although conditions may remain constant at each given point in space.

supply per unit mass of the active layer, which characterizes its temperature and aggregate state, may also increase or decrease in the process, depending on the heat content of the material introduced. One may distinguish the periods and the amount of heat gain or loss for any of the heat exchange processes by the indications of an increase or decrease of the average heat content per unit mass of the active layer.

The heat fluxes associated with the movement of material include the amounts of heat produced by the temperature of the material and the amounts of latent heat of fusion in liquid water, which are not reflected in the state of the temperature. These latter include the latent heat of fusion of water obtained from the vaporization and condensation processes $80m_{vc}$, the latent heat of rain water $80m_{liq}$, the latent heat of the runoff water $80m_{water}$ and of the water in the accumulating (or ablating) layer $80h_a\delta\alpha$.

Let W indicate the integral sum of the heat gain by the active layer during the year as a result of all the heat fluxes except the latent heat of fusion and let F indicate the integral sum of the heat losses during the year as a result of similar, oppositely directed, heat fluxes; L represents the latent heat of fusion of water which has entered the active layer $80(m_{vs} + m_{liq})$ and S represents the latent heat of fusion of the water which has left the active layer $80(m_{water} + h_a\delta\alpha)$. Then the heat balance equation for the stationary process will be:

$$W - F + L - S = 0 \qquad (5)$$

Thus, we have two simple basic relationships for the stationary process: the moisture balance equation (1) and the heat balance equation (5). A comparison of the two shows that $L = 80\mathcal{N}_{liq}$, $S = 80M$ and $L - S = 80(\mathcal{N}_{liq} - M)$. On the other hand, from (1) we get:

$$\mathcal{N}_{liq} - M = A - \mathcal{N}_{sol}$$

By substituting the $L - S$ value in the heat balance equation, after appropriate transformations, we get:

$$F + 80\mathcal{N}_{sol} - W = 80A \qquad (6)$$

i.e., for a stationary process the integral sum of the heat loss and the heat necessary for melting the solid atmospheric precipitation minus the integral sum of the heat gain are equal to the latent heat of fusion of the layer of ice accumulation or ablation.

In this form, all terms in the material-energy balance equation correspond to factors which determine the nature of the ice formation processes (see Fig. 121).

All the magnitudes which enter into the given equations are variable and when any one of them changes, equality is attained by a highly complex change in the whole combination of heat and moisture exchange processes, radiation and circulation processes and the resultant processes of ice formation. A complete picture of the behavior of the ice formation processes can be had only if continuous recordings are made of all the items in the material-energy balance and this has not yet been done for any point on the earth's surface. However, ordinary meteorological data give an approximate picture of the total annual material-energy balance.

The sum total of the processes of heat exchange between the active layer and the atmosphere is comprised of the mean annual air and surface temperatures and the temperature of the lower boundary of the active layer (the level of the zero annual amplitude of temperature fluctuations), which may differ considerably under certain conditions. These magnitudes represent the most important characteristics of the ice formation processes. The annual sum of solid precipitation can be judged by the amount of precipitation, the depth and the density of the snow cover. Finally, the magnitudes of the heat gain and loss during the year can be characterized approximately by the amplitudes of the annual, diurnal and aperiodic surface temperature fluctuations or, if these are constant, by the amplitudes of such fluctuations for the air above the earth's surface. The temperature fluctuations increase as the heat exchange processes intensify.

Thus, although accurate data are not yet available on the material-energy balance, one can still make a general outline of the relationship between the main types of ice formation and climate. Naturally, this relationship may be somewhat equivocal. Various combinations of the behavior of some of the meteorological elements may give an identical result in the annual heat and moisture balance and thus in the ice formation processes. However, undoubtedly this equivocality lies within narrow bounds, because of the genetic tie between the behavior of the individual meteorological elements. The factors which determine the type of ice formation are important characteristics of climate. Abundant precipitation, which is a characteristic feature of maritime climate, is regularly associated with small-amplitude periodic temperature fluctuations, while small amounts of precipitation, which are a distinctive feature of continental climate, are associated with large-amplitude temperature fluctuations.

With this in mind, we shall attempt to examine the spatial distribution of the main types of ice formation and their relationship to climate.

CHAPTER XVIII

THE ZONES OF ICE FORMATION

THE RECRYSTALLIZATION ZONE

The structure of the ice formation processes is simplest in the absence of melting, i.e., when the thermal balance of the earth's surface is such that there will be sufficiently low, negative surface temperatures the year around. Under such conditions, only solid precipitation falls and the entire influx of energy, whether it be radiational, convective or sublimational, is expended on temporarily increasing the temperature of the surface layer and, in part, on volatilizing the ice. Thus, the temperature maxima do not exceed zero degrees centigrade and melting does not occur. The material-energy balance equation (6) for this zone, neglecting the vaporization and sublimation processes, may be divided into two independent equations:

$$F = W \tag{7}$$

and

$$N = A_1 \tag{8}$$

In this zone, liquid water and ice, taken in the petrographic sense, do not occur on the surface. In places where the precipitation balance is positive, the surface is composed solely of snow that becomes ice at a considerable depth owing to the weight of the upper layers. The whole complex of processes which develop under these circumstances has been described in the section on the cold type of ice formation. It is based on the compression-settling process, accompanied by sublimation perecrystallization in the snow diagenesis stage and by recrystallization in the stages of firnification and ice formation. On moving downward, the various types of snow which comprise the upper, more or less differentiated part of the profile become a uniform layer of recrystallization firn; still lower they become primary-recrystallization ice; while on slopes where plastic flow occurs the firn immediately becomes secondary-recrystallization ice.

The rate of conversion of snow into ice increases as the amount of falling snow increases, but in this case the ice formation process occurs at a greater depth below the surface. On the other hand, when the annual increment of solid precipitation is slight, the increased loading from above and settling occur more slowly and ice formation takes place at a lesser depth. On an average, the firn-ice boundary in the regions of recrystallization ice formation lies at a depth of the order of 30–50 m.

At present, the Antarctic continent with the shelf ice of its seas (except for a narrow coastal zone), most of central Greenland and probably the summits of the highest mountains in various latitudes[1] belong to the zone of recrystallization ice formation.

The temperature regime typical of the zone of recrystallization ice formation, at least at very high elevations above sea level under present conditions, is created by the ice itself or, to be more exact, by the snow. The snow cover has exceptional radiation properties: it has an enormous reflecting capacity (in a dry, uncontaminated state, on an average, it has an albedo of 80–90%), owing to which incident radiation heats it but slightly, but despite this it has a high normal radiant emissivity (close to that of an absolutely black body) because of the very large surface area of the snowflakes. Owing to this latter property and the low thermal conductivity of snow, very intense cooling of the snow surface occurs during periods when the radiation equilibrium is negative. Furthermore, the advective transfer of heat by air masses cannot penetrate far into the regions of glaciation, because a large amount of heat is absorbed to melt the snow and ice.

Thus, the snow cover itself, in regions where conditions permit its retention, changes the heat balance of the surface to a considerable extent and helps maintain a low negative temperature. The regions of ice sheet glaciation are the coldest on earth. The absolute minimum temperatures at the earth's surface (of the order of $-70°C$) are always associated with a temperature inversion and are approximately identical at the Siberian "cold pole" and in regions of ice sheet glaciation,[2] which evidently can be explained by the establishment of radiation equilibrium with the higher layers of the atmosphere at that temperature. However, the summer and average annual temperatures of the regions of ice sheet glaciation are

---

[1] For example, in the Himalayas the level at which melting ceases is considered to be 1000 m above the firn line, i.e., 5750 m (R. Finsterwalder, 1937). Apparently this estimate is too low. However, the mountain summits which rise another 3 km should reach the recrystallization zone.

[2] During the warm winter of 1930/31, minimum temperatures of $-64°$ to $-65°C$ were recorded in the center of the Greenland ice sheet in January, February and March, while in Verkhoyansk the average minima were $-62°C$.

incomparably lower than those of northern continents not covered by an ice sheet (see Table 5).

TABLE 5

Average temperature	Eismitte (center of the Greenland ice sheet, 71°11′ N, 39°54′ W)	Verkhoyansk (67°5′ N)
Warmest month	−13.7	+15.5
Coldest month	−51.0	−50.1
Annual	−32.5	−15.9

One may assume that the temperatures of central Antarctica are still lower.[3] The temperature regime changes abruptly even in the comparatively small ice-free sections of land surrounded by ice at the highest latitudes. For example, an average July temperature of +6°C and absolute maxima above +15°C were recorded in Pearyland (82°N) at the northern extremity of Greenland (Fristrup, 1950).

To create a positive balance of solid precipitation in the recrystallization zone, more solid precipitation must fall than is volatilized to the atmosphere. Volatilization is very slow at low temperatures. In regions of sheet glaciation, it is compensated somewhat by sublimation and plays practically no role in the material balance. The annual influx of precipitation in the zone of recrystallization ice formation varies within quite wide limits. In the Himalayas, where precipitation falls from ascending air when the monsoon passes over the mountain range, it is estimated that more than 8000 mm of precipitation fall annually at heights greater than 6000 m (R. Finsterwalder, 1937). In central Greenland and on the Antarctic coast, where precipitation falls primarily from ascending air currents in cyclones, the precipitation amounts to 300–400 mm/year, while in the region of the South Pole, the "land of cirrus precipitation," which falls in descending air currents in an anti-cyclone and strikes the supercooled surface-adjacent layer, the precipitation amounts to only 5 mm/year, according to the calculations of some researchers (Church, 1942).

Thus, the amount of precipitation depends largely on local circulation conditions. Furthermore, theory indicates that the zone of

---

[3] [The most recent data (1963) indicate the following for central Antarctica: warmest month −32.8°C, coldest month −69.8°C, annual −55.5°C – D.K.]

recrystallization ice formation and also the chionosphere[4] and cryosphere in general must have an upper limit created by insufficient atmospheric moisture and the predominance of volatilization over sublimation. This was pointed out in the latter part of the nineteenth century (Tyndall, 1861, and Heim, 1885).

Within the recrystallization zone itself, the positive material balance of the surface may be destroyed by erosion (deflation) of the snow, thanks to which many mountain massifs in Antarctica and eastern Greenland are situated amidst the ice sheet but are not covered by ice and have slopes gentle enough for snow to accumulate on their surface.

THE RECRYSTALLIZATION-INFILTRATION ZONE

The transition from the recrystallization to the infiltration zone of ice formation is caused by the melting of part of the solid precipitation and by the arrival of part of the precipitation in liquid form. These changes are associated with an increase of air temperature above the freezing point, be it for only brief intervals. The air temperature in the atmosphere increases downward at an average of 0.5–0.6°C per 100 m. It also increases horizontally with decreasing geographic latitude, and, further, there is a considerable horizontal temperature gradient between the periphery and the center of an ice sheet (for instance, in Greenland it is 11°/500 km). Melting and the amount of precipitation which falls in the liquid phase increase in these directions.

Fine water droplets may exist in the atmosphere in a supercooled state at very low temperatures. Therefore, by way of exception, thin ice crusts may form on the snow surface in any part of the zone of recrystallization ice formation, owing to the freezing of supercooled cloud or fog droplets. However, the formation of ice crusts begins to play a conspicuous role only in regions where the snow cover melts slightly from time to time. Owing to the low temperature of the underlying snow, the melt water freezes in the pores at the very surface, forming ice interlayers from a few millimeters to not more than a few centimeters thick. Thus, thin and widely spaced interlayers of fine-grained infiltration ice appear in the vertical cross section between the snow and the recrystallization firn. These interlayers indicate brief periods of melting of the snow surface.

---

[4] The chionosphere is the potential zone of dominance of accumulation over loss of solid atmospheric precipitation in the annual balance on a horizontal surface. The concept was introduced by S. V. Kalesnik (1939, p. 28).

There is no clearly defined boundary between the regions of purely recrystallization ice formation and the regions with inter-layers of buried melt crust. There is a very gradual transition be-tween them, because the temperature maxima in the surface layer of air vary greatly with time. At present, only Antarctica (with the exception of the coastal zone from several kilometers to several tens of kilometers wide) is not subject to any melting whatsoever. In Greenland, an air temperature of $+0.5°C$ was observed even in the central part of the northern ice cap at an elevation of 3100 m, while the temperature reached $+5°C$ on the southern ice cap at an ele-vation of 2700 m. Correspondingly, individual ice interlayers or lenses were detected even at elevations of 2970 and 3030 m. In rare, individual cases, evidently slight melting may occur everywhere in Greenland, up to the highest points of the ice sheet (3350 m above m.s.l.).

Ice stratification is encountered more and more frequently toward the margin of the Greenland ice sheet and becomes the rule at elevations of about 2400–2500 m or at 200 km from the edge of the ice sheet. Beginning at this level, ice stratification is a characteristic sign of summer snow layers, indicating that brief melting may occur annually at the local mean maximum temperatures. In Greenland, this transitional zone of snow with ice interlayers extends down to approximately the 2000 m level, forming a belt more than 100 km wide which fringes the central, colder part of the ice sheet. The mean annual air temperature within this zone is about $-20°$ to $-25°C$, and the mean temperature of the warmest month is correspondingly $-4°$ to $-7°C$.[5]

The position of the recrystallization-infiltration zone has not yet been established for other regions.

THE "COLD" INFILTRATION ZONE

When melting becomes more intense during downward movement in the transitional recrystallization-infiltration zone, the tem-perature of the upper layers of snow also increases in the summer period and, consequently, the cold reserve, which prevents the

---

[5] The data given here and later on the position of the ice formation zones in Greenland were obtained by comparing all published data of expeditions which investigated the Greenland ice sheet, reference to which would occupy too much space. The most valuable data were gathered by the expeditions of A. Wegener in 1929 and 1930–31, J. Koch and A. Wegener in 1912–1913 and A. de Quervain in 1912. The data of the French expedition of 1949–1951 could not be taken into consideration.

infiltration of melt water into the snow, decreases. Thus, the primary ice interlayers become thicker and more like firn, with porous sections, and their crystals become larger. Water penetrates deeper and deeper, firn-ice interlayers form farther from the surface and a layer of regelation firn formed from snow under the influence of melt water appears above. The sharp differentiation into thin ice interlayers and snow unaffected by the melting processes disappears. At first, snow layers (although only in a narrow strip) still remain between the firn layers, which form the upper parts of the annual layers. As soon as infiltration begins because of summer heating of the snow, a very slight increase of melting suffices to drench the entire annual snow layer with melt water. This snow then becomes regelation firn. Therefore, the cold infiltration zone has a quite distinct upper boundary, insofar as this is permitted in general by the changes in the meteorological conditions from year to year. As already noted, this boundary lies at a height of approximately 2000 m, about 80 km from the edge of the ice sheet, on the western slope of the central part of the Greenland ice sheet.

It is characteristic of the cold infiltration zone that the water produced by surface melting is expended entirely on infiltration densification and ice formation,[6] without creating runoff. All atmospheric precipitation remains within the active layer, except for what is usually a negligible amount of moisture that evaporates into the atmosphere and is compensated by sublimation and condensation. In the process of melting and infiltration, part of the material is removed from the annual accumulation layer, but then refreezes in the firn layer, increasing the mass and the density of the layers deposited in previous years. Therefore, under stationary conditions, the loss of material from the surface during the first year of existence of deposited snow is compensated, on an average, by infiltration from new layers in the years that follow. Thus, there is merely a redistribution of material, but on the whole, for the active layer, the amount of precipitation is equal to the annual increment:

$$N = A \tag{9}$$

Since $N = N_{sol} + N_{liq}$, it follows from (6) that

$$W + 80 N_{liq} = F \tag{10}$$

i.e., the entire heat loss from the surface is balanced by the heat influx of the active layer and the latent heat of crystallization of the liquid precipitation.

---

[6] For a description of the processes of infiltration ice formation, see Chap. XIII.

The processes of infiltration densification and ice formation are associated with the heating of the rock by freezing water, which releases the latent heat of crystallization. The magnitude of the heating is quite considerable:

$$\Delta t = \frac{80\Delta\delta}{0.5\delta} = 160\ \frac{\Delta\delta}{\delta}$$

where δ is the initial density of the firn and $\Delta\delta$ is the infiltration densification.

Heating continues until the temperature reaches $0°C$ and the rock becomes permeable for the descending melt water, after which infiltration extends to the deeper layers. The absence of runoff indicates that the infiltration heating does not reach the lower limit of the active layer. Below the layer heated to $0°C$ by the melt water, there is a layer with a negative temperature that remains within the active layer and in it the warm summer wave is propagated by conductive and diffusive-sublimation heat transfer.

In the annual balance, the sum of the heat lost from the surface F, which reduces the heat content of the active layer, may be divided into two components, of which one is extinguished by the heat influx of the active layer during the cold period before melting begins, and the other, larger portion F_T is the "cold reserve" of the active layer before melting begins and heat is lost in the periods of cooling during the melt season. However, as we have already noted, this second element plays a secondary role in the ice formation processes.

Similarly, the sum of the heat influx consists of two parts, of which one is expended directly on increasing the temperature of the active layer and the other, W_T, is expended on melting the upper surface. The absence of runoff, which applies to the described subzone of ice formation, is represented as

$$W_T + 80N_{liq} < F_T$$

and the boundary conditions for this subzone, from the standpoint of the quantitative relationship between the intensity of melting and freezing, is

$$0 \leqslant W_T + 80N_{liq} < F_T \tag{11}$$

i.e., the amount of heat expended on melting, together with the latent heat of crystallization of the liquid precipitation, comprises a magnitude sufficiently large to wet the entire annual layer of snow, but smaller than the cold reserve of winter freezing plus the heat lost during the melt period.

Thus, in the cold infiltration zone, all the thermal energy expended on melting the surface is retained in the active layer and is released during the freezing of the melt water. It does the work of infiltration densification, but in the final analysis is expended on increasing the temperature of the firn.

Under these conditions, firn becomes ice by two processes: settling and infiltration densification. Settling is a slow process which in itself cannot transform firn into ice except considerably below the active layer, but infiltration densification can occur at a different rate. Under the examined conditions, because of the adequate cold reserves in the active layer, the rate of infiltration densification is limited by the relationship between the amount of liquid water or the rate of melting and the amount of falling solid precipitation. The rate of ice formation increases as melting increases and as the amount of falling snow decreases. At the same time, the rate of crystal growth associated solely with infiltration densification and not with settling also increases.

Any increase of surface melting leads to an increase in the depth of penetration of melt water and to the extension of the infiltration processes to a thicker layer. However, because of settling and recrystallization, the ice formation process does not end within the active layer but at depths of the order of 20–40 m below the surface, in the layer which has a constant negative temperature.

Thus, a cross section of ice rocks in the cold infiltration zone is composed of the following (proceeding downward):

(1) snow less than one year old (not present during the melt period);

(2) a layer of regelation and infiltration firn with interlayers, lenses and irregular bodies of infiltration ice in relatively small quantities, total thickness of the order of 20–40 m;

(3) infiltration-recrystallization ice with interlayers, lenses and irregular bodies of infiltration ice on slopes, transformed in varying degree into secondary-recrystallization ice;

(4) veins of congelation ice in fissured areas, primarily in the lower part of the cross section comprised of ice.

The amount of infiltration ice in the total mass depends on the relative role of infiltration in the process of firn densification and, consequently, on the relationship between the intensity of the surface melting and the amount of solid precipitation deposited $\dfrac{W_T + 80 \mathcal{N}_{liq}}{80 \mathcal{N}_{sol}}$, i.e., in the final analysis, on its location within the described zone of ice formation: in the upper part, near its boundary with the recrystallization zone, melting is slighter and there is less infiltration ice; farther down, the melting intensifies and the infiltration ice content increases.

The relationship between the intensity of melting and the amount of falling solid precipitation, peculiar to the cold infiltration zone, is determined approximately by the following conditions. The water obtained from the melting of some portion of the solid atmospheric precipitation and from rain, freezes in the firn pores during the process of infiltration densification. If the solid precipitation in the active layer is not to become ice, the volume of the ice which forms annually due to freezing of water in the firn pores must remain smaller than the volume of the pores of the annual firn increment. In calculating the volume of ice per unit area, one may substitute the corresponding water equivalent.

During the melting process, the snow cover becomes regelation firn and settles greatly; hence the lowering of the snow surface cannot be attributed solely to loss by runoff of melt water. Therefore, let us differentiate these two processes arbitrarily, considering that settling with the transformation of snow into regelation firn takes place before melting and runoff, and in our computations we shall use the snow layer equivalents of the thickness and density of the layers of regelation firn.

The total thickness h of the annual layer of solid precipitation converted into regelation firn consists of the thickness h_T of the melting layer and the thickness h_a of the layer that remains after melting, i.e.,

$$h = h_T + h_a$$

The density of the upper layer of regelation firn h_a immediately after thawing is δ_{upper}. Before descending to the lower limit of infiltration over a number of years by infiltration densification (without settling), this layer will reach a density of δ_{lower}, while its thickness will remain constant (since settling is not considered). The increase in mass of the layer during this time from $h_a \delta_{upper}$ to $h_a \delta_{lower} = A = \mathcal{N} = \mathcal{N}_{sol} + \mathcal{N}_{liq}$ yields a value which, on the average, is equal to the amount of liquid water which participates in the infiltration process annually. This consists of melt water $W_T/80 = h_T \delta_{upper}$ and rain water $\mathcal{N}_{liq}$. Hence we get the following equation:

$$W_T + \frac{\delta_{upper}}{\delta_{lower}} 80 \mathcal{N}_{liq} = \frac{\delta_{lower} - \delta_{upper}}{\delta_{lower}} 80 \mathcal{N}_{sol} \qquad (12)$$

or, considering the comparatively small amount of liquid precipitation in the cold infiltration zone:

$$W_T + 80\mathcal{N}_{liq} \approx \frac{\delta_{lower}\ \delta_{upper}}{\delta_{lower}}\ 80\mathcal{N}_{sol} \qquad (12')$$

Equation (12) defines the ultimate quantitative relationship between the heat W_T expended on melting the surface and the amount of solid and liquid atmospheric precipitation in the zone of infiltration ice formation in the absence of runoff, i.e., under conditions of a cold regime. This relationship depends on the magnitude of the relative infiltration densification $\frac{\delta_{lower} - \delta_{upper}}{\delta_{lower}}$ for the period of time when the firn passes from the upper part of the cross section (density δ_{upper}) to the lower limit of percolation of water (density δ_{lower}, without consideration of settling).

The δ_{upper} and δ_{lower} values are not identical everywhere in the cold infiltration zone. To get an idea of their order of magnitude, on an average, we can assume that $\delta_{upper} \approx 0.48$ and $\delta_{lower} \approx 0.80$; thus, from (12′) we find that the critical value of the heat of melting and the amount of liquid precipitation will be $W_T + 80\mathcal{N}_{liq} \approx 0.4 \times 80\mathcal{N}_{sol}$. Consequently, the boundary conditions for the described zone are:

$$0 \leqslant W_T + 80\mathcal{N}_{liq} < 0.4 \times 80\mathcal{N}_{sol} \qquad (13)$$

i.e., the melting and liquid precipitation deposit should be sufficient to wet the entire annual layer of snow and to convert it into regelation firn, but it should not exceed approximately 40% of the amount of solid precipitation being deposited.

Thus, the cold infiltration zone of ice formation, which is situated below the recrystallization zone, differs from the latter in that in it the structural transformation of all the snow into firn and part of the subsequent firn densification occur under the influence of partial melting and freezing. However, in contrast to the lower zones of the cryosphere, there is no runoff here; the sum of the precipitation is equal to the annual material increment and all the heat expended on melting remains within the active layers. On the other hand, the infiltration densification is not intensive enough to curtail ice formation in the active layer. The conditions for this type of ice formation process are as follows:

$$W_T + 80\mathcal{N}_{liq} < F_T$$

and

$$W_T + 80\mathcal{N}_{liq} < 0.4 \times 80\mathcal{N}_{sol}$$

In other words, the sum of the heat expended on melting and the latent heat of fusion of liquid precipitation should be smaller than the cold reserve of winter freezing, while melting and the liquid precipitation deposit should not exceed approximately 40% of the amount of solid atmospheric precipitation.

Owing to melting and the infiltration of melt water, the temperature regime at the surface and in the active layer in the cold infiltration zone varies considerably compared to that of the recrystallization zone. "Blunting" of the summer maxima because of the expenditure of heat on melting the snow and firn is a characteristic feature of the temperatures of the surface layer of air. In the absence of melting, the curves of the diurnal trend of the air temperature are more or less symmetrical, provided there is no disturbance by aperiodic fluctuations, but as soon as heat begins to be expended on surface melting, the maxima become smoothed, usually amounting to no more than a few degrees above zero. A temperature inversion occurs in the surface layer of air, causing the formation of convective air currents, by which heat is conducted to the melting surface. The temperature inversion due to melting is especially strong in the case of advection of warm air masses.

A still greater change is observed in the temperature regime of the active layer. The infiltration of gravitational melt water, which releases 80 cal/g of latent heat during freezing in the deeper layers of firn, is an incomparably more effective heat transmission factor than are molecular heat conduction and the sublimation processes. The transfer of heat downward with the melt water in the firn is considerably faster than the propagation of the cold temperature wave in winter and the warm wave in spring before thawing begins. Consequently, the mean annual temperature in the lower part of the active layer is higher than it would be in the absence of infiltration heat transfer at a given mean annual air temperature. The mean temperature of the firn can exceed the mean annual air temperature by as much as several degrees (in some cases, apparently, by as much as ten degrees).

The energy expended on melting the surface, which is transferred downward and would otherwise have been expended on raising the temperature of the surface and the surface-adjacent layer of air, acts as the heat source for increasing the firn temperature. Thus, heat is redistributed in the active layer, as a result of which the surface becomes cooler and the lower horizons warmer. However, reduction of the surface temperature leads to a change in the thermal balance of the surface toward an increased heat flux by attenuation of its natural radiation and an increase of the convective and sublimation-condensation influx of heat from the air. Simultaneously, during melt periods the radiational influx of heat increases because of the reduction of the albedo of the darker melting surface. In the final analysis, this heat excess, received anomalously by the cold surface and retained in the lower part of the active layer, also acts as a source of the anomalously high temperatures in the firn and the whole layer of underlying rock.

Consequently, in regions where firn is subject to melting, it warms the underlying rock. It acts as a creel or a trap; heat is captured by the firn and the firn, in turn, gives the heat easy access to the interior and does not allow the heat to return, because of its low heat conductivity. Owing to the higher temperatures within the earth, any layer of rock usually exerts a warming effect on its adjacent layer, provided the temperature does not reach the melting point of these rocks. This effect is expressed quantitatively by the following temperature increase below the given layer:

$$\Delta t = h\frac{dt}{dz} = W_{\text{int}}\frac{h}{k} \tag{14}$$

where h is the layer thickness; dt/dz is the temperature gradient, W_{int} is the thermal flux from the earth toward the surface and k is the coefficient of thermal conductivity of the rock.

However, the warming influence of the porous ice rock on the underlying layer considerably exceeds the ordinary influence of other rocks. This is manifested in the large vertical gradient of the mean annual temperatures in the active layer, exceeding the normal gradient which corresponds to the molecular thermal conductivity of firn.

Since increased melting is all that is required to transform a recrystallization zone into a cold infiltration zone, the bottom of the cold infiltration zone everywhere borders on areas and sectors belonging to the zone of recrystallization ice formation. Although little study has been devoted to the subject, it may be asserted that the cold infiltration zone should develop in the upper reaches of the firn basins of mountain glaciers at sufficient elevations, on the Arctic and Antarctic islands and on the edge of the Greenland ice sheet. Insofar as we can judge from available data, this zone is situated at heights of 2000 to 1400 m in the middle section of the western slope of the Greenland ice sheet, forming a band approximately 60 km wide. In this band, the mean annual temperature is −15° to −20°C, while the mean temperature of the warmest month is approximately −1° to −4°C and the annual precipitation amounts to about 450 mm.

Further, the lower boundary of the cold infiltration zone separates the entire upper half of the cryosphere from the lower half, which has its special features. In the upper, recrystallization zone of the cryosphere, the largest differences in the material-energy balance do not cause any changes in the nature of the ice formation processes. Ice formation is of the recrystallization type whether 5 mm or 8000 mm of solid precipitation fall: complete uniformity prevails. A certain horizontal differentiation begins in the cold infiltration zone, which is manifested only in a quantitative difference in the relative role of settling and infiltration densification of the firn. However, beginning with the lower boundary of the cold infiltration zone, the quantitative horizontal differentiation becomes a qualitative one, manifested in a change of the type of ice formation processes, which finally leads to asymmetry of the entire lower half of the cryosphere.

The transition from the cold infiltration zone to the lower zones of ice formation may be caused by the disturbance of one or both of the above-cited boundary conditions:

$$W_T + 80 N_{liq} < F_T$$

or

$$W_T + 80 N_{liq} < 0.4 \times 80 N_{sol}$$

Disturbance of the first condition alone, i.e., an increase in the sum of heat expended on melting and the latent heat of liquid precipitation over the cold reserve of winter freezing results in the following: infiltration heating of the entire active layer to the melting point, elimination of the cold regime and runoff of melt water within the glacier and below it.

A disturbance of the second condition alone, i.e., an increase in the amount of melt and rain water to approximately 40–50% of the amount of solid atmospheric precipitation, results in the following: the pores of the unmelted remnant of firn fill with melt water, the firn becomes infiltration ice in a single melt season and the melt water runs off along the surface.

Correspondingly, under various conditions the cold infiltration zone transforms downward into a "warm" infiltration zone in the first case and into an infiltration congelation zone with a cold regime in the second case.

If both boundary conditions are disturbed, the nature of the ice formation process will be determined by the relationship between the magnitude of the cold reserve of winter freezing and the cold of crystallization of solid precipitation: when

$$F_T < 0.4 \times 80 N_{sol} \tag{15}$$

the processes follow the type of the "warm" infiltration zone, but when

$$F_T > 0.4 \times 80\mathcal{N}_{sol} \tag{16}$$

they are of the type of the infiltration congelation zone.

THE "WARM" INFILTRATION ZONE

The upper boundary of the "warm" infiltration zone is the level at which the sum of the heat expended on melting and of the latent heat of the liquid precipitation is just sufficient for infiltration heating to bring the entire active layer to the melting point: $W_T + 80\mathcal{N}_{liq} = F_T$. At the same time, the condition $W_T + 80\mathcal{N}_{liq} < 0.4 \times 80\mathcal{N}_{sol}$ at the upper boundary of the "warm" infiltration zone is not disturbed and, consequently:

$$F_T < 0.4 \times 80\mathcal{N}_{sol}$$

i.e., the cold reserve of winter freezing and the heat loss during the melt period are less than approximately 40% of the latent heat of fusion of the solid precipitation.

Such conditions are characteristic of a maritime climate with a large amount of atmospheric precipitation, small-amplitude temperature fluctuations, a relatively warm winter and slight freezing of the rock layer. In an extreme case, freezing may practically not occur in a typical oceanic climate and the whole layer of ice rock may be at a near-zero temperature the year round. Conditions quite similar to these are characteristic of the firn cap of southeast Iceland, for example, where snow layers up to 7 m thick with a constant near-zero temperature are precipitated in a single year, so that the snow remains wet for many months in layers deposited at positive temperatures.

Under extreme oceanic conditions, where $F_T \to 0$, the entire intake of heat by the surface is expended on melting the solid precipitation, while all the melt and rain water percolates through the firn layer and runs off along the channels within and below the glacier. Despite the abundance of water, infiltration densification does not occur and ice forms exclusively by settling and paratectonic perecrystallization.

Owing to the abundance of precipitation under conditions of an oceanic climate, thick layers of firn may accumulate annually; very active glaciation develops and persists at a relatively high air temperature. At the lower boundary of the "warm" infiltration zone, not only may the mean temperature of the warmest month reach values several degrees above zero, but the mean annual temperature can exceed the melting point by as much as 1–1.5°C in places. Under such conditions, glaciation owes its existence to the reserves of the latent cold of crystallization of the solid atmospheric precipitation and develops despite the relatively high temperature of the ambient medium.

Extreme conditions, whereby complete freezing (i.e., freezing through) does not occur, are generally unattainable, but conditions approximating this extreme and intermediate conditions with relatively slight freezing are characteristic of the firn basins of most regions of mountain glaciation. The earlier "classical" alpine glaciology, which paid little heed to the ice formation processes, was familiar only with glaciation fed by the "warm" infiltration zone and unjustifiably ascribed general importance to the regularities observed under these conditions.

Under conditions typical of the "warm" infiltration zone, the ice formation processes in general differ little from those of the cold zone and consist of settling with paratectonic perecrystallization and infiltration densification. Ice formation may cease in the active layer, depending on the intensity of infiltration densification, but usually it goes deeper than the active layer, as in the case of the cold infiltration zone. However, in this case, the firn becomes ice by settling under conditions of a "warm" regime rather than a cold regime, and, correspondingly, it occurs somewhat more rapidly (nearer the surface) because of greater plasticity and because the firn grains do not freeze together.

Usually a firn layer 10–15 m thick freezes through during the cold season and a constant melting point is maintained all year round below this layer. By the time the melt season begins, when slow heating from above has already commenced, the temperature of the firn layer decreases quickly with depth, reaching a minimum of −2° to −10°C (depending on the winter air temperatures) at a depth of 2–3 m, and then increases more slowly to zero at the lower boundary of the active layer. During a good part of the melt season, the percolating water freezes in the firn pores and warms the firn downward, layer by layer, until the entire cold reserve is used up, after which the gravitational water begins to flow freely through the active layer to the ice boundary and farther along the cracks and channels within and beneath the glacier. Only a small quantity of suspended capillary water freezes in autumn and winter, during the refreezing of the firn.

The rate of infiltration densification of the firn and the rate of ice formation are limited by the cold reserve of winter freezing and the loss of heat during the melt season F_T. Excess amounts of solid pre-cipitation and infiltration water are available, but there is not enough cold to freeze the water in the pores of the firn layer. However, the relative role of infiltration densification is determined not only by the magnitude of the cold reserve of the active layer but also by the length of time the firn remains in the active layer, i.e., by the number of infiltration heating cycles experienced by the firn. This is well illustrated by a comparison of the ice formation conditions in the Alps and on Spitsbergen. In the Alps, at an elevation of 3500 m, the annual firn increment is 3–5 m and the active layer is 15 m thick. Consequently, the firn does not remain in the active layer more than 4–5 years, while on the Isachsen firn plateau (Isachsenfonna) on Spitsbergen, the corresponding figures are 40 cm, 10 m and 25 years. Therefore, on Spitsbergen the firn densifies in the active layer by infiltration to a state close to that of ice, while in the Alps the main factor is settling.

The length of time the firn remains in the active layer is a function not only of the depth of freezing but also of the magnitude of the annual firn increment and thus of the amount of solid precipitation and the intensity of melting. Thus, the rate of infiltration ice forma-tion in the warm infiltration zone is directly proportional to the cold reserve of winter freezing F_T and the intensity of melting W_T and is inversely proportional to the amount of solid precipitation N_{sol}, i.e.,

$$\frac{F_T \times W_T}{80 N_{sol}} \qquad (17)$$

Hence, the rate of infiltration ice formation, the relative amount of infiltration ice and the depth at which the main mass of firn becomes ice within the described zone vary in two directions, vertically downward and horizontally from a maritime toward a continental climate.

At the upper boundary of the zone, the available cold reserve is not sufficient to convert the firn into ice in the active layer and the transformation of firn into ice by settling and paratectonic pere-crystallization ceases at a depth of the order of 40 m under conditions of a warm regime. Vertically downward, the annual firn increment decreases more rapidly than the cold reserve of winter freezing; therefore, the rate of infiltration ice formation increases downward, the infiltration ice content of the firn layer increases and the role of settling decreases compared to the role of infiltration densification. Thus, the firn layer gradually becomes thinner from the upper boundary of the warm infiltration zone downward, until the firn is completely wedged out.

A gradual reduction of the firn thickness has been verified, for instance, in the upper reaches of the Great Aletsch glacier in the Alps, where the firn is more than 30 m thick at 3500 m, only 20 m thick at 3330 m and wedges out at 3020 m.

The wedging out of the firn layer downward is caused by the complete runoff of all precipitation, not by the rapid transformation of firn into ice. As long as there is even a slight firn residue, some time will be required to convert it into ice by infiltration processes. The tapering of the firn layer downslope is not a regular, gradual process. The firn wedges out relatively rapidly over a short distance at the lower limit of the firn layer.

The structure of the layer of ice rock in the "warm" infiltration zone differs little from that of the "cold" infiltration zone. The stratification, proceeding downward, is as follows:

(1) snow less than one year old, absent during the melt period;

(2) a layer of regelation and infiltration firn with interlayers, lenses and irregular bodies of infiltration ice in relatively small amounts, total thickness from 40 m in the upper part of the zone to zero in the lower part;

(3) infiltration-recrystallization ice with interlayers, lenses and irregular bodies of infiltration ice, becoming secondary-recrystallization ice, to a greater or lesser extent, on the slopes. There is considerably less vein congelation ice in the warm zone than in the cold zone, owing to the lack of cold in the lower part of the cross section, which consists of ice.

The lower limit of the "warm" infiltration zone is known in glaciology as the *firn line* or the *firn limit*. Below it, the annual balance of solid atmospheric precipitation becomes negative, ablation exceeds accumulation and only ice that has been displaced from the higher zones of ice formation as avalanches or glaciers can exist during the warm season. On glaciers with a "warm" regime, the firn line is the boundary between the higher regions of accumulation and the lower regions of ablation. In this case, only the zone of seasonal ice formation lies below the firn line. This alternation of zones is characteristic of the maritime regions of glaciation or at least of continental regions with not too severe a climate.

There is a gradual change in the horizontal range of the "warm" infiltration zone, from maritime to continental climate, similar to the vertical change. In a continental climate there is less precipitation and a greater amplitude of temperature fluctuations; therefore, the winter freezing and summer melting are more intense. Hence, the very combination of conditions is created which intensifies infiltration ice formation at the expense of the slower recrystallization.

This leads to an increase in the amount of infiltration ice and a reduction of the firn thickness and, finally, to the disturbance of the boundary condition $F_T < 0.4 \times 80 N_{sol}$ and to a transformation of the "warm" infiltration zone into an infiltration congelation zone.

Under the transitional conditions of regions with moderate continental climate, the vertical sequence of zones differs from that of a maritime climate.

Because of the "warm" regime of the described zone, the material increment in the active layer is smaller than the sum of solid precipitation and the relationship between them is regulated by the distribution of heat loss and gain during the year, in agreement with equation (6). Part of the material runs off in the form of melt water, removing with it a certain amount of heat. However, the heat loss along the channels inside and beneath the glacier below the active layer is not reflected in the temperature regime of the underlying ice, which maintains a constant melting point. Therefore, the firn also exerts a warming effect on the underlying rock in the "warm" infiltration zone, as it does in the higher cold zone. However, the magnitude of the heating increases downward in the cold zone as melting increases, while it decreases downward in the "warm" zone because the mean annual air temperature approaches the melting point of ice in this direction.

It has been established that the firn basins of Alpine glaciers have a "warm" regime at heights where the mean annual air temperature is −7°C (Hughes and Seligman, 1939). However, other conditions being equal, the temperature regime of the active layer will change substantially when the firn becomes ice. In contrast to firn, ice does not have a warming effect on the underlying rock, since the heat expended on melting is lost to the active layer because of the surface runoff of melt water.

Although the amount of heat expended on melting is greater than the cold reserve of winter freezing when the boundary condition $F_T < 0.4 \times 80 N_{sol}$ is disrupted, usually the cold reserve is great enough to convert part of the firn into ice. As soon as a continuous layer of ice forms, water from more remote melt areas runs off along its surface, carrying with it a great quantity of heat. Therefore, although the firn regime may be "warm," a cold regime may persist below the firn in the glaciers and native rocks of regions with a moderate continental climate, i.e., the temperature may be negative at the level of the zero annual amplitude of temperature fluctuations. Then there will be an infiltration congelation zone below the "warm" infiltration zone, instead of a zone of seasonal ice formation (Fig. 122).

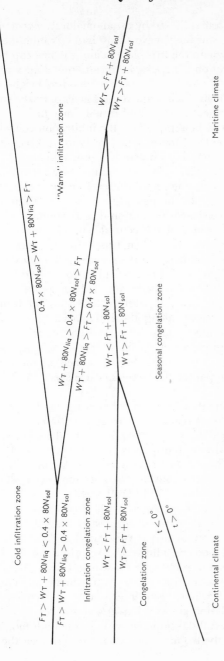

FIG. 122. Diagram of the vertical distribution of ice formation zones in regions with a climate transitional between maritime and continental.

N_{sol} – annual sum of solid precipitations; F_T – cold reserve of winter freezing and heat lost during the melt season; W_T – sum of the heat expended on melting; N_{liq} – annual sum of liquid precipitations; t – temperature at the base of the layer of annual fluctuations.

Boundaries between zones

Cold infiltration and infiltration congelation: $F_T > W_T + 80N_{liq} = 0.4 \times 80N_{sol}$;
cold infiltration and "warm" infiltration: $F_T = W_T + 80N_{liq} < 0.4 \times 80N_{sol}$;
"warm" infiltration and infiltration congelation: $W_T + 80N_{liq} > F_T = 0.4 \times 80N_{sol}$;
triple point: $F_T = W_T + 80N_{liq} = 0.4 \times 80N_{sol}$.

This alternation of zones, caused by the anomalously warm regime in the firn region, has been noted on Northeast Land (Nordaustlandet) and on Spitsbergen, where the firn plateau and the firn cap belong to the "warm" infiltration zone, despite mean annual air temperatures of as much as $-7°$ and $-8°C$ at a corresponding height, while lower down there are cold glaciers and a thick layer of frozen rock.

Characteristically, the "warm" infiltration zone may also disappear horizontally and be replaced by the infiltration congelation zone in a more continental climate, owing solely to less precipitation while the annual and monthly air temperatures remain the same. The change from a "warm" to a cold temperature regime in the active layer and the underlying rock is due exclusively to elimination of the warming influence of the firn while it is being transformed rapidly into ice by accelerated infiltration densification.

Evidently, the melt water of the central part of some ice caps, which have a "warm" regime in their firn-warmed central region and a cold regime in their peripheral ice zone, generally does not have access to the periphery of the caps, but it would be difficult to determine the further fate of this melt water without special study.

In other cases, melt water apparently first runs off from the "warm" central firn region along the interglacial channels and then water blocked by the "cold" ice of the peripheral zone discharges under pressure onto the glacier surface. This may explain the water fountains that gush forth from channels in the ice, observed in the southern part of the Greenland ice sheet (A. Nordenskiöld, 1886).

Another type of anomaly in the vertical alternation of zones of ice formation occurs in desert regions, where even an intense influx of radiation heat is expended on volatilization from the snow surface without melting and without the appearance of liquid water, because the air is so dry. In the Chilean and Argentine Andes, cases have been recorded where the snow surface does not melt even when the air temperature increases to $+15°C$ (Troll, 1942).

Under such conditions, instead of the infiltration zone there is a unique *lower desert variant of the recrystallization zone*. In this case, the perecrystallization of snow to firn is very rapid and apparently is basically sublimation perecrystallization. According to Catalano, one can almost follow the process under a magnifying glass. Such processes, which are unaccompanied or nearly unaccompanied by the appearance of melt water, result in characteristic sharp-pointed forms of radiation ablation known as *nieve penitente* (penitent snow). These processes reach full development only in the high mountains of the subtropics and the tropics at the boundary between the zone of eternal snow above and dry deserts in the depressions or valleys isolated by the mountains below. Unfortunately, practically no study has been made of the behavior of the ice formation processes under such conditions. Locally less sharply defined but similar conditions are encountered in dry depressions and valleys up to high latitudes, as manifested by the occurrence of incompletely developed, initial forms of the penitent snow. Therefore, one must consider the possibility of local formation of recrystallization firn and ice everywhere at the lower boundary of the infiltration zone in a climate that is considerably warmer than normal for the zone of recrystallization ice formation.

THE INFILTRATION CONGELATION ZONE

The direct transition vertically downward from a cold infiltration zone to an infiltration congelation zone of ice formation occurs under conditions where the cold reserve of winter freezing in the active layers remains greater than the heat of melting and liquid precipitation ($W_T + 80N_{liq} < F_T$), but where the amount of melt and rain water is adequate to fill all the pores of the unfrozen firn remnant ($W_T + 80N_{liq} \approx 0.4 \times 80N_{sol}$). This is observed in regions of continental climate, where the cold reserve of winter freezing in the active layer exceeds the amount of latent heat of fusion of the solid atmospheric precipitation by approximately 40%:

$$F_T > 0.4 \times 80N_{sol} \qquad (18)$$

In contrast to the small and nearly imperceptible change in the character of the ice formation processes during the transition from the cold to the "warm" infiltration zone, a considerable and obvious change is observed at the upper boundary of the infiltration congelation zone.

Although there is not enough melt and rain water to fill the pores of the unmelted firn remnant, this firn can become ice only at a great depth, through pressure exerted by the higher layers. Under such conditions, which are characteristic of the cold infiltration zone, the main mass of rock in the upper part of the cross section will consist of firn in which the infiltration ice may comprise only individual layers, lenses and irregular inclusions.

Actually, only a small amount of untransformed firn need remain each year so that in subsequent years melt water will be expended on filling the pores of the layers of earlier years and so that new layers will be preserved as firn. In this case, infiltration extends for a considerable distance from the surface and the firn density and the infiltration ice content of the firn gradually increase with depth along this profile.

However, as soon as melt and rain water appear in an amount in excess of what is required to fill the pores of the unmelted firn remnant, the firn at the lower limit of water percolation will convert entirely into ice. A water-impermeable layer will form, with a relatively large heat conductivity, which can easily transfer the heat of crystallization downward. Every year the upper boundary of this layer rises, owing to the freezing of water dammed up in the firn pores, and soon reaches the surface. There is a frequent alternation of ice and firn layers in the transitional zone, because the underlying firn is isolated from the melt water when a continuous interlayer of ice appears amid the firn and will not become infiltration ice.

The following example, observed by the author in a region where the mean annual air temperature is about $-12°C$, illustrates the change of the material balance and structure of the surface layer during the transition from a cold infiltration to an infiltration congelation zone of ice formation.

The transitional zone extended about 30 m vertically, chiefly because the amount of snow deposited was reduced considerably by increased wind action at a low level. The increased wind action was due to the local topography. Higher, in the infiltration zone, $N = A = 760$ mm of precipitation was deposited annually, of which 200 mm melted and were used entirely for infiltration (including about 5 mm that fell as rain); consequently

$$W_T + 80N_{liq} = 16,000 \text{ cal/cm}^2 < 0.4 \times 80N_{sol} = 24,320 \text{ cal/cm}^2$$

Under these conditions, a layer of firn with interlayers of infiltration ice appeared at the surface, with individual layers on an average 95 cm thick and with a mean density of 0.6 g/cm³ at the top, increasing slowly downward.

Only 540 mm of precipitation were deposited 35 m farther downslope, of which about 215 mm melted or fell as rain, i.e.,

$$W_T + 80N_{liq} = 17,200 \text{ cal/cm}^2 \approx 0.4 \times 80N_{sol} = 17,280 \text{ cal/cm}^2$$

The surface consisted of alternating layers of ice and firn, with ice predominating. The annual layer was 40 cm thick, with an average density of about 0.8 g/cm³. In periods of intense melting, a small part of the melt water ran off laterally from this transitional zone over the surface of the upper ice layer beneath the firn into the infiltration congelation zone and into the glacier cracks.

Only 275 mm of precipitation were deposited another 25 m

farther downslope. Of these, 225 mm melted or fell in the form of rain, i.e., 80% of the total amount or twice that required to fill the pores of the unmelted firn remnant. The upper part of the cross section consisted of ice with an average density of about 0.9 g/cm³, which was covered by a meter-thick layer of snow by the end of the accumulation season. In periods of moderate melting, the water froze in the pores at the surface of the ice and when the melting was intense, the water ran off along the ice into the ablation region and, in part, into the cracks, washing out channels and cavities in the firn. By the end of the melt season, the firn was completely melted or remained in the form of isolated patches and melt water ran off horizontally along the exposed ice surface. Of the 225 mm of water mentioned above, 165 mm ran off and 60 mm froze in the firn pores, forming an annual layer of ice not more than 12 cm thick. The upper part of this layer was subjected to melting at the end of the summer and part of the melt water refroze in the form of extruded congelation ice. Finally, a layer of ice 10.6 cm thick remained of the meter-thick layer of snow and below it lay infiltration ice with lenses of infiltration congelation ice, while above it was a small amount of extruded congelation ice. Annual ice layers 5–6 cm and 2–3 cm thick were observed at lesser absolute heights, where the melting was more intense.

Thus, the infiltration congelation zone of ice formation had the following characteristics. The cold regime was maintained in the layer of ice rock, but melt and rain water began to run off along the surface. Thanks to the warm surface runoff, the ice temperature at the level of the zero annual amplitudes of temperature fluctuations was lower than in the non-ice rock, other conditions being equal, because the temperature maxima had been cut off short of the melting point. The surface balance of solid precipitation remained positive $(A > 0)$, but the layers of annual accumulation became much thinner than those of the cold infiltration zone because part of the material was lost in the form of runoff and the remainder of its mass became dense ice.

The amount of solid precipitation remaining on the surface in the form of ice depends to a great extent on the thermal balance of the active layer, according to equation (6), and on the slope of the surface, the presence of cracks and generally the conditions of the surface drainage. In other words, as the temperature of the underlying ice decreases, the rate of melting decreases, the surface slope decreases and the path length of the runoff water increases, more and more of the water freezes in the firn pores or on the exposed ice surface and less drains off. If the active layer has not accumulated a large cold reserve during the winter and if too little cold has arrived at the surface from below during the melt season, the layer of solid precipitation in this zone will not be able to withstand summer melting. A positive balance of solid precipitation is created by the cold reserve of winter freezing, not by the latent cold of crystallization of the solid atmospheric precipitation, as in the "warm" infiltration zone. Under these circumstances, glaciation owes its existence to the low temperature of the ambient medium, which permits it to develop despite the small amount of atmospheric precipitation.

Congelation ice-veins develop especially well in this zone, as well as in the lower ablation regions of cold glaciers; in the fissured areas these veins develop on such a scale that one may regard them as a special internal source of glacier nourishment.

The cross section of ice in the infiltration congelation zone, proceeding downward, is composed as follows:

(1) snow less than one year old, which becomes firn during melt periods (by the end of the melt periods it disappears completely or nearly disappears);

(2) a layer of infiltration ice with a distinct, thin stratification, containing interlayers and lenses of infiltration congelation and extruded congelation ice;

(3) vertical veins of congelation ice;

(4) secondary-recrystallization ice on slopes, at a depth where ice flow can be detected.

As melting increases and the amount of precipitation decreases downward in the infiltration congelation zone, the annual ice layers gradually become thinner until a zero balance of solid precipitation is reached, i.e., until the boundary between the regions of glacier accumulation and ablation is reached. The infiltration congelation zone of ice formation and the ablation zone of glaciers show the following characteristic differences: in the infiltration congelation zone, infiltration ice with a smooth, slippery surface lies beneath the snow or firn and the surface conforms with the bedding, while in the ablation zone there is a layer of destruction ice ("melt crust") beneath the snow; this layer is regenerated in winter, but as a rule it has the buried "cryoconite horizon" of the bottoms of dust wells, while the surface of the ice intersects the bedding.

The infiltration congelation zone of ice formation is characteristic of regions of continental climate where the average annual temperature is just a few degrees below zero and the average temperature of the warmest month is close to zero. As the continentality of the climate increases, the same kind of change takes place in this zone as in the case of downward movement, i.e., the layer of annual accumulation becomes thinner and thinner, while the vertical distance between the upper and lower limits of the zone keeps increasing. The infiltration congelation zone is weakly developed in the transitional regions, where it borders on the "warm" infiltration zone above. However, in regions of more severe continental climate, it becomes as much as 400 m thick, and in some regions even 600 m thick.

This zone includes extensive glacier areas, especially in the Arctic regions. Because of the infiltration congelation zone of ice formation, the boundary between the accumulation and ablation areas in regions of cold glacier development does not coincide with the firn line, but lies some hundreds of meters below it. Therefore, the investigators who have tried to determine the boundary between the accumulation and ablation regions of cold glaciers by alpine standards often unjustly classified glaciers fed from the infiltration congelation zone as "dead" glaciers, i.e., glaciers which had lost their source of nourishment. The author (Shumskii, 1947*b*) made this same mistake when he distinguished a zone of "unstable relictal glaciation" in the Soviet Arctic, when actually it was quite stable relictal glaciation with infiltration congelation nourishment. This type of nourishment also occurs in many regions classified as "stable relictal glaciation," where previous investigators either failed to note the absence of firn or did not mention it, being unable to explain it. A considerable part of the glaciation of the Canadian Arctic Archipelago also belongs to this type, as is clear from the data of the American investigators (e.g., Ward, 1950), who have not yet established the laws of this phenomenon. Undoubtedly, the zone of infiltration congelation ice formation also occurs in Greenland below the firn line and in continental mountain regions with slight precipitation, in particular the eastern Pamir Mountains and, apparently, the eastern margins of the Tien-Shan and Altai Mountains of the Soviet Union.

GLACIATION AND PERMAFROST

In a maritime climate, where the glaciation develops chiefly because of the reserves of the latent cold of crystallization of solid atmospheric precipitation, the level of the zero balance of solid precipitation on the earth's surface is simultaneously the lower limit of the region where locally formed ice rocks exist the year round. The situation is different in continental climates where glaciation develops because of the low temperature of the medium, not because

of abundant atmospheric precipitation. Here melting (or volatilization) of the entire annual layer of solid precipitation, which permits
a considerable increase of summer temperature, is not generally
associated with elimination of the cold regime of the rock layer in the
rather broad zone below the snow line. The mean annual temperatures remain low enough to maintain a constant negative temperature at the level of the zero annual amplitudes, including a fairly
thick layer of underlying rocks, and rocks containing free and not too
saline water are "permanently" frozen.[7]

As we have seen, most of the higher-lying zones of the cryosphere,
which have a positive balance of solid precipitation and in which
glaciation develops at the earth's surface, also have a cold temperature regime in their fairly thick surface layer of rock. The recrystallization, recrystallization-infiltration, cold infiltration and infiltration congelation zones of ice formation require a negative
temperature at the level of the zero annual amplitudes. The magnitudes of negative temperature at the level of the zero annual amplitudes, the ice thickness and the vertical temperature gradient
determine whether the cold regime, i.e., the temperature below the
melting point of ice at the given hydrostatic pressure, will extend to
the underlying non-ice rock as well as to the ice, in other words,
whether frozen ground (a frozen state of the rock) will develop
beneath the glacier.

Ice, firn and snow may exert either a warming or a cooling influence on the underlying rock, depending on the conditions. However, as a rule, the snow and ice exert a cooling effect only at the
boundary with the atmosphere and the adjacent air, since this
influence is associated with the change of the radiational balance
caused by increased albedo and natural radiation of the snow surface
and with the heat lost to melting, i.e., the heat expended on overcoming the latent cold of crystallization of the ice. Surface cooling
can be transmitted to the underlying rocks only indirectly, through
the layer of snow and ice. In this case, it counters the direct warming
effect of the ice rocks. The cooling effect definitely prevails only in
regions with a positive average annual air temperature, where heat is
expended on melting, not on increasing the surface temperature,
and it also predominates in cold regions where the snow melts and
runs off late each year and acts as a greater hindrance to summer
warming than to winter freezing. In other cases, the warming effect
generally prevails. This warming effect is threefold.

First, in regions with a negative mean annual temperature, the

---

[7] We use the term "frozen" exclusively for rock cemented by ice.

firn, upon melting, increases the temperature at the level of the zero annual amplitudes, owing to the greater rate of infiltration heating compared with freezing. Second, the ice rocks in a cold regime increase the temperature of the underlying rock, in proportion to the thickness of the rock, by a value equal to the product of its thickness and the temperature gradient, according to equation (14). Third, if there is movement in the ice layer, an additional heat source appears, viz., internal and external friction, which makes the value of the temperature gradient in a cold glacier greater than it would be if only the earth's heat flux were involved. In a "warm" glacier, the heat of friction and the incoming earth's heat are expended on the internal and bottom melting of the ice.

Since the kinetic energy of a glacier is negligible, all the potential energy of position during the descent of a glacier to positions of less absolute height is converted into heat, while in the case of a cold regime, it is expended on raising the temperature. If the heat of friction is released evenly throughout the glacier, the increase of the ice temperature during a descent of h meters will be

$$\Delta t = A \frac{h}{c}$$

or 0.47°C/100 m descent; here A is the thermal equivalent of work and c is the specific heat of the ice, namely, 0.47°C per 100 m descent. This is about equal to the average vertical temperature gradient in the atmosphere and is approximately sufficient for the ice itself, on descending, to assume a temperature corresponding to the mean annual air temperature at each given level.

Actually, the release of heat in a glacier is distributed unevenly, both in the vertical profile, because of the differences in the intensity of deformation, and in the direction of flow, because of the longitudinal transfer of pressure and energy. The heat release is maximum at the glacier bed, and also at the edges in the case of sheet glaciation, especially in tributaries which move rapidly because of the pressure of the ice sheet. Therefore, the temperature gradient decreases from the surface toward the bed of the glacier and this decrease is greater in rapidly moving glaciers than in the slow-moving central portion of an ice sheet. The temperature gradient at the top of the glacier is greater than the normal gradient in stationary ice, while it is smaller than the normal gradient at the bed of the glacier, because of the thermal barrier which disturbs the uniformity of the geothermal heat flux. As Lagally (1932a) has shown, the mean temperature gradient between the surface and the bed (at depth h) in a cold glacier with viscous flow is equal to the arithmetic mean of the actual gradient at the surface $\left|\dfrac{dt}{dz}\right|_0$ and the normal gradient in stationary ice $\dfrac{W_{int}}{k}$

$$\frac{T_h - T_0}{h} = \frac{1}{2}\left(\frac{dt}{dz}\bigg|_0 + \frac{W_{int}}{k}\right) \tag{19}$$

The geothermal gradient measured in the surface layers of cold glaciers varies from 14 m/°C for a rapidly moving tributary of the Greenland ice sheet (Koch and Wegener, 1930) and 20 m/°C in the Ross Ice Shelf to 67 m/°C, according to the somewhat doubtful indirect data of seismic soundings 120 km from the edge of the Greenland ice sheet (Brockamp, 1935).

If the geothermal heat flux is assumed to be 53 cal/cm²/year, the most probable average value of the geothermal gradients will be 30 m/°C in cold glaciers for the stationary ice of the central part of ice caps and sheets, with an average of at least 20 m/°C for the most rapidly moving glaciers.

The thickness l of the layer with a cold regime will be approximately equal to the product of the temperature at the level of the zero annual amplitudes T_0 and the magnitude of the average geothermal gradient $\dfrac{\overline{dz}}{dt}$:

$$l \simeq T_0 \frac{\overline{dz}}{dt} \tag{20}$$

For a more exact calculation, one must consider the reduction of the melting point of ice under pressure.

Thus, the layer with a cold regime will be from 20 T_0 to 30 T_0 meters thick. In regions where the temperature at the level of zero annual amplitudes is $-30°C$ (in the recrystallization zone), the cold regime penetrates approximately 900 m beneath the surface of the ice sheet; in regions where this temperature is $-10°C$ (in the infiltration congelation zone), the cold regime penetrates 200–300 m, etc.

If the glacier is thicker than this, the ice will be at the melting point farther down and thus the glacier will be of the mixed "cold-warm" type and will be underlain with thawed rocks. However, if the glacier is not as thick as the above, it will be cold to the bed and will be underlain with frozen rocks.

However thick the ice may be in the central part of the glacier, as a rule frozen ground will develop along the margins of the glaciers and on the glacier-free adjacent areas in regions of continental climate, because the lower boundary of the infiltration congelation zone in these regions is situated at the level of sufficiently low mean annual atmospheric isotherms.

Thus, the problem of the relationship between glaciation and permafrost is solved. Active glaciation with alimentation in the warm infiltration zone is incompatible with permafrost, but typical development of an infiltration congelation zone presumes the existence of frozen ground beneath thin glaciers and in the periglacial region. On the other hand, the presence of well developed frozen ground is a direct indication that the boundary between the accumulation and ablation regions of glaciers in a given region does not coincide with the firn line, but that a fairly broad infiltration congelation zone lies between them.

THE CONGELATION ZONE

From the standpoint of the processes of ice rock formation, the permafrost region should be regarded as a zone of congelation ice formation, the lowest of the zones of the cryosphere where ice rocks exist the year round. The fundamental difference between it and the higher zones of ice formation consists in the negative balance of solid atmospheric precipitation on the earth's surface and, thus, no continuous ice cover accumulates here.

The supposition that glaciation develops exclusively because of the low temperature of the ambient medium despite a small amount of solid atmospheric precipitation applies more to the congelation zone than to the higher infiltration congelation zone.

As already noted, the low surface temperature at the present rate of influx of solar radiation can be maintained continuously, the year round, only if there is a continuous snow-ice cover. As soon as this cover disappears, the summer temperature increases abruptly. With very low winter and negative mean annual air temperatures, the mean temperatures of the warmest month in the congelation zone become as much as several degrees above zero in regions where the cold ocean monsoons penetrate, while farther from the ocean they may reach $+15°$ to $+20°C$.

As a rule, under such conditions there is no constant surface glaciation except on small specially favored areas in the upper part of the congelation zone. In regions where the mean temperature of the warmest month is greater than approximately $10°C$, forest vegetation develops, agriculture becomes possible and the territory is suitable for various economic activities. However, beginning at depths of just 0.1 to 3.0 m beneath the protection of the slowly thawing layer of rock, the temperature remains constantly negative. In the congelation zone, glaciation passes from the surface into the earth's crust, where ice rock can exist for a long time because of intense winter freezing.

Thus, in the congelation zone ice accumulation falls within known bounds and cannot disrupt the mechanical equilibrium unless other factors, such as melting, intervene. Stresses and strains in ice bodies are caused primarily by volumetric changes which occur during temperature fluctuations of the active layer and in most cases these stresses and strains change direction periodically, without progressive movement. Thus, glaciation is stationary in the congelation zone.

Since the ice of the upper zones of the cryosphere moves but slightly, the glacier material is actually removed from the water cycle, traversing a short path in a very long time. For example, in the Greenland ice sheet, according to quite reliable estimates, part of the ice derives from the end of the last glacial epoch (approximately 10,000 years ago), while in the Antarctic it derives from the maximum of the last glacial epoch (approximately 25,000 years ago). In contrast to this, a considerable part of the ice in the congelation zone appears, in general, to have been preserved for the entire lifetime of the frozen ground in the given place.

With few exceptions, all the ice in the described zone belongs to the congelation ice group, i.e., it forms by the freezing of water, and not from solid atmospheric precipitation. Atmospheric precipitation, which at first is fairly evenly distributed over the surface in a fluid, liquid state, is redistributed according to the features of the surface topography and the water-permeability of the surface rocks. Various conditions of moistening and melting of the surface layer are created, which determine whether and how congelation ice will form. The granulometric composition, cementation, and the plastic, thermal and other properties of the rock, the nature of the plant cover, etc., are also very important. To a great extent, the conditions of ice formation in the congelation zone depend on the diversity of local factors and, therefore, the distribution of ice rock is highly irregular. Furthermore, some zonal regularities, which have been studied but little, are also involved in this distribution.

Perennial vein ice, *segregation* and *injection ice* and, in native rocks, *vein ice* are the main, persistent and widely distributed ice rocks of the congelation zone.

Perennial vein ice develops in the finely dispersed and organic mineral frozen rocks, primarily of alluvial origin. It forms even now in the upper or northern part of the congelation zone, chiefly in the flood plains of rivers, while the deposits of the ancient terraces contain large beds of fossil ice of Pleistocene, "syngenetic," perennial ice-vein origin. No perennial vein ice exists at present in the more southerly regions and the fossil ice forms are represented by only comparatively small epigenetic formations (stages of a high flood plain).

Segregation ice occurs in the congelation zone wherever there are finely dispersed or organic-mineral rocks (clays, argillaceous soils, sandy loams, peat) which freeze in a not too compact, moist state.

The multiannual ice injections of "taliks"[8] beneath lakes are distributed over a large area of the congelation zone, except for its southern periphery, and are adapted to regions where alluvial deposits develop. Since the large injections are always associated with positive forms of the relief and their roof is subject to comparatively rapid destruction, after which the ice melts out, injection ice of this type is usually young. It is widely developed in the flood plains of rivers, on young terraces and in the thermokarst depressions, but is never found on ancient terraces, since such ice melted out long ago in the ancient terraces. The multiannual injections at the points of emergence of subpermafrost water are found only on the southern periphery of a congelation zone which has thin frozen rock, in regions of complex tectonic structure.

On the surface and in the active layer, the ice formation processes behave basically as they do in the zone of seasonal ice formation, but the low winter temperatures and the presence of frozen ground leave their mark: the *ice covers of water* develop to a considerably greater extent, *seasonal ice injections* form and *icings* (i.e., *hydroeffusives*) develop, consisting primarily of *extruded* ice but also of *infiltration* and ordinary congelation ice with *ice mounds* containing *rhythmic congelation ice*.

Seasonal ice injections are widely distributed and become large at the southern periphery of the congelation zone, which has a thick active layer, while farther north they become weaker and weaker and disappear entirely at the northern periphery, where the surface layer affected by seasonal melting is too thin. Within this zone, the seasonal ice injections are most widely distributed in the regions of dissected relief and are less widely distributed in mountain regions with coarse-skeleton soils (where river icings predominate instead of underground icings) and are much less widely distributed in the plains.

The congelation zone also includes ablation regions with glaciers that get their nourishment from higher zones of the cryosphere.

---

[8] [See note 2, Chap. X. – D.K.]

Furthermore, the so-called *snowbank* and *drift glaciers* are widely developed in the upper part of the congelation zone, in places where the topography is favorable for the accumulation of wind-blown snow or places protected from the sun's rays. Snowbank glaciers differ from glaciers only in that they are stationary and, as a rule, consist of *infiltration ice* or *firn.* Here we are dealing with isolated areas in which the processes follow the type of ice formation found in higher zones, because of the local abundance of deposited solid precipitation or decreased melting and, naturally, the conditions of the nearest infiltration congelation zone, with the immediate transformation of snow into ice, are created at least as often as the conditions of the cold infiltration zone, where the upper part of the cross section is composed primarily of firn.

The cold regime of the congelation zone creates conditions favorable for the *preservation* of surface ice rocks, snowbank glaciers, the dead ice of the glaciers, hydroeffusives, blocks of river, lake and sea ice, etc., provided they are *buried* beneath an alluvium layer thick enough so that it will not melt through completely.

Thus, in essence, one may find all types of congelation and metamorphic ice rocks among the underground ice of the congelation zone, with the sole exception of recrystallization firn. Actually, most of the underground ice consists of *epigenetic* formations (with respect to the enclosing rocks); in particular, the main mass of the formerly enigmatic fossil or stone ice can be classified as perennial vein ice. However, almost all varieties of surface congelation and metamorphic ice apparently can be found in small amounts, primarily in mountain regions, in the form of buried ice syngenetic with the enclosing rocks. Hence, the ice rocks of the congelation zone have the most diverse facies composition and are most difficult to analyze.

As follows from the definition itself, the lower limit of the congelation zone (the southern limit in the northern hemisphere) is approximately the 0°C temperature level at the depth of the zero amplitudes of seasonal temperature fluctuations. (It is possible that frozen ground may not form at subzero temperatures because of salinification or the binding of water by the surface of dispersed rocks.) Usually, this limit does not coincide with the zero annual air temperature isotherm, but passes above it (to the north of it). The magnitude of the deviation may vary greatly, depending on a number of factors, namely, the snow cover, the topography, the vegetation, the composition of the rock, hydrogeologic conditions, etc., and also on the history of the development of the frozen ground. Examination of the influence of these factors of the frozen ground regime is really a subject for the cryopedologist.

The congelation zone includes extensive territories, chiefly in the northern continents, which have a cold continental climate, i.e., Asia and North America. In Asia, it includes northern Mongolia to 46°N (Sumgin, 1940; Sumgin *et al.*, 1940) as well as northern and eastern Siberia and the adjacent islands. In North America, it takes in most of Alaska, northern Canada and Labrador and the glacier-free parts of the Canadian Archipelago and Greenland (except for the southern coast). In Europe, frozen ground occurs only in the extreme northern and north-eastern parts of the continent and on the glacier-free islands of the European Arctic.

Besides these major regions, the congelation zone includes the high mountain massifs and the plateau of Central Asia, i.e., Tibet, the Kuenlun Shan (K'un Lun Shan), Karakorum, the eastern Pamirs and, in part, the eastern sections of the Tien Shan and Altai Mountains and other mountain ranges. Characteristically, the researchers who dealt with Central Asia often erroneously described typical icings (naleds), which were hydroeffusives in river valleys at elevations of 4000–5000 m, as "firn fields" (De Terra, Shaw and others), because they were unfamiliar with the forms of glaciation in the congelation zone.

In the rest of the world, the congelation zone apparently includes only the glacier-free parts of the Antarctic ice sheet. Evidently, it would be unrealistic to assume that frozen ground develops in the mountain regions of other continents near the snow line. Unless the climate is sufficiently continental, the "warm" infiltration zone comprises the lower zone of ice formation and this excludes the possibility of a cold temperature regime. As a rule, the ice-free surface areas above the snow line in mountains consist of steep exposures of native rocks, where the typical ice formation processes of the congelation zone do not occur.

THE SEASONAL CONGELATION ZONE

The lower part of the cryosphere has the following characteristics: solid precipitation falls and the air temperature periodically drops below the melting point of ice, but the surface has a negative solid precipitation balance and the rock layer does not have a cold regime. The ice rocks in this zone form and exist periodically and regularly over a fairly long cold season, with the exception of the ablation regions of glaciers which descend into the upper part of this zone from the higher zones of the cryosphere and the small glaciers and snowbank glaciers, which exist under especially favorable topographic conditions near the boundary of the "warm" infiltration zone. In regions with a maritime climate, the zone of seasonal ice formation is bounded above by the "warm" infiltration zone, while in regions with a continental climate, it is bounded by the congelation zone.

The typical ice rocks of this zone are: the *ordinary congelation ice* of the first two stages of congelation ice formation, namely, the *ice covers of water* and the *snow cover*, and, in regions with a sufficiently continental climate, interlayers of *segregation ice* in the active layer of the soil. In regions with a maritime climate, there is practically no seasonally frozen ground and the snow lies on incompletely frozen soil. The metamorphic ice formation processes do not play an essential role in this zone; the snow cover converts, in part, into ice only during the runoff of melt water and sometimes in small river icings (hydroeffusives).

Most of the zone of seasonal ice formation, which includes over 30% of the land surface of the earth, belongs to the most densely populated and most utilized regions of the earth.

Another region, not included in the zone of seasonal ice formation and comprising slightly less than 50% of the land surface of the earth, is situated between the tropics and at less than 1500 m above m.s.l. (Bonacina, 1938), where frosts and solid atmospheric precipitation in the form of hail are the exception.

CHAPTER XIX

DISTRIBUTION OF THE PROCESSES OF DYNAMIC METAMORPHISM

In contrast to the processes of ice formation, the processes of dynamic metamorphism are not directly dependent upon climate; consequently they are azonal. Local factors play the main role in the distribution of dynamometamorphic ice, which often is complex and diverse. We shall summarize only the most general laws of structure of ice bodies comprised of dynamometamorphic ice.

There are three principal agencies of dynamic metamorphism. External dynamic influences play the leading role in the ice cover of water. Temperature fluctuations and the attendant changes in volume dominate in the immobile underground ice and, in part, in the surface ice of the congelation zone, while the natural weight of ice is the main factor in glaciers and avalanches.

The nature and intensity of the external dynamic influences, i.e., the wind, agitation and flow, have their specific laws, which are not affiliated with the ice cover; they depend primarily on the dimensions of the reservoir, the dip of the river bed and the volume of stream water. The external influences result in cataclasis, fracture and crushing of the ice cover, leading to the formation of *compression-cataclastic ice* (ice breccia and conglomerates), often cemented by new generations of congelation ice.

The phenomena of dynamic metamorphism are least widespread in the immobile ice of the congelation zone and leave only a slight impression on the primary structure, so that one can hardly speak of this ice as dynamometamorphic. The phenomena of dislocation metamorphism, i.e., the appearance of cracks, fractures and faults, the cataclasis of crystals and the flattening of air bubbles in the lower part of the perennial veins, play the main role in the ice of the perennial veins, the hydrolaccoliths and the ice mounds of the surface icings. The ultimate cause of these phenomena is always the freezing of water, whereby the increase of volume during freezing in a closed space is always important in hydrolaccoliths and icing

441

mounds, while the ice which formed in the cracks of perennial veins plays the passive role of a wedge during the subsequent thermal expansion of the rock.

In contrast to the immobile ground ice of the congelation zone and the passively moving ice covers of water, the main mass of sedimentary ice is dynamometamorphic, because it moves actively under its own weight. Only a rather thin ice layer in which the weight pressure does not exceed the elastic limit escapes dynamic metamorphism; such layers lie immobile in snowbank glaciers or are transported passively by the deeper ice in glaciers, eventually entering the deep, flowing zone in the accumulation region or melting away in the ablation region.

The movement of glaciers, which is complex in nature, profoundly alters the primary structure of sedimentary-metamorphic ice, but in most cases the original character of the ice can still be identified. This movement leads to the various phenomena of dislocation metamorphism and also to paratectonic perecrystallization and even to temporary melting of the ice due to friction or local excess pressure. Various types of dynamometamorphic ice result. These types have already been described in the sections on *secondary-recrystallization*, *friction-regelation*, *compression-regelation* and *friction-cataclastic* ice, to which the *clastic* ice forms have been added. These are the indirect result of movement by gravitational crushing.

Secondary-recrystallization ice, which comprises the main mass of glaciers, retains vestiges of its primary structure, mainly textural features. Indistinct traces of sedimentary stratification or stratification from the metamorphic stage of ice formation, quite deformed congelation veins, tension cracks, thrust and fracture planes, zones of crushing and folding, regelation lenses, regelation bands and moraine inclusions, taken together, create tectonic structures which are sometimes highly complex and are inferior in size alone to the regions of intensive tectogenesis of the earth's crust. Thus, the conditions for sedimentary-metamorphic ice formation may be comparatively uniform at the surface, but deeper down, especially in the bottom layers of the glacier, the processes of dynamic metamorphism create a diversity of facies composition as great as that of the epigenetic ice in the congelation zone of ice formation.

The increase of atmospheric ice on the elevated parts of the earth's surface disrupts mechanical equilibrium, which strives to re-establish itself during the movement of glaciers. The more rapid this increase is or, to be more exact, the more rapid the increase with elevation, the faster the glacier will flow. The magnitude of the ice increment with height above the snow line, which is a measure of glacier activity and which has been termed the *energy of glaciation* (Shumskii, 1947*a*), reaches a maximum in a maritime climate and decreases with continentality. This is manifested in the greater thickness of glaciers in the regions of maritime climate. In regions with a large energy of glaciation, ice sheets are relatively steep and convex, but as the energy of glaciation decreases, they become flatter and less active. This is quite evident in the case of the Greenland ice sheet: its southern sector, situated within the sphere of influence of the Icelandic low, is active and thick with respect to its horizontal dimensions, while its northern sector, situated in the cold continental region of the "arctic wind divide," is very flat and slow moving. As the continentality of the climate increases, the layer of the earth's crust which has a cold regime becomes thicker. This layer is entirely absent in the regions where a "warm" infiltration zone develops, while it extends to the rocks of the glacier bed in the infiltration congelation and congelation zones.

In line with these changes, generally the processes of dynamic metamorphism are less intense in the colder continental regions. The climate has some indirect influence (through the glacier activity and the temperature regime of the ice layer) on the dynamic metamorphic processes as well, in that they increase or decrease the intensity of these processes. However, the general picture is considerably obscured by local morphological factors, which exert a greater influence on the intensity and nature of the processes of dynamic metamorphism.

The temperature regime also exerts a direct influence on ice structure. One result of the cold regime in the layer of glacier ice is the high pressure of the air included in the secondary-recrystallization ice which passed through the deep parts of the glacier. The air pressure in the compression-regelation ice also yields quantitative data on the temperature regime of the ice. Evidently, the temperature regime also affects the size and structure of the friction-regelation and compression-regelation ice bodies.

Finally, the tectonic structures and petrographic features of dynamometamorphic ice are a function of the morphological and local dynamic conditions, about which we can make only some general remarks here.

Secondary-recrystallization ice is the product of plastic flow. Friction-regelation and friction-cataclastic ice result from gliding along the internal fracture planes. Lamellar thrusts, folding, fluidal structure and lenses of compression-regelation ice result from local longitudinal shearing and compression caused by the resistance of projections of the glacier bed, the ice areas overloaded with moraine and the tapering glacier termini with too gentle a slope. Finally, the open cracks, which give rise to congelation veins, result from stress, which can be longitudinal, oblique or transverse with respect to the direction of flow.

The layer of primary sedimentary-metamorphic ice in the accumulation region of the glacier surface becomes thinner as the slope of the glacier surface becomes steeper. Apparently, this layer becomes very thick in the nearly horizontal central region of ice sheets and caps.

As the conditions of ice flow, primarily the size of the cross section, the inclination of the bed, the inclination of the surface and the direction of flow, become more uniform, the role of plastic flow in glacier movement increases, the glacier grains become larger and the crystallographic orientation of the grains becomes more uniform, other conditions being equal. Regular crystallographic orientation is associated with the direction of flow; specifically, the main crystal axes tend to be oriented linearly, perpendicular to the direction of flow, in other words, the basal planes are arranged in the direction of flow. Usually the air inclusions, which are elongated in the direction of flow, are flattened in the basal plane.

As the conditions of ice flow become more variable and the distance from the sources of nourishment become greater, the role played by slipping along the bed and along the internal fracture planes become greater and the complex tectonic structures that appear as a result of longitudinal compression and stress in the glacier become more developed.

The more even the bed is and the more stable the rocks that comprise it, the greater will be the role of slipping along the bed and the smaller will be the role of slipping along the internal fractures.

However, as a rule, glaciers have a fairly well developed bottom zone of folds and thrusts, because of the irregularities of the bed and the abundance of moraine material on the bed, even in the lower layers of ice. Friction-regelation and friction-cataclastic ice are associated with thrusts, while macrofluvial composition and the formation of compression-regelation ice are associated with folding.

The relationship of the elements of these structures, and also of congelation veins and seams from tension cracks, with vestiges of the primary stratification and the crystallographic orientation of the enclosing secondary-recrystallization ice, usually provide the means for establishing the behavior of the processes of dynamic metamorphism and the general picture of the morphologic and dynamic conditions under which a given part of a glacier formed.

CHAPTER XX

THE STRUCTURE OF
THE CRYOSPHERE

The laws of the geographic distribution of ice rocks, which we have already examined, can now serve as the basis for depicting the distribution of ice within the cryosphere, i.e., the structure of the cryosphere.

The cryosphere, which is bounded above and below by zones of high temperature, contains part of the earth's surface together with a fairly thick adjacent layer of the earth's crust and the lower part of the atmosphere. The moisture content of the atmosphere decreases greatly at some distance from the earth's surface and so, actually, ice appears only within the troposphere. Thus, the cryosphere is approximately 8–12 km deep.

Both the upper and the lower boundaries of the cryosphere dip at the poles and rise at the equator. The characteristic hypsometric indexes of the upper and lower limits of the lowest position of the cryosphere in high latitudes are approximately +8 km and −0.6 km with respect to the level of the World Ocean and the highest position of the cryosphere in the low latitudes has corresponding indexes of about +17 km and +6.5 km. Both boundaries change position with time: very slowly within the earth's crust and rapidly in the atmosphere, depending on the meteorological processes. Specifically, the lower boundary drops to sea level in the middle latitudes for a time each year and occasionally reaches the equator.

In the cryosphere ordinary ice exists either as a mineral in a dispersed state (in the troposphere and hydrosphere), as a component of polymineralic rocks (in the lithosphere) or as fairly large ice bodies composed of monomineralic ice rocks. These latter are concentrated exclusively on the land or water surface and in the upper layers of the earth's crust.

The atmospheric part of the cryosphere has three zones (proceeding downward):

(1) the upper zone of cirrus clouds with skeletal-prismatic ice crystals;

(2) the middle zone of altostratus and altocumulus clouds with solid ice crystals of the intermediate growth type;

(3) the lower zone of nimbostratus clouds with skeletal-tabular ice crystals.

On entering the cryosphere, the earth's surface and the adjacent part of the earth's crust become an arena for the ice formation processes (i.e., the formation of ice rocks), which differ in different parts of the cryosphere. As we have shown above, the ice formation processes are distributed zonally. In this sense, one may say that the surface part of the cryosphere consists of ice rocks which develop in the different zones of ice formation. The ice formation processes depend on the heat and moisture balance of the earth's surface and, consequently, on the state and processes of the atmosphere. Therefore, there must be a definite connection (which still has not been investigated) between the structure of the atmospheric part of the cryosphere and the conditions of ice formation on the part of the earth's surface which is rising to that level. Meanwhile, we still must examine the structure of the surface and atmospheric parts of the cryosphere separately.

Somewhat less than half of the total land area of the earth,[1] which lies between the tropics at less than 1500 m above sea level, is almost always outside the cryosphere, more than 30% of the land surface enters the cryosphere annually and belongs to the zone of seasonal ice formation and about 20%, or 30,000,000 km², is always within the cryosphere. Most of this area is located in the high latitudes, with only a negligible portion of it in the highlands of the temperate and tropical zones.

It has been observed that the structure of the cryosphere, like that of the earth's crust, is asymmetrical and that this asymmetry is the indirect result of the asymmetry of the earth's crust. The structure of the earth's crust is different in the regions of continental massifs and ocean deeps. The uneven distribution of mountain and water masses, which have quite different thermal properties, leads to the differentiation of maritime and continental climates, with a whole series of transitional types. This differentiation is responsible for the difference in the structure of the cryosphere in littoral and continental regions, a difference which is obvious from a comparison of the schematic vertical profiles of the cryosphere given in Table 6.

This asymmetry is evident in the lower half of the cryosphere, beginning with the cold infiltration zone, because the lower half of

---

[1] Total land area of the earth, about 149,000,000 km².

Table 6

Schematic Vertical Profiles of the Cryosphere

Maritime climate	Continental climate
Recrystallization zone	Recrystallization zone
Recrystallization-infiltration zone	Recrystallization-infiltration zone
Cold infiltration zone	Cold infiltration zone
....	xxxxxxxxxxxxxxxxxxxxxxxxxxxxx
"Warm" infiltration zone	Infiltration congelation zone
xxxxxxxxxxxxxxxxxxxxxxxxxxxxxxx	Congelation zone
Seasonal congelation zone	....
	Seasonal congelation zone

.... lower limit of the cold regime in the rock layer

xxxxxxxxx firn limit

————— boundary between the accumulation and ablation zones of glaciers ("the snow line," the lower limit of the chionosphere)

the cryosphere is a region of unstable dynamic equilibrium, where the temperature continually passes across the melting point of ice. This does not occur in the recrystallization zone and is limited above by the lack of moisture, by the equilibrium between sublimation and volatilization. However, when melting occurs, ice can be preserved by the reserves of the latent cold of crystallization at 0°C and by the cold reserves of winter freezing. In the first instance, the ice masses which accumulate atmospheric cold in the latent form must be large in order to survive intensified melting. In the second instance, there must be a rapid rate of removal of heat from the surface, because ice has a small heat capacity, and thus there must be a large temperature gradient, in other words, intense freezing. Actually, both factors always participate to a certain extent in preserving ice in the lower part of the cryosphere, although the latent cold of crystallization of atmospheric precipitation plays the dominant role in regions of typical maritime climate, while the cold of winter freezing plays the main role in regions of continental climate. However, the enormous latent heat of fusion of ice is a more active factor in preserving the positive ice balance on the earth's surface; therefore, the boundary between the accumulation and ablation regions of glaciers or the limit of the chionosphere drops considerably lower in the regions of maritime climate than in continental regions. Ice cannot remain on the earth's surface in regions of continental climate when the amount of solid precipitation is slight and the melting intense, even when freezing is very intense, because ice is a poor conductor of heat. However, very favorable conditions are created for the retention of ice during severe freezing when there is a protective surface layer of non-ice rock and the glaciation proceeds from the surface into the earth's crust. Therefore, the constant (non-seasonal) lower boundary of the cryosphere in continental regions (which coincides with the limit of the cold regime in the rock layer) drops much lower than in maritime regions. Thus, the lower boundary of the chionosphere descends toward the sea, which acts as a source of atmospheric precipitation, but in quite high latitudes the lower boundary of the entire cryosphere descends in the heart of the continents which are a source of cooling in winter and in the mean annual balance, despite intense heating in summer.

The vertical division of the cryosphere into a latitudinal cross section is depicted schematically in Fig. 123. The cold infiltration and infiltration congelation zones, which occupy an intermediate position in the cryosphere, do not extend far vertically (e.g., only about 800 m in the central part of western Greenland). Thus, the outer zones, i.e., the recrystallization and congelation zones, occupy most of the 8–12-km deep cryosphere.

However, the climatic indexes, which indicate the degree of continentality of climate, vary not only with distance from the maritime influences but also with the macrorelief of the surface. In most cases, mountain uplands that are not too massive and that rise distinctly above the general level of the earth's surface have a maritime climate with small amplitude temperature fluctuations and large amounts of precipitation. Thus, the surface cryosphere structure depicted in Fig. 123 applies only to quite high latitudes, where the lower limit of the cryosphere drops close to the level of the plains. In warmer regions, where only isolated uplands reach the high cryosphere, the cryosphere has a typically maritime structure, even above the continents. Naturally, this change occurs gradually, so that regions having the continental type of cryosphere structure in the central regions of the continents become narrower southward in the northern hemisphere until they wedge out altogether, giving way to the expanding regions with a maritime cryosphere structure. The expansion of regions with the continental type of cryosphere structure

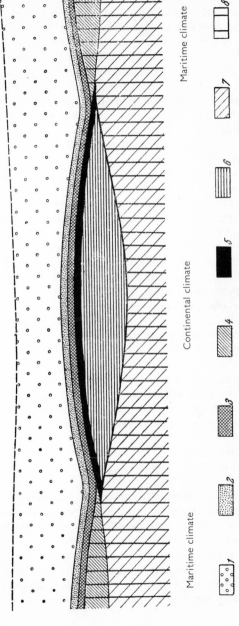

FIG. 123. Schematic vertical latitudinal cross section of the cryosphere. 1. recrystallization zone; 2. recrystallization-infiltration zone; 3. cold infiltration zone; 4. "warm" infiltration zone; 5. infiltration congelation zone; 6. congelation zone; 7. seasonal congelation zone; 8. warm regime in the rock layer.

at the expense of regions with a maritime structure takes place from the continents toward the seas in high latitudes. From the standpoint of climate-forming influences, the sea surface in a cold climate approximates the continental type, because of increasing iciness which considerably decreases the temperature minima and, together with the low temperature, reduces the role of the water basins as sources of atmospheric moisture compared with warm seas.

The influence of this increased continentality in cold high latitudes and the increased oceanity at the level of the cryosphere in the low latitudes can be traced clearly on the world glaciological map. In high latitudes even the small islands have a continental type of cryosphere structure with infiltration congelation and congelation zones below. Even Spitsbergen, which is situated in a region influenced by a warm sea current, has a cryosphere structure that is transitional between maritime and continental, in which the "warm" infiltration zone of ice formation is replaced below by infiltration congelation and congelation zones. In the northern hemisphere, the continental type of cryosphere structure advances southward in the form of tongues within the Asian and American continents and penetrates farthest as isolated islands in the high plateaus of Central Asia. However, the less massive uplands within the continents, even those situated considerably farther north, belong to the regions with the maritime type of cryosphere structure.

Perhaps the following statistics will give an even more graphic picture of the influence of increasing continentality at the cryosphere level in high latitudes. A comparison of the areas of the earth's surface that have different types of cryosphere structure shows this striking result: of the approximately 31,000,000 km² of land surface continually within the cryosphere, 99.1% belongs to regions with a continental type of cryosphere structure and only 0.9%, or about 270,000 km², belongs to regions with the maritime type of cryosphere structure.

We have classified the area of the earth's surface that lies within the cryosphere by zones of ice formation, in conformity with the data of Table 7.

The land area that is continually within the cryosphere is divided almost evenly between the recrystallization and congelation zones and only about 2.4% of the total area belongs to the intermediate, i.e., the infiltration, zones (0.9% belongs to the "warm" type of glaciation, which is fed from the "warm" infiltration zone).

Evidently the infiltration zones (cold, "warm" and infiltration congelation), which have the most complex ice formation processes because of the superposition of processes from both the outer zones,

TABLE 7

Zone of ice formation	Approximate area of the earth's surface in km²	Percentage of total land area continuously within the cryosphere
Recrystallization and recrystallization-infiltration zones	14,950,000	48.2
Infiltration and infiltration congelation zones with their zones of glacier ablation	750,000	2.4
Congelation zone	15,700,000	49.4
TOTALS	31,400,000 km²	100.0%

are merely a transitional, unstable state of the earth's surface characteristic chiefly of the mountain regions and the steep margins of the ice sheets. The broad plains regions within the cryosphere, which have a considerable climate-forming influence of their own, can belong to only one of the two outer zones, recrystallization or congelation, i.e., they will either be under the ice sheet or in the permafrost region. The reason for this is that the earth's surface can be in only two relatively stable states:

(1) the cold state, where it consists of snow and ice and is at negative temperatures, and

(2) the warm state, where it consists of high-temperature rocks and is at a positive temperature.

Generally, all other states are unstable, because at positive temperatures they result in melting of the snow and ice and at negative temperatures they lead to deposition of a snow cover or, in summer, they result in radiational heating to a positive temperature, at least with the present intensity of solar radiation.

When the quantity of solid atmospheric precipitations is slight, the transition from a cold stable state of the surface to a warm state takes place easily, but if the winter is cold enough frozen ground develops below the surface and conditions characteristic of the congelation zone appear, i.e., the surface conditions change acutely twice a year while a cold regime is maintained at a depth.

When there is much solid precipitation and the precipitation balance of the broad plains region is positive because of the cooling effect of the snow, the surface becomes a recrystallization zone, except for a narrow marginal strip.

Actually, ice sheets are created by the spread of mountain glaciers, because (at least at present) only ice can cause the snow line to drop to sea level, even at the poles, as is evident from the example of Pearyland.

Thus, in warm regions where the cryosphere rises to the level of high mountains, it has the maritime type of climate with a "warm" infiltration zone below. This type embraces only the small upland regions of the earth's surface which reach high latitudes in regions of typically maritime climate (Iceland, Scandinavia, Alaska) and which retreat into the subtropical latitudes in the heart of continents (the southern slopes of the mountain system of Central Asia).

The cryosphere structure becomes continental in the polar and subpolar regions, where the cryosphere drops to the general level of the earth's surface, and is characterized by a cold temperature regime in the rock layer beneath the surface. The moister cold regions belong to the recrystallization zone, while the drier and relatively warm regions belong to the congelation zone of ice formation. They are separated by the narrow transitional belt of cold infiltration and infiltration congelation zones, which includes a relatively small area of mountain regions and the margins of ice sheets.

Special conditions prevail in the central polar part of regions where the earth's surface always lies within the cryosphere. Owing to the distance from the sources of moisture and the prevailing anticyclone, the amount of atmospheric precipitation decreases to 80–100 mm/year in the region of the arctic wind divide and, apparently, to even less in the regions of the South Pole (possibly to 5 mm).[2] In the recrystallization zone of the central part of the Antarctic, this leads merely to decreased nourishment of the ice sheet, a condition characteristic of the areas near the upper limit of the cryosphere. The ice sheets in the Arctic are considerably less developed owing to the continentality of most of the subarctic regions, where the surface belongs to the congelation zone of ice formation. Consequently, the temperature and height of the cryosphere are generally greater in the Arctic than in the south polar region.

Since the ice sheet is not continuous in the region of the arctic wind divide, a reduction of the amount of solid precipitation leads to a secondary lifting of the intermediate infiltration zones of ice

---

[2] [The most recent data (1963) indicate that the mean annual precipitation at the South Pole is 7 mm water equivalent. – D.K.]

formation in conjunction with large fluctuations of their hypsometric position caused by local factors. Thus, the recrystallization zone narrows in these regions and yields to the lower congelation zone. This is manifested most clearly in northern Greenland, where the lower boundary of the infiltration congelation zone in the coastal strip of Crown Prince Christian's Land lies at sea level (Koch and Wegener, 1912, p. 50), while it rises to 1200 m and higher to the northwest, in Pearyland (Fristrup, 1950). There can be no snow on the high plateau of Pearyland in summer, because there is no snow there even in winter. The little snow that falls is swept away by winds into the valleys and the sea, so that travel by dogsled is restricted to the ice of the fjords. Considerable local radiational heating of the surface occurs in connection with the absence of snow in summer.

During periods of general cooling and reduction of the amount of atmospheric moisture in the central arctic region, evidently the congelation zone should expand even more at the expense of the upper zones of the cryosphere, which are actually discontinuous at the present time (Shumskii, 1947a, b).

A schematic meridional or radial cross section of the cryosphere should be approximately as shown in Fig. 124. In regions of maritime climate, the boundary of the continental type of cryosphere structure retreats to higher latitudes and the recrystallization zone expands at the expense of the congelation zone, i.e., ice sheets develop.

In continental regions, on the other hand, the boundary of the maritime type of cryosphere structure shifts into the lower latitudes and the congelation zone expands at the expense of the recrystallization zone, glaciers develop only in the mountains, and the plains become regions of development of frozen ground and stationary congelation ice (Shumskii, 1947a, p. 54).

This whole complex system changes continually with time: in the continental type of cryosphere structure, the cryosphere drops or rises and the polar caps expand or contract because of variations in the intensity of the general atmospheric circulation, while local changes in the cryosphere occur because of changes in the surface relief, the distribution of land and sea and local changes in the circulation of the water and air. During the last glacial epoch, the area of surface glaciation of land alone more than doubled (33,600, 000 km²), while it nearly quadrupled during the epoch of maximum Quaternary glaciation (55,000,000 km²), covering more than one third of the present land area of the earth (von Klebelsberg, 1948–49). Evidently, the regions belonging to the congelation zone of ice formation expanded at least that much. The extent of glaciation has changed

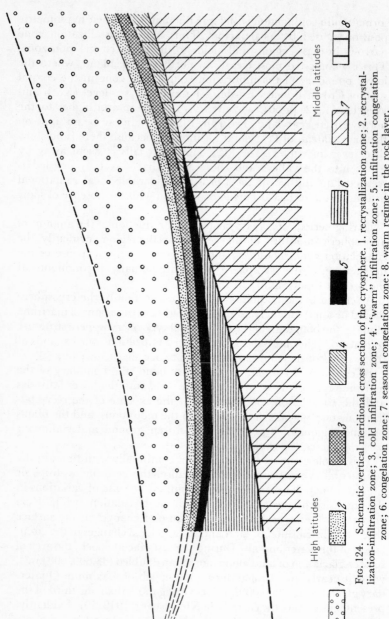

FIG. 124. Schematic vertical meridional cross section of the cryosphere. 1. recrystallization zone; 2. recrystallization-infiltration zone; 3. cold infiltration zone; 4. "warm" infiltration zone; 5. infiltration congelation zone; 6. congelation zone; 7. seasonal congelation zone; 8. warm regime in the rock layer.

considerably even in historic times. It has been established that the climate of the Atlantic coastal regions was milder in the middle ages than at present. There was a distinct advance of glaciation in the seventeenth to nineteenth centuries, in places reaching its greatest advance since the last glacial epoch, while at present we are witnessing a considerable retreat of glaciation in most regions of the earth.

CONCLUSIONS

In presenting the principles of structural glaciology, I could not help but touch on most of the other branches of theoretical glaciology and rely on data from investigations of the glaciation of specific regions, although their systematic description is really a matter for regional glaciology. This universality is quite natural, since any subdivision of glaciology is arbitrary and is dictated not so much by the content as by the plan and purpose of the presentation. The need for including material from almost all branches of glaciology supports the central, the principal role, which I have assigned to structural glaciology in my scheme (Fig. 1). All this also establishes the theoretical significance of structural glaciology as a branch of science without which, in essence, it would be impossible to arrive at the proper solution of a single major problem connected with the study of ice.

In the future, structural glaciology will find practical applications as diverse as its theoretical applications. With this is mind, let us again stress its two basic aspects:

(1) investigation of the structure and composition of the natural ice types as a basis for understanding their physical properties;

(2) investigation of the structure and composition of the natural ice types as the key to understanding their genesis, the process and conditions of their formation and, consequently, their forms of bedding and distribution. The distribution of ice types is important enough to be treated separately.

Undoubtedly, it would be of great practical interest to be able to determine the probable form of bedding of underground ice bodies on the basis of ice sample studies. However, it is even more essential to be able to intepret the climatic and geological-geomorphological conditions of the appearance and continued existence of ice. In this respect, ice can be studied much more thoroughly and accurately than any other rock. Ice rocks, which are extremely sensitive to changes in external conditions because of their unique physical properties, are special natural chronicles that record the heat and moisture balance of the earth's surface, the temperature regime of the rock mass, and, to a considerable extent, the physical processes which occur in them. Changes of climate, reflecting the state of glaciation of the cryosphere as a whole and of its elements, are recorded in nature by the geological activity of the ice and by the ice itself, i.e., by its structure and properties. Thus far, geologists and geomorphologists have relied almost exclusively on traces of the geological activity of ice, chiefly of glaciers, to recreate the history of the relief, climate and landscape. The geological-geomorphological results of the formation and melting of various types of congelation ice, i.e., perennial veins, segregation and injection ice, have attracted less attention, because the conditions and processes of their formation are little understood. Structural glaciology will certainly play an important role in finding a more complete and accurate explanation for the meaning of the traces left by these ice types in the relief and in friable deposits. However, structural glaciology should make its chief contribution to the science of paleogeography, in that the study of ice itself—fossil, epigenetic, buried and contemporary glacier ice, particularly ice caps and ice sheets which are often very old—offers considerable possibilities for paleogeographic studies. These possiblities are especially important for the permafrost regions, which contain a large quantity of ice of different genesis among the Quaternary deposits.

It would take too much space here to list all the conclusions that can be drawn concerning the conditions of ice rock formation based on the geological-petrographic study of individual samples, to say nothing of whole cross sections, because essentially this book is an analysis of and an establishment of the possiblities of drawing such conclusions. Paleogeographic deductions in general should be based on complete mastery of the method and the factual data, not on ready prescriptions. This applies even more to paleoglaciological reconstructions, if one considers the embryonic state of structural glaciology.

It should merely be emphasized that the study of ice affords the possibility of establishing the zone or, when an entire cross section is studied, even part of the zone of ice formation. In turn, this makes it possible to give the quantitative characteristics of the main indexes of climate for the period of ice formation. At present this can be done only empirically, but in the future it will also be done analytically as complex investigations of the material-energy balance of the surface and its connection with climate and ice structure progress. Undoubt-edly, the thickness of the layer of annual sedimentary-metamorphic ice increment, the character of the ice and the relative content of its many variants in cross section, the size of the crystals and, in ice which has been metamorphosed by flow, the position of the initial intersertal air inclusions, as well as other signs, are the most accurate indications of the amount of precipitation and the temperature regimes of the air and the surface at the time of the ice formation.

Although the author is quite conscious of the imperfection and inadequacy of what may now be offered as the principles of structural glaciology, he feels this book should be published. The method of investigation presented in this book justifies its publication. The author feels that if this method is adopted and developed, it will open new possiblities for glaciology and for the employment of glaciology to meet the requirements of the grandiose development of our country.

LITERATURE CITED

TRANSLATOR'S NOTE

The attached version of the Shumskii bibliography differs somewhat from the original. Shumskii lists the Russian and the non-Russian items separately; I list them together, alphabetically by author. Shumskii cites all periodical literature by the spelling and title at the time of publication; I list periodicals by their most recent title, according to the *Union List of Serials*[1] and the *Serial Publications of the Soviet Union, 1937–1957*.[2] I believe this will save the reader considerable time in locating the material in the libraries of the United States and Canada.

The Shumskii bibliography contains numerous misprints. Consequently, I have attempted to find and see all the items listed. The entries followed by letter symbols indicate that I have actually seen the items in one of the libraries of the Boston area, at the Library of Congress, or in one of the special bibliographies listed. The items which I have not been able to find are indicated by an asterisk and any further information which the reader might supply about them would be greatly appreciated. The Library of Congress system of transliteration has been followed.

Key to the Symbols

AFCRL	Air Force Cambridge Research Laboratories, Research Library, Bedford, Mass.
DLC	Library of Congress, Washington, D.C.
MH	Widener Library, Harvard University
MHBot	Botanical Library, Harvard University
MHCh	Chemistry Library, Harvard University
MHMc	McKay Library, Harvard University
MHMi	Mineralogy Library, Harvard University
MHPh	Physical Research Library, Harvard University
MHZ	Library of the Museum of Comparative Zoology, Harvard University
MIT	Science Library, Massachusetts Institute of Technology
USGS	U.S. Geological Survey Library, Washington, D.C.

---

[1] [Gregory, W. (ed.), *Union List of Serials in Libraries of the United States and Canada*, 2nd. ed., New York, The H. W. Wilson Co., 1943. 3066 pp. (and Supplements). – D.K.]

[2] [Smits, R. (compiler), *Serial Publications of the Soviet Union 1939–1957*, Washington, D.C., Cyrillic Bibliographic Project. Library of Congress, 1958. 459 pp. – D.K.]

AB   *Arctic Bibliography*, Washington, D.C., by the Arctic Institute of North America for the Department of Defense, 1953 +

MAB   *Meteorological Abstracts and Bibliography*, American Meteorological Society, Boston, Mass., 1950 +

SIP   *Annotated Bibliography on Snow, Ice and Permafrost*, SIPRE Report 12, Washington, D.C., Science Division, Library of Congress, 1951 +

BIBLIOGRAPHY

*Abolin, R. I., *Geografwheskoe Obshchestvo SSSR, Chitinskii Otdel, Zapiski*, 9: 19, 1913.

Adams, J. M., "The polar properties of single crystals of ice," *Royal Society of London, Proceedings*, Series A, 128(A808): 588–591, 1930. MH

Adams, J. M., and W. Lewis, "The production of large single crystals of ice," *Review of Scientific Instruments*, 5(11): 400–402, 1934. MHPh

Agassiz, L., *Nouvelles études et expériences sur les glaciers actuels, leur structure, leur progression et leur action physique sur le sol* (Recent studies and experiments on present-day glaciers, their structure, their progression and their physical activity on the ground), Paris, V. Masson, 1847. 598 pp. MHZ

Ahlmann, H. W., "Scientific results of the Swedish-Norwegian Arctic Expedition in the summer of 1931. Part 1. The cartography of the coast-districts of North-East Land and its environments," *Geografiska Annaler*, 15(1): 1–68, 1933. See pp. 9–24. MHZ

——, "Contribution to the physics of glaciers," *Geographical Journal*, 86(2): 97–113, 1935. MHZ

——, "Scientific results of the Norwegian-Swedish Spitsbergen Expedition, 1934. Part 7. The firn structure on Isachsen's Plateau," *Geografiska Annaler*, 18(1): 48–73, 1936. MHZ

—— and E. G. Droessler, "Glacier ice crystal measurements at Kebneskajse, Sweden," *Journal of Glaciology*, 1(5): 268–274, 1949. MHZ

—— and A. Tveten, "The recrystallization of snow into firn and the glaciation of the latter," *Geografiska Annaler*, 5(1): 52–58, 1923. MHZ

*Al'tberg, V. Ia., *Podvodnyi led* (Underwater ice), Moscow, 1939.

——, "Struktura l'da" (Ice structure), in Veinberg, B. P., *et al.*, *Led. Svoistva, vozniknovenie i ischeznovenie l'da* (Ice. Its properties, appearance and disappearance), Moscow, Gostekhizdat, 1940, pp. 228–238. AB 43599

—— and V. F. Troshin, "O novykh formakh kristallicheskogo l'da" (New forms of crystalline ice), *Leningrad. Gosudarstvennyi Gidrologicheskii Institut, Izvestiia*, No. 32: 93–107, 1931. DLC

Andreev, V. N., "Gidrolakkolity (bulgunniakhi) v Zapadno-Sibirskikh tundrakh" (Hydrolaccoliths in the West Siberian tundras), *Geografwheskoe Obshchestvo SSSR, Izvestiia*, 68(2): 186–210, 1936. MHZ

Arnol'd-Aliab'ev, V. I., "Ob issledovanii fizicheskikh svoistv tverdykh gidrometeorov" (Investigation of the physical properties of solid hydrometeors), *Meteorologiia i Gidrologiia*, 5(3): 15–27, 1939. MHMc

Bader, H., "Mineralogische und strukturelle Charakterisierung des Schnees und seiner Metamorphose" (Mineralogical and structural characterization of snow and its metamorphism), *Beiträge zur geologischen Karte der Schweiz, Geotechnische Serie, Hydrologie*, No. 3: 1–62, 1939. USGS

———, "Theory of non-calorimetric methods for the determination of the liquid water content of wet snow," *Schweizerische Mineralogische und Petrographische Mitteilungen*, 28(1): 355–361, 1948. MHMi

———, "The significance of air bubbles in glacier ice," *Journal of Glaciology*, 1(8): 443–451, 1950. MHZ

———, "Introduction to ice petrofabrics," *Journal of Geology*, 59(6): 519–536, 1951. MHZ

Baer, K. E., "Expédition à Novaia Zemlia et en Laponie. Tableau physique des contrées visitées" (Expedition to Novaya Zemlya and Lapland. Physical description of the regions visited), *Akademiia Nauk SSSR, Bulletin Scientifique*, 3(11/12): 171–191, 1838. See p. 187. MHBot

Bain, G. W., "Measuring grain boundaries in crystalline rocks," *Journal of Geology*, 49(2): 199–206, 1941. MHZ

Baranov, I. Ia., "Nabliudeniia nad zamerzaniem vody" (Observations of the freezing of water), *Akademiia Nauk SSSR, Komitet po Vechnoi Merzloty, Trudy*, 6: 167–171, 1938. SIP 1782

*———, *Gidrogeologiia SSSR* (Hydrogeology of the USSR), No. 17, *Vostochnaia Sibir'* (Eastern Siberia), Book 2, 1940.

———, "Nekotorye ledianye obrazovaniia na poverkhnosti pochvy" (Some ice formations on the soil surface), *Priroda*, 38(10): 47–50, 1949. MHZ

Barendrecht, H. P., "Dimorphie des Eises" (Dimorphism of ice), *Zeitschrift für anorganische Chemie*, 11: 454–455, 1896. MHCh

Barrat, T., and H. R. Nettleton, "Thermal conductivity of liquids and solids," in *International Critical Tables*, New York, McGraw-Hill Book Co., Inc., 1929, Vol. 5, pp. 218–231. N.B.: "Thermal conductivity of crystals," pp. 231–232. MHPh

Becke, F., "Die Krystallform des Traubenzuckers und optisch activer Substanzen im Allgemeinen" (The crystal form of grape sugar and optically active substances in general), *Mineralogische und Petrographische Mitteilungen*, 10(6), Report 16: 464–498, 1899. N.B.: p. 294. MHMi

Beilby, G. T., *Aggregation and flow of solids*, London, Macmillan and Co., Ltd., 1921. 256 pp. MH

Bentley, W. A., "Studies of frost and ice crystals," *U.S. Weather Bureau, Monthly Weather Review*, 35(9): 397–403; 35(10): 439–444; 35(11): 512–516; 35(12): 584–585, 1907. MHMc

Bentley, W. A. and W. J. Humphreys, *Snow crystals*, New York, Dover Publications, Inc., 1962. 227 pp. MH

Bernard, M. A., and W. T. Wilson, "A new technique for the determination of heat necessary to melt snow," *American Geophysical Union, Transactions*, 22(1–B): 178–181, 1941. AFCRL

Bertin, A., "Sur la constitution de la glace glaciaire" (The constitution of glacier ice), *Académie des Sciences, Paris, Comptes Rendus*, 63: 346–351, 1866. AFCRL

Bertin, M., "Sur la structure optique de la glace" (The optical structure of ice), *Annales de Chimie et de Physique*, 5ème Série, 13(1): 283–288, 1878. MHCh

Beskow, G., "Tjälbildningen och tjällyftningen" (Frost mound formation and frost heaving), *Sveriges Geologiska Undersökning*, Series C, Vol. 26, No. 3, Report No. 375, 1935. 242 pp. MHZ

Bluemcke, A., and H. Hess, "Untersuchungen am Hintereisferner" (Investigations conducted on the Hintereisferner), *Deutscher und Oesterreichischer Alpenverein, Wissenschaftliche Ergänzungshefte*, Vol. 1, No. 2, 1899. DLC

Bonacina, L. C. W., "Snow as a form of precipitation and factors controlling distribution over the globe," *International Geodetic and Geophysical Union, Association of Scientific Hydrology, Bulletin*, 23: 79–90, 1938. SIP 2658

Bonshtedt, E. M., "Ledianye stebel'ki" (Ice columns), *Priroda*, 9/10 (10–12): 73–74, 1921. MHZ

Bossolasco, M., "Zur Frage der Gletschereisbildung durch tägliches Schmelzen und nächtliches Wiedergefrieren des Firnschnees" (On the question of glacier ice formation by the diurnal melting and the nocturnal refreezing of the firn snow), *Zeitschrift für Gletscherkunde*, 18(1/3): 189–191, 1930. MHMi

[Brewster, D.,] "Optical structure of ice," (entered under Miscellanea, regarding Dr. D. Brewster), *Quarterly Journal of Science, Literature and Art*, Vol. 4, Article XVI, I, p. 155, 1818. MH

Bridgman, P. W., "Water, in the liquid and five solid forms, under pressure," *American Academy of Arts and Sciences, Proceedings*, 47(13): 439–558, 1912. AFCRL

———, "The pressure-volume-temperature relations of the liquid, and the phase diagram of heavy water," *Journal of Chemical Physics*, 3(10): 597–605, 1935. MHCh

———, "The phase diagram of water to 45,000 kg/cm²," *Journal of Chemical Physics*, 5(12): 964–966, 1937. MHCh

———, "Recent work in the field of high pressures," *Reviews of Modern Physics*, 18(1): 1–93, 1946. MH

Brockamp, B., "Überlegungen zur Temperaturverteilung im Inlandeis auf Grund seismischer Ergebnisse" (Considerations of the temperature distribution in the inland ice, based on seismic results), *Deutsche Grönland-Expedition Alfred Wegener, 1929 und 1930–1931, Wissenschaftliche Ergebnisse*, Leipzig, F. A. Brockhaus, 1935. pp. 41–51. AB 2215

———— and H. Mothes, "Seismische Untersuchungen auf dem Pasterzegletscher" (Seismic studies on the Pasterze glacier), *Zeitschrift für Geophysik*, 6(8): 482–500, 1930. N.B.: p. 490. MH

Buchanan, J. Y., "On ice and brines," *Royal Society of Edinburgh, Proceedings*, 14(123): 129–147, 1887. MH

————, "Ice and its natural history," *Royal Institution of Great Britain, Proceedings*, 19(102): 243–277, 1908. MH

Bucher, E., "Beitrag zu den theoretischen Grundlagen des Lawinenverbaus" (Contribution to the theoretical principles of avalanche defense structures), *Beiträge zur geologischen Karte der Schweiz, Geotechnische Serie, Hydrologie*, No. 6, 1948. 113 pp. MHMi

Bucher, W. H., "The importance of the Ross shelf-ice to structural geology," *American Geophysical Union, Transactions*, 23(2): 697–699, 1942. AFCRL

Bunge, A. A., "Einige Worte zur Bodeneisfrage" (Some remarks on the question of ground ice), *Vsesoiuznoe Mineralogicheskoe Obshchestvo, Zapiski*, Seriia 2, 40(1): 203–209, 1903. MHZ

Burton, E. F., and W. F. Oliver, "The crystal structure of ice at low temperatures," *Royal Society of London, Proceedings*, Series A, 153(878): 166–171, 1935. MH

Cahn, R. W., "Recrystallization of single crystals after plastic bending," *Institute of Metals, Journal*, 76(1212): 121–143, 1949. AFCRL

Carol, H., "Beobachtungen zur Entstehung der Rundhöcker" (Observations on the formation of dressed rocks), *Die Alpen*, 19: 173–180, 1943. DLC

————, "Über einen Versuch, den Gletscheruntergrund mittelst Einstiegs durch ein Strudelloch zu erreichen" (An attempt to reach the lower layers of a glacier through an eddy hole), *Die Alpen*, 31(6): 180–184, 1945. DLC

————, "The formation of 'Roches Moutonnées,' " *Journal of Glaciology*, 1(2): 57–59, 1947. AFCRL

Chamberlin, R. T., "Instrumental work on the nature of glacier motion," *Journal of Geology*, 36(1): 1–30, 1928. MHMi

————, "Glacier movement as typical rock deformation," *Journal of Geology*, 44(1): 93–104, 1936. MHZ

Chamberlin, T. C., "Glacial studies in Greenland," *Journal of Geology*, 2(7): 649–666, 1894. MHZ

————, "Glacial studies in Greenland, II. The glaciers of Disco Island," *Journal of Geology*, 2(8): 768–788, 1894. MHZ

Chamberlin, T. C., "Glacial studies in Greenland, III. Coast glaciers between Disco Island and Inglefield Gulf," *Journal of Geology*, 3(1): 61–69, 1895. MHZ

——, "Glacial studies in Greenland, IV. Glaciers of the Inglefield Gulf Region," *Journal of Geology*, 3(2): 198–218, 1895. MHZ

——, "Glacial studies in Greenland, V–VII. The Redcliff Peninsula," *Journal of Geology*, 3(4): 469–480; 3(5): 565–582; 3(6): 668–681, 1895. MHZ

——, "Glacial studies in Greenland, VIII. The Krakokta glacier," *Journal of Geology*, 3(7): 833–843, 1895. MHZ

——, "Glacial studies in Greenland, IX. The Tuktoo glacier," *Journal of Geology*, 4(5): 582–592, 1896. MHZ

——, "Glacial studies in Greenland, X. The Bowdoin glacier," *Journal of Geology*, 5(3): 229–240, 1897. MHZ

——, *A contribution to the theory of glacial motion*, Chicago, University of Chicago Press, 1904. 16 pp. SIP 8200

Chirvinskii, P. N., "Sushchestvuet li kristallicheskaia raznost' vody pravil'-noi sistemy?" (Does the crystalline form of the cubic system of water exist?), *Ezhegodnik po Geologii i Mineralogii Rossii*, Novo-Aleksandriia, 14(9): 280–282, 1912. DLC

——, "Shestovato-voloknistyi led" (Columnar fibrous ice), *Geograficheskoe Obshchestvo SSSR, Izvestiia*, 68(6): 878–880, 1936. MHZ

Church, J. E., "Snow and snow surveying; Ice," in Meinzer, O. E. (ed.). *Hydrology*, New York, Dover Publications, Inc., 1949. pp. 83–148. MHZ

Correns, C. W., "Über die Erklärung der sogenannten Kristallisationskraft" (On the definition of the so-called crystallizing force), *Akademie der Wissenschaften, Berlin. Physikalisch-Mathematische Klasse, Sitzungsberichte*, No. 11: 81–88, 1926. AFCRL

Cotta, B., *Geologische Fragen* (Questions of geology), Freiberg, J. G. Engelhardt, 1858. 344 pp. N.B.: p. 81. MHZ

Croce, K., "Calorimetry," (Re: I. G. Halliday's "The liquid water content of snow"), *Journal of Glaciology*, 1(8): 456, 1950. MHZ

Curie, M. P., "Sur la formation des cristaux et sur les constantes capillaires de leur différentes faces" (The formation of crystals and the capillary constants of their various faces), *Société Française de Minéralogie, Bulletin*, 8(6): 145–150, 1885. MHMi

Deeley, R. M., "Glacier granule-markings," *Geological Magazine*, Decade 5, 7(3): 112–114, 1910. MHZ

—— and G. Fletcher, "The structure of glacier-ice and its bearing upon glacier-motion," *Geological Magazine*, Decade 4, 2(4): 152–162, 1895. MHZ

—— and P. H. Parr, "The viscosity of the Hintereis Glacier," *London, Edinburgh and Dublin Philosophical Magazine and Journal of Science*, Series 6, 26: 85–111, 1913; 27: 153–176, 1914. MH

Demorest, M., "Ice-deformation in the flow of glaciers," *American Geophysical Union, Transactions*, Vol. 22, Part II, p. 525, 1941. MHZ

————, "Ice sheets," *Geological Society of America, Bulletin*, 54(3): 363–399, 1943. MHZ

De Quervain, M., "Schnee als kristallines Aggregat" (Snow as a crystalline aggregate), *Experientia*, 1(7): 207–212, 1945. MHCh

————, "Das Korngefüge von Schnee" (The granular structure of snow), *Schweizerische Mineralogische und Petrographische Mitteilungen*, 28(1): 518–527, 1948. MHMi

————, "Korngrössenanalyse von Altschnee durch Sedimentation" (Grain-size analysis of old snow by sedimentation), *Schweizerische Bauzeitung*, 66(9): 117–118, 1948. MHMc

Devaux, J., "Sur la formation des glaciers par fusion diurne et regel nocturne des névés" (The formation of glaciers by diurnal fusion and nocturnal regelation of snow), *Académie des Sciences, Paris, Comptes Rendus*, 185: 1602–1604, 1927. AFCRL

————, "L'économie radiothermique des champs de neige et des glaciers" (Radiation and thermal properties of snow fields and glaciers), *Annales de Physique*, 20: 5–67, 1933. SIP 661

Devik, O., "Supercooling and ice formation in open waters," *Geofysiske Publikasjoner*, 13(8), 1942, 19 pp. MH

Dobrowolski, A. B., *Historja naturalna lodu* (Natural history of ice), Warsaw, 1923. 940 pp. AB 4027

————, "La glace au point de vue pétrographique" (Ice from the petrographic point of view), *Société Française de Minéralogie, Bulletin*, 54(1/2): 5–19, 1931. MHMi

————, "La symmétrie des cristaux de glace" (The symmetry of ice crystals), *Société Française de Minéralogie, Bulletin*, 56(6/7/8): 335–346, 1933. MHMi

Dolgov, S. I., *Issledovaniia podvizhnosti pochvennoi vlagi i ee dostupnosti dlia rastenii* (Investigations of the mobility of soil moisture and its availability for plants), Moscow, Akademiia Nauk SSSR, Pochvennyi Institut im. V. V. Dokuchaeva, 1948. 205 pp. MH

Donchenko, R. V., and A. R. Shul'man, "Nachal'nye fazy deformatsii l'da" (The initial phases of ice deformation), *Leningrad. Gosudarstvennyi Gidrologicheskii Institut, Trudy*, No. 16(70): 101–103, 1949. SIP 4891

Dorsey, N. E., "Supercooling and freezing of water," *Journal of Research of the National Bureau of Standards*, 20(6): 799–808, 1938. MH

————, *Properties of ordinary water-substance*, New York, Reinhold Publishing Corp., 1940. 673 pp. AFCRL

————, "The freezing of supercooled water," *American Philosophical Society, Transactions*, New Series, 38(3): 247–328, 1948. MHZ

Dranitsyn, D. A., "O nekotorykh zonal'nykh formakh rel'efa krainiago Severa" (Some zonal forms of the relief of the Far North), *Pochvovedenie*, 16(4): 21–68, 1914. SIP 6660

Drescher, F. K., "Ein grosses Universal-Drehinstrument zur Gefüge-untersuchung" (A large universal rotation instrument for structural research), *Zentralblatt für Mineralogie, Geologie und Palaeontologie*, Abteilung A, 5: 167–172, 1932. MHMi

Drygalski, E. von, "Grönlands Eis und sein Vorland" (Greenland's ice and its foreland), *Gesellschaft für Erdkunde zu Berlin, Grönland Expedition, 1891–1893*, Berlin, W. H. Kühl, 1897. Vol. 1, 555 pp. MHZ

————, "Das Eis der Antarktis und der subantarktischen Meere" (The ice of Antarctica and the subantarctic ocean), *Deutsche Südpolar-Expedition 1901–1903*, Berlin, Vereinigung Wissenschaftlicher Verleger, Vol. 1, No. 4, 1921, pp. 367–709 and plates. DLC

Dumanskii, A. V., "Teploty smachivaniia i gidrofil'nost' dispersnykh sistem" (The heats of wetting and the hydrophilic nature of disperse systems), *Kolloidnyi Zhurnal*, 12(5): 319–325, 1950. MHCh

Eckel, O., and C. Thams, "Untersuchungen über Dichte-, Temperatur- und Strahlungsverhältnisse der Schneedecke in Davos" (Investigations on conditions of density, temperature and radiation of the Davos snow cover), *Beiträge zur geologischen Karte der Schweiz, Geotechnische Serie, Hydrologie*, No. 3: 272–340, 1939. USGS

Emden, R., "Über das Gletscherkorn" (The glacier grain), *Schweizer-ische Naturforschende Gesellschaft, Neue Denkschriften*, 33(1): 1–44, 1893. SIP 11522

Engeln, O. D. von, "The motion of glaciers," *Science*, New Series 80(2079): 401–403, 1934. MHZ

————, "The motion of glaciers," *Science*, New Series, 81(2106): 459–461, 1935. MHZ

*Ermakov, N. P., *L'vovskoe Geologicheskoe Obshchestvo, Mineralogicheskii Sbornik*, 2: 53, 1948.

Ermolaev, M. M., (a) *Instruktsiia dlia ekspeditsionnogo izucheniia iskopaemogo l'da kak geograficheskogo faktora* (Instructions for field study of fossil ice as a geographic factor), Leningrad, Izdatel'stvo Arkticheskogo Instituta, 1932. 42 pp. AB 4678

————, (b) "Geologicheskii i geomorfologicheskii ocherk ostrova Bol'shogo Liakhovskogo" (Geological and geomorphological sketch of Great Liakhov Island [ostrov Bol'shogo Liakhovskogo]), *Akademiia Nauk SSSR, Sovet po Izucheniiu Proizvoditel'nykh Sil, Trudy, Seriia Iakutskaia*, 7: 147–228, 1932. AB 4670

*Fersman, A. E., *Geokhimiia* (Geochemistry), Leningrad, ONTI-Khim-teoret., 1934. Vol. 1. N.B.: p. 292.

*Figurin, A. E., *Russia. Gosudarstvennyi Admiral'teistvennyi Departament, Zapiski,* 5: 275, 1823.

Filippova, L. I., and A. R. Shul'man, "O relaksatsii napriazhenii vo l'du" (Elastic deformation in ice), Leningrad. *Gosudarstvennyi Gidrologicheskii Institut, Trudy,* 16(70): 96–100, 1949. SIP 4890

Fedosov, A. E., "Mekhanicheskie protsessy v gruntakh pri zamerzanii v nikh zhidkoi fazy: (Mechanical processes in soils during the freezing of the liquid phase), *Akademiia Nauk SSSR, Institut Geologicheskikh Nauk, Trudy,* 35(4): 1–42, 1940. SIP 3851

Finsterwalder, R., "Die Gletscher des Nanga Parbat" (The glaciers of Nanga Parbat), *Zeitschrift für Gletscherkunde,* 25: 57–108, 1937. MHZ

———, "Some comments on glacier flow," *Journal of Glaciology,* 1(7): 383–388, 1950. MHZ

Finsterwalder, S., "Der Vernagtferner, seine Geschichte und seine Vermessung in den Jahren 1888 und 1889" (The Vernagtferner Glacier, its history and its measurement in 1888 and 1889), *Deutscher und Oesterreichischer Alpenverein, Graz, Zeitschrift, Wissenschaftliche Ergänzungshefte,* Vol. 1, No. 1, 1897, 112 pp. MHZ

———, "Bericht der internationalen Gletscherkommission" (Report of the International Glacier Commission), *International Geological Congress,* 9, *Vienna, 1903, Compte Rendu,* 1904, 2 vols; see pp. 161–169. (Congrès géologique international de Vienne, 1903, Comptes Rendus). MHZ

———, "Beobachtungen über die Art der Gletscherbewegung" (Observations on the mechanism of glacier movement), *Akademie der Wissenschaften, Munich, Mathematisch-Physikalische Klasse, Sitzungsberichte,* 42(1): 1–9, 1912. MHZ

———, "Über die innere Reibung des Eises und die Bestimmung der Gletschertiefe" (The internal friction of ice and the determination of glacier depth), a commentary on Somigliana's article (q.v.), *Zeitschrift für Gletscherkunde,* 15(1): 55–59, 1926. MHZ

Flint, R. F., and M. Demorest, "Glacier thinning during deglaciation. Part 1. Glacier regimens and ice movement within glaciers," *American Journal of Science,* 240(1): 29–66, 1942. MHZ

Forbes, J. D., *Occasional papers on the theory of glaciers,* Edinburgh, A. and C. Black, 1859. 278 pp. MHZ

Frenkel', Ia. I., *Kineticheskaia teoriia zhidkostei* (The kinetic theory of fluids), Moscow, Izdatel'stvo Akademii Nauk SSSR, 1945. 423 pp. MH

———, "Obshchaia teoriia geterofaznykh fluktuatsii i predperekhodnykh iavlenii" (General theory of heterophase fluctuations and pretransitional phenomena), *Zhurnal Eksperimental'noi i Teoreticheskoi Fiziki,* 9(8): 952–962, 1939. DLC

Fristrup, B., "Meteorology and glaciology" in "A preliminary account of the Danish Pearyland Expedition," *Arctic,* 3(1): 3–13, 1950. See pp. 9–12. AFCRL

*Fritsman, E. Kh., *Priroda vody. Tiazhelaia voda* (The nature of water. Heavy water), Leningrad, 1935.

*Futterer, K., *Oberrheinischer Geologischer Verein in Diedenhofen, Bericht über d. 34. Versammlung*, April, 1901, p. 1.

Gallwitz, H., *Eiskeile und glaziale Sedimentation* (Ice wedges and glacial sedimentation), Berlin, Akademie-Verlag, 1949. 24 pp. AB 22012

Gerrard, J. A. F., M. F. Perutz, and A. Roch, "Measurement of the velocity distribution along a vertical line through a glacier," *Royal Society of London, Proceedings*, Series A, 213(1115): 546–558, 1952. MH

Goldschmidt, V. M., "Geochemische Verteilungsgesetzte der Elemente" (Geochemical laws of distribution of the elements), *Norske Videnskaps-Akademi, Oslo, Skrifter, Matematisk-Naturvidenskablig Klasse*, No. 3, 1923. 17 pp. MHZ

――, "Geochemie" (Geochemistry), in *Handwörterbuch der Naturwissenschaft*, 2nd ed., Jena, Gustav Fischer, 1934, Vol. 8, pp. 886–904. MHZ

Gol'dshtein, M. N., "Puchenie gruntov pri promerzanii" (Frost heaving during freezing), *Moscow. Vsesoiuznyi Institut Zheleznodorozhnogo Transporta, Trudy*, 16: 33–129, 1948. SIP 6897

Golovkov, M. P., "K petrografii l'da Karskogo moria" (The petrography of Kara Sea ice), *Leningrad. Vsesoiuznyi Arkticheskii Institut, Trudy*, 60: 7–40, 1936. AB 5899

――, "Issledovanie l'da Kungurskoi peshchery" (Investigation of the Kungur Cave ice), *Leningrad. Universitet. Uchenye Zapiski, Seriia Geologo-Pochvenno-Geograficheskaia*, 21(5): 11–35, 1939. SIP 8017

Gorodkov, B. N., "Prilednikovye landshafty pleistotsena na severe Azii" (Pleistocene glacial landscapes of northern Asia), *Akademiia Nauk SSSR, Doklady*, 61(3): 513–516, 1948. MHZ

*Grigor'ev, A. A., *Akademiia Nauk SSSR. Komissiia po Izucheniiu Chetvertichnogo Perioda*, Vol. 1: 31, 1932.

――, *Subarktika* (The subarctic). *Opyt kharakteristiki osnovnykh tipov fiziko-geograficheskoi sredy* (Essay on the characteristics of the basic types of the physical-geographic medium), Moscow, Izdatel'stvo Akademii Nauk SSSR, 1946. 170 pp. MH

Grigor'ev, D. P., "Kak obrazuiutsia druzy mineralov" (The formation of mineral druses), *Priroda*, 36(9): 25–32, 1947. MHZ

Gross, R., and H. Möller, "Über das Kristallwachstum in röhrenförmigen Hohlräumen" (Crystal growth in a tubular space), *Zeitschrift für Physik*, 19(5/6): 375–387, 1923. MH

Gurevich, M. I., "Protsessy peremeshcheniia talykh vod v snezhnom pokrove i vodootdacha iz snega" (Processes of melt water migration in a snow cover and water delivery from the snow), *Leningrad. Gosudarstvennyi Gidrologicheskii Institut, Trudy*, No. 14(68): 177–217, 1949. SIP 5315

Haefeli, R., "Schneemechanik mit Hinweisen auf die Erdbaumechanik" (Snow mechanics with references to soil mechanics), *Beiträge zur geologischen Karte der Schweiz, Geotechnische Serie, Hydrologie*, No. 3: 63–242, 1939. USGS

———, "Entwicklung und Probleme der Schnee- und Gletscherkunde in der Schweiz" (The development and problems of snow and glacier study in Switzerland), *Experientia*, 2(1): 1–7, 1946. MHCh

———, "The development of snow and glacier research in Switzerland," *Journal of Glaciology*, 1(4): 192–201, 1948. MHZ

———, "Some observations on glacier flow," *Journal of Glaciology*, 1(9): 496–500, 1951. MHZ

———, H. Bader, and E. Bucher, "Das Zeitprofil, eine graphische Darstellung der Entwicklung der Schneedecke" (The time profile, a graphic representation of the development of a snow cover), *Beiträge zur geologischen Karte der Schweiz, Geotechnische Serie, Hydrologie*, No. 3: 243–254, 1939. USGS

Haff, J. C., "Preparation of petrofabric diagrams," *American Mineralogist*, 23(9): 543–574, 1938. MHMi

Hagenbach-Bischoff, E., "Le grain du glacier" (Glacier grains), *Bibliothèque Universelle, Archives des Sciences Physiques et Naturelles*, 3rd period, 7(10): 343–366, 15 October, 1882. DLC

———, "Das Gletscherkorn" (Glacier grains), *Naturforschende Gesellschaft, Basel, Verhandlungen*, 7(1): 192–216, 1882. AFCRL

———, "Weiteres über Gletschereis" (More about glacier ice), *Naturforschende Gesellschaft, Basel, Verhandlungen*, 8: 821–832, 1889. AFCRL

Halliday, I. G., "The liquid water content of snow measurement in the field," *Journal of Glaciology*, 1(7): 357–361, 1950. MHZ

———, [see Croce, K., *Journal of Glaciology*, 1(8): 456, 1950.] MHZ

Hamberg, A., "Studien über Meereis und Gletschereis" (Sea ice and glacier ice studies), *Svenska Vetenskapsakademien, Bihang til Handlingar*, 21(2): 1–13, 1895. MH

———, "Zur Kenntnis der Vorgänge im Erdboden beim Gefrieren und Auftauen sowie Bermerkungen über die erste Kristallisation des Eises in Wasser" (Soil processes during freezing and thawing and remarks on the first crystallization of ice in water), *Geologiska Föreningens i Stockholm, Förhändlingar*, 37(5): 583–619, 1915. MHZ

———, *Struktur und Bewegungsvorgänge im Gletschereise nebst Beiträgen zur Morphologie der arktischen Gletscher* (Structure and movement processes in glacier ice and contributions to the morphology of glaciers), Stockholm, Centraltryckeriet, 1932, pp. 69–124. AB 45407

Hawkes, L., "Some notes on the structure and flow of ice," *Geological Magazine*, 67(789): 111–123, 1930. MHZ

Heim, A., *Handbuch der Gletscherkunde* (Handbook of glaciology), Stuttgart, J. Engelhorn, 1885. 560 pp. MHZ

———, *Bergsturz und Menschenleben* (Landslides and human life), Zürich, Fretz und Wasmuth Verlag, 1932. 218 pp. SIP 12854

———, "Über Eis-Trümmerströme und eiszeitliche Bergstürze" (Ice rubble streams and landslides of the glacial period), *Zeitschrift für Gletscherkunde*, 22(1/5): 222-224, 1935. MHZ

Hellmann, G., *Schneekrystalle. Beobachtungen und Studien* (Snow crystals. Observations and studies), Berlin, Rudolf Mückenberger, 1893. 66 pp. MHZ

Hess, H., *Die Gletscher* (Glaciers), Braunschweig, F. Vieweg und Sohn, 1904. 426 pp. MHZ

———, "Der Hintereisferner 1893 bis 1922, ein Beitrag zur Lösung des Problems der Gletscherbewegung" (The Hintereisferner glacier, 1893 to 1922, a contribution to the solution of the problem of glacier movement), *Zeitschrift für Gletscherkunde*, 13(4/5): 145–203, 1924. MHZ

———, "Zur Strömungstheorie der Gletscherbewegung" (On the flow theory of glacier movement), *Zeitschrift für Gletscherkunde*, 19(4/5): 221–250, 1931. MHZ

———, "Das Eis der Erde" (The earth's ice), in Gutenberg, B. (ed.), *Handbuch der Geophysik*, Vol. 7, No. 1, 1933, pp. 1–121. AB 7039

———, "Die Bewegung im Innern des Gletschers" (Movement within a glacier), *Zeitschrift für Gletscherkunde*, 23(1/3): 1–35, 1935. MHZ

———, "Über den Zustand des Eises im Gletscher" (The condition of ice in a glacier), *Zeitschrift für Gletscherkunde*, 25: 1–16, 1937. MHZ

———, "Zur Physik des Gletschers" (Glacier physics), *Petermanns Geographische Mitteilungen*, 85(7/8): 241–244, 1939. MH

Holzner, J., "Über die Aufwachsung der Kristalle" (Crystal growth), *Zeitschrift für Kristallographie, Mineralogie und Petrographie*, 65(3), Report 13: 161–208, 1927. MHMi

Höppler, F., "Die Plastizität des Eises" (The plasticity of ice), *Kolloid-Zeitschrift*, 97(2): 154–160, 1941. MHCh

Howard, A. D., "Further observations of the Ross Shelf ice, Antarctica," *Geological Society of America, Bulletin*, 59(9): 919–926, 1948. MHZ

Hughes, T. P., and G. Seligman. "The temperature, melt water movement and density increase in the névé of an alpine glacier," *Royal Astronomical Society of London, Monthly Notices, Geophysical Supplement*, 4(9): 616–647, 1939. SIP 2752

———, M. F. Perutz and G. Seligman, [see Seligman, G., *Geographical Journal*, 97(5): 295–307, 1941.] MHZ

Ivanov, K. E., and V. V. Lavrov, "Ob odnoi osobennosti mekhanizma plasticheskoi deformatsii l'da" (One special feature of the mechanism of the plastic deformation of ice), *Zhurnal Tekhnicheskoi Fiziki*, 20(2): 230–231, 1950. MHPh

Johnsen, A., "Untersuchungen über Kristallzwillinge und deren Zusammenhang mit anderen Erscheinungen" (Investigations of crystal twins and their relationship to other phenomena), *Neues Jahrbuch für Mineralogie, Geologie und Palaeontologie, Beilage-Band*, 23(2): 237–344, 1907. See p. 326. MHZ

Johnson, W. A., "Estimation of spatial grain size," *Metal Progress*, 49(1): 87–92, 1946. MHMc

Johnston, J., and L. H. Adams, "On the effect of high pressures on the physical and chemical behavior of solids," *American Journal of Science*, Series 4, 35(207), Report 19: 206–253, 1913. See p. 214. MHZ

Kachurin, L. G., (*a*) "Zamerzanie monodispersnykh vodnykh aerozolei" (Freezing of monodisperse aqueous aerosols), *Akademiia Nauk SSSR, Izvestiia, Seriia Geofizicheskaia*, No. 2: 43–49, 1951. SIP 3287

———, (*b*) "Zamerzanie polidispersnykh vodnykh aerozolei" (Freezing of polydisperse aqueous aerosols), *Akademiia Nauk SSSR, Izvestiia, Seriia Geofizicheskaia*, No. 2: 50–55, 1951. SIP 3288

Kachurin, S. P., *O genezise naibolee rasprostranennykh iskopaemykh l'dov Severa* (The genesis of the most widely distributed fossil ice types of the North), Moscow, Akademiia Nauk SSSR, Institut Merzlotovedeniia im. V. A. Obrucheva, 1946. 38 pp. SIP 772

Kalb, G. "Gesetzmässige Aufwachsung der Kristalle und Zwillingsverwachsung" (Regular growth of crystals and intergrowth of twins), *Zentralblatt für Mineralogie, Geologie und Palaeontologie*, No. 17/18: 285–288, 1920. See p. 286. MHMi

———, "Herrscht Zufall oder Gesetz beim Festwachsen der Kristalle auf ihrer Unterlage?" (Do crystals grow to their base by law or by chance?), *Zentralblatt für Mineralogie, Geologie und Palaeontologie*, No. 5/6: 65–70, 1920. See pp. 66, 69. MHMi

———, "Kristalltracht und Aufwachsung des Eises" (Crystal habit and the growth of ice), *Zentralblatt für Mineralogie, Geologie und Palaeontologie*, No. 5: 129–134, 1921. MHMi

Kalesnik, S. V., *Obshchaia gliatsiologiia* (General glaciology), Leningrad, Izdatel'stvo Narkomprosa RSFSR, 1939. SIP 4551

Khanina, S. K., and A. R. Shul'man, "Izuchenie techeniia estestvennykh l'dov" (Study of the flow of natural ice bodies), *Leningrad. Gosudarstvennyi Gidrologicheskii Institut, Trudy*, No. 16(70): 89–95, 1949. SIP 4819

*Khar'kov, V. E., *Metody uplotneniia i uborki snega na aerodromakh* (Methods of compacting and removing snow on airfields), Moscow, 1944.

Klebelsberg, zu Thumberg, R. von, *Handbuch der Gletscherkunde und Glazialgeologie* (Handbook of glaciology and glacial geology), Vienna, Springer Verlag, 1948/1949. 2 vols. 1028 pp. AFCRL

Klocke, F., "Über die optische Struktur des Eises" (The optical structure of ice), *Neues Jahrbuch für Mineralogie, Geologie und Palaeontologie*, No. 3/4: 272–285, 1879. MHMi

Koch, J. P., and A. Wegener, "Die glaciologischen Beobachtungen der Danmark-Expedition. Danmark-expeditionen til Grønlands nordostkyst, 1906–1908" (The glaciological observations of the Denmark Expedition to the northeast coast of Greenland, 1906–1908), *Meddelelser om Grønland*, 46(1): 1–77, 1912. MHZ

————— and —————, "Wissenschaftliche Ergebnisse der Dänischen Expedition nach Dronning Louises-Land und quer über das Inlandeis von Nordgrönland 1912–13 unter Leitung von Hauptmann J. P. Koch" (Scientific results of the Danish expedition to Queen Louise Land and the traverse across the inland ice of North Greenland, 1912–13, under the leadership of Captain J. P. Koch), *Meddelelser om Grønland*, 75(1): 1–676, 1930. MHZ

Kolkmeijer, N. H., and J. C. L. Favejee, "Structure emulsoid sol particles and their hydration film," *Nature*, 132(3337): 602–603, 1933. AFCRL

Kolmogorov, A. N., "K voprosu o 'geometricheskom otbore' kristallov" (The problem of the "geometric selection" of crystals), *Akademiia Nauk SSSR, Doklady*, 65(5): 681–684, 1949. MHZ

Koloskov, P. I., "K voprosu o faktorakh i protsessakh firnizatsii snega" (Factors and processes of snow firnification), *Akademiia Nauk SSSR, Izvestiia, Seriia Geograficheskaia i Geofizicheskaia*, 9(5/6): 503–506, 1945. AB 23371

Kondrat'eva, A. S., "Teploprovodnost' snegovogo pokrova i fizicheskie protsessy, proiskhodiashchie v nem pod vliianiem temperaturnogo gradienta" (Thermal conductivity of the snow cover and physical processes in it caused by the temperature gradient), *Akademiia Nauk SSSR. Fiziko-mekhanicheskie svoistva snega i ikh ispol'zovanie v aerodromnom i dorozhnom stroitel'stve*, Moscow, Sovet po izucheniiu proizvoditel'nykh sil, Aerodromno-dororzhanaia Komissiia, 1945. See p. 14. AB 35658

König, H., "Eine kubische Eismodifikation" (A cubic modification of ice), *Zeitschrift für Kristallographie, Mineralogie und Petrographie*, 105(4): 279–286, 1944. MHMi

Konovalov, E. P., "Kratkii otchet o rabote na Zarevshanskom lednike v 1932 g." (Brief report on the work on the Zarevshan glacier in 1932), *Lednikovye Ekspeditsii Vtorogo Mezhdunarodnogo Poliarnogo Goda*, Vol. 3: 369–415, 1936. SIP 12913

Kragel'skii, I. V., "Fiziko-mekhanicheskie svoistva snegovogo pokrova" (Physical-mechanical properties of the snow cover), *U.S.S.R. Armiia. Upravlenie Voenno-Vozdushnykh Sil. Sbornik materialov po stroitel'stvu i ekspluatatsii zimnikh aerodromov*, No. 1: 13–31, 1942. AB 52459

—————, "O metodike opredeleniia tverdosti i plotnosti snegovykh pokrytii" (Methods of hardness and density determination of snow covers), *Akademiia Nauk SSSR. Fiziko-mekhanicheskie svoistva snega i ikh ispol'zovanie v aerodromnom i dorozhnom stroitel'stve*, Moscow, Sovet po izucheniiu proizvoditel'nykh sil, Aerodromno-dorozhnaia Komissiia, 1945, pp. 61–66. SIP 1878

Krastanow, L., "Über die Bildung der unterkühlten Wassertröpfen und der Eiskristalle in der freien Atmosphäre" (The formation of undercooled water droplets and ice crystals in the free atmosphere), *Meteorologische Zeitschrift*, 57(10): 357–371, 1940. MH

———, "Beitrag zur Theorie der Tropfen- und Kristallbildung in der Atmosphäre" (Contribution to the theory of drop and crystal formation in the atmosphere), *Meteorologische Zeitschrift*, 58(2): 37–45, 1941. MH

*Kropotkin, P. A., *Geograficheskoe Obshchestvo SSSR, Zapiski po Obshchei Geografii*, 7(1), 1876.

*Kuz'min, P. P., "Opyt issledovaniia teplovogo i vodnogo balansa snegotaianiia" (Investigation of the heat and water balance of snowmelt), *Leningrad. Gosudarstvennyi Gidrologicheskii Institut, Trudy*, No. 1(55): 11, 1947.

*———, "Intensivnost' snegotaianiia kak funktsiia elementov energeticheskogo balansa" (Intensity of snowmelt as a function of the elements of the energy balance), *Leningrad. Tsentral'nyi Institut Prognozov, Trudy*, No. 5(32): 43, 1947.

*———, "Issledovanie i raschet snegotaianiia" (Investigation and calculation of snowmelt), *Leningrad. Gosudarstvennyi Gidrologicheskii Institut, Trudy*, No. 7(61): 5, 1948.

Laemmlein, G. G., "Sekundäre Flüssigkeitseinschlüsse in Mineralien" (Secondary fluid inclusions in minerals), *Zeitschrift für Kristallographie, Mineralogie und Petrographie*, 71(3): 237–256, 1929. MHMi

———, "Geometrical selection in a growing crystal aggregate," *Akademiia Nauk SSSR, Doklady*, 48(3): 168–171, 1945. MHZ

Lagally, M., "Versuch einer Theorie der Spaltenbildung in Gletschern" (Attempt at a theory of crack-formation in glaciers), *Zeitschrift für Gletscherkunde*, 17(1/3): 285–301, 1929. MHMi

———, "Die Zähigkeit des Gletschereises und die Tiefe der Gletschern" (The viscosity of glacier ice and glacier thickness), *Zeitschrift für Gletscherkunde*, 18(1/3): 1–8, 1930. MHMi

———, (a) "Zur Thermodynamik der Gletscher" (The thermodynamics of glaciers), *Zeitschrift für Gletscherkunde*, 20(4/5): 199–214, 1932. MHZ

———, (b) "Die Bewegung des 'toten Eises' an der Pasterze" (The movement of "dead ice" on the Pasterze glacier), *Zeitschrift für Gletscherkunde*, 20(4/5): 215–221, 1932. MHZ

———, "Mechanik und Thermodynamik des stationären Gletschers" (Mechanics and thermodynamics of a stationary glacier), *Beiträge zur angewandte Geophysik, Ergebnisse der kosmischen Physik*, Leipzig, Akademische Verlagsgesellschaft, 1934. Supplementband 2, pp. 1–94. MHMi

Landau, L. D., "O ravnovesnoi forme kristallov" (The equilibrium form of crystals), in *Sbornik posviashchennyi semidesiatiletiiu Akademika A. F. Ioffe* (Collection of articles dedicated to the 70th anniversary of Academician A. F. Ioffe), Moscow, Izdatel'stvo Akademii Nauk SSSR, 1950, pp. 44–49. MHPh

*Lange, O. K., "Materialy dlia klassifikatsii podzemnykh vod" (Data for the classification of underground waters), *Gidrologicheskii S"ezd v 1924 g.*, *Trudy*, Leningrad, Vol. 1, 1925.

Lebedev, A. F., *Pochvennye i gruntovye vody* (Soil and ground waters), Moscow, Izdatel'stvo Akademii Nauk SSSR, 1936. 314 pp. SIP 5900

Le Chatelier, H., "Über das Gleichgewicht chemischer Systeme bei ungleichförmigem Druck" (The equilibrium of chemical systems with irregular pressure), *Zeitschrift für physikalische Chemie*, 9(3): 335–338, 1892. MHCh

Leffingwell, E. de K., "The Canning River region, northern Alaska," *U. S. Geological Survey, Professional Paper 109*, Washington, D.C., U.S. Government Printing Office, 1919. 251 pp. MHZ

Lehmann, O., *Molekularphysik* (Molecular physics), Leipzig, W. Engelmann, 1888–1889. 2 Vols. MH

*Levinson-Lessing (Loewinson-Lessing), F. Iu., *Petrografiia* (Petrography), 5th ed., Leningrad. 1940.

Loewe, F., "Das Klima des Grönlandischen Inlandeises" (The climate of the inland ice of Greenland), in *Handbuch der Klimatologie* (Climatological handbook) by W. Köppen and R. Geiger, Berlin, Gebrüder Borntraeger, 1935, Vol. 2, Part K, No. 3, pp. K68–K99. MIT

Lohmann, H., *Das Höhleneis unter besondere Berücksichtigung einiger Eishöhlen des Erzgebirges* (Cave ice with special emphasis on some ice caves of the Erzgebirge), Dresden, B. G. Teubner, 1895. 40 pp. MHZ

Lonsdale, K., [see Seligman, G., *Journal of Glaciology*, 1(8): 442, 1950.] MHZ

Lopatin, I. A., "Nekotoriia svedeniia o ledianykh sloiakh v vostochnoi Sibiri" (Some information on ice strata in East Siberia), *Akademiia Nauk SSSR, Zapiski*, Vol. 29, Supplement 1, Sankt Peterburg, 1876. 32 pp. AB 10332

Lütschg-Loetscher, O., "Über Niederschlag und Abfluss im Hochgebirge. Sonderstellung des Mattmarkgebietes" (Precipitation and runoff in the high mountains, with particular application to the Mattmark region), *Schweizerischer Wasserwirtschaftsverband, Verbandsschrift* No. 14: 1–479, 1926. SIP 10260

McConnel, J. C., "On the plasticity of an ice crystal," *Royal Society of London, Proceedings*, 48(294): 259–260, 1890; 49(299): 323–343, 1891. MH

———— and D. A. Kidd, "On the plasticity of glacier and other ice," *Royal Society of London, Proceedings*, 44(270): 331–367, 1888. MH

McFarlan, R. L., "The structure of ice II," *Journal of Chemical Physics*, 4(1): 60–64, 1936. MHCh

————, "The structure of ice III," *Journal of Chemical Physics*, 4(4): 253–259, 1936. MHCh

Maksimovich, G. A., "Peshchernye l'dy" (Cavern ice), *Geograficheskoe Obshchestvo SSSR, Izvestiia*, 79(5): 537–549, 1947. SIP 1062

Mallet, R., "On the brittleness and non-plasticity of glacier ice," *London, Edinburgh and Dublin Philosophical Magazine and Journal of Science*, Series 3, 26(176): 586–592, 1845. MH

Markov, K. K., "Sovremennye problemy gliatsiologii i paleogliatsiologii" (Contemporary problems of glaciology and paleoglaciology), *Voprosy Geografii*, Sbornik 1: 127–156, 1946. MH

Mawson, D., "A contribution to the study of ice-structures," in *British Antarctic Expedition, 1907–1909, Reports on the Scientific Investigations*, Vol. 2, *Geology*, London, William Heinemann, 1916. See p. 1. SIP 10463

Meinardus, W., "Die hypsographischen Kurven Grönlands und der Antarktis und die Normalform der Inlandeisoberfläche" (The hypsographic curves of Greenland and the Antarctic and the normal form of the inland ice surface), *Petermanns Geographische Mitteilungen*, 72(5/6): 97–105, 1926. MH

————, "Bemerkungen zur Form der Inlandeisoberfläche Grönlands" (Remarks on the form of the inland ice surface of Greenland), *Zeitschrift für Gletscherkunde*, 20(1/3): 94–100, 1932. MHZ

Mercanton, P. L., "Le glacier du Rhône" (The Rhone glacier), *Schweizerische Naturforschende Gesellschaft, Neue Denkschriften*, 52: 37–190, 1916. MHZ

————, "Rapports sur les variations périodiques des glaciers des Alpes suisses. La pression des bulles gazeuses dans le glacier" (Reports on the periodic variations of the glaciers of the Swiss Alps. The pressure of gas bubbles in a glacier), *Schweizer Alpenklub, Jahrbuch*, 38th Report, 1917, pp. 151–153. MH

————, "Bismuth and ice. The growth of the glacier grain," *Journal of Glaciology*, 1(7): 393–394, 1950. AFCRL

Meyer, J., and W. Pfaff, "Zur Kenntnis der Kristallisation von Schmelzen. III" (Contribution to knowledge of the crystallization of melts, Part 3), *Zeitschrift für anorganische Chemie*, 224(3): 305–314, 1935. MHCh

Middendorf, A. F., *Puteshestvie na sever i vostok Sibiri. Sever i Vostok Sibiri v estestvenno-istoricheskom otnoshenii.* Ch. 1, Vyp. 3, *Klimat Sibiri* (A journey to northern and eastern Siberia. Northern and eastern Siberia from the viewpoint of natural history. Part 1, No. 3, The climate of Siberia), Sankt Peterburg, Typografiia Imperatorskoi Akademii Nauk, 1862. AB 11373

Molchanov, I. V., "O stroenii i strukture ozernogo l'da v sviazi s meteorologicheskimi usloviiami" (The structure and composition of lake ice in connection with meteorological conditions), *Leningrad. Gosudarstvennyi Gidrologicheskii Institut, Izvestiia*, 14: 31–51, 1925. SIP 11687

Morgan, J., and B. E. Warren, "X-ray analysis of the structure of water," *Journal of Chemical Physics*, 6(11): 666–673, 1938. MHCh

Moskvitin, A. I., "Ledianye klin'ia—klinovidnye treshchiny i ikh strati-graficheskoe znachenie" (Ice wedges—wedgelike cracks and their significance in stratigraphy), *Moskovskoe Obshchestvo Ispytatelei Prirody, Biulleten', Novaia Seriia, Otdel Geologicheskii,* 48(2): 55–72, 1940. MHZ

———, "O sledakh merzloty i neobkhodimosti ikh raspoznavaniia" (Traces of permafrost and the need for recognizing them), *Merzlotove-denie,* 2(1): 3–22, 1947. AB 11795

Moss, R., "The physics of an ice-cap," *Geographical Journal,* 92(3): 211–231, 1938. MHZ

Mügge, O., "Über die Plasticität der Eiskrystalle" (The plasticity of ice crystals), *Neues Jahrbuch für Mineralogie, Geologie und Palaeontologie, Ab-handlungen,* 2(3): 211–228, 1895. MHZ

———, "Über die Structur des grönlandischen Inlandeises und ihre Bedeutung für die Theorie der Gletscherbewegung" (The structure of Greenland's inland ice and its importance for the theory of glacier movement), *Neues Jahrbuch für Mineralogie, Geologie und Palaeontologie,* 2(3): 123–136, 1899. MHZ

———, "Weitere Versuche über die Translationsfähigkeit des Eises, nebst Bemerkungen über die Bedeutung der Structur des grönlandischen Inlandeises" (Further study on the translation capacity of ice, with remarks on the significance of the structure of Greenland's inland ice), *Neues Jahrbuch für Mineralogie, Geologie und Palaeontologie, Abhandlungen,* 2(2): 80–98, 1900. MHZ

———, "Die regelmässigen Verwachsungen von Mineralen verschiedener Art" (The regular intergrowths of different kinds of minerals), *Neues Jahrbuch für Mineralogie, Geologie und Palaeontologie, Beilage-Band,* 16(3): 335–475, 1903. See p. 455. MHZ

Nakaya, U., and Y. Sekido, "General classification of snow crystals and their frequency of occurrence," *Sapporo, Japan. Hokkaido Imperial University, Faculty of Science, Journal,* Series 2, Physics, 1(9): 243–264, 1936. MH

——— and ———, "Allgemeine Klassifikation der Schneekristalle und die Häufigkeit ihres Vorkommens" (General classification of snow crystals and their frequency of occurrence), *Deutsche Akademie der Luftfahrtforschung, Mitteilungen,* 2(1): 9–35, 1943. MHMc

Nakaya, U., Y. Toda, and S. Maruyama, "Further experiments on the artificial production of snow crystals," *Sapporo, Japan. Hokkaido Imperial University, Faculty of Science, Journal,* Series 2, Physics, 2(1): 13–57, 1938. MH

———, ——— and ———, "Weitere Versuche zur künstlichen Herstellung von Schneekristallen" (Further experiments on the artificial production of snow crystals), *Deutsche Akademie der Luftfahrtforschung, Mitteilungen,* 2(1): 71–127, 1943. MHMc

Nansen, F., "Grönlands Inlandeis" (Greenland's inland ice), *Petermanns Geographische Mitteilungen, Ergänzungsheft* 23, No. 105: 68–95, 1892. MH

Nebol'sin, S. I., "Kak taet sneg" (Snow melt), *Meteorologicheskii Vestnik*, 35: 120–127, 1925. SIP 6788

Neher, J., "Schneeuntersuchungen im Gelände" (Snow investigations in the field), *Beiträge zur geologischen Karte der Schweiz, Geotechnische Serie, Hydrologie*, No. 3: 255–272, 1939. USGS

Niggli, P., "Einführung" (Introduction) to "Der Schnee und seine Metamorphose" (Snow and its metamorphism), *Beiträge zur geologischen Karte der Schweiz, Geotechnische Serie, Hydrologie*, No. 3: IX–XXIII, 1939. USGS

Nikiforov, K., "O nekotorykh dinamicheskikh protsessakh v pochvakh v oblasti rasprostraneniia pochvennoi merzloty" (Some dynamic processes in permafrost soils), *Pochvovedenie*, 14(2): 49–74, 1912. SIP 6727

Nordenskiöld, A. E., *Grönland. Seine Eiswüsten im Innern und seine Ostküste. Schilderung der Zweiten Dickson'schen Expedition ausgeführt im Jahre 1883* (Greenland. Its inland ice deserts and its east coast. Description of the Second Dickson Expedition conducted in 1883), Leipzig, F. A. Brockhaus, 1886. 505 pp. MH

Nordenskiöld, G., "Preliminärt meddelande rörande en undersökning af snökristaller" (Preliminary report on snow crystal research), *Geologiska Föreningens i Stockholm, Förhandlingar*, 15(3), Report 150: 146–158, 1893. MHZ

Nye, J. F., "The flow of glaciers and ice-sheets as a problem in plasticity," *Royal Society of London, Proceedings*, Series A, 207(1091): 554–572, 1951. MH

——, "A method of calculating the thicknesses of the ice-sheets," *Nature*, 169(4300): 529–530, 1952. AFCRL

——, "The mechanics of glacier flow," *Journal of Glaciology*, 2(12): 82–93, 1952. MHZ

——, "A comparison between the theoretical and the measured long profile of the Unteraar glacier," *Journal of Glaciology*, 2(12): 103–107, 1952. MHZ

Odell, N. E., "The glaciers and morphology of the Franz Josef Fjord region of North-East Greenland," *Geographical Journal*, 90(2): 111–125; 90(3): 233–258, 1937. MHZ

Oiia, A. Ia., "Vodnyi balans snegotaianiia pod pologom lesa" (The water balance of snow melt under a forest canopy), *Leningrad. Gosudarstvennyi Gidrologicheskii Institut, Trudy*, No. 16(70): 21–45, 1949. SIP 4784

Orowan, E., "Joint meeting of the British Glaciological Society, the British Rheologists' Club and the Institute of Metals," *Journal of Glaciology*, 1(5): 231–240, 1949. MHZ

Ostwald-Luther-Drucker, *Fiziko-Khimicheskie Izmereniia* (Physical-chemical measurements), Leningrad, Parts I and II, 1935, a Russian translation based on Ostwald, W., *Ostwald-Luther Hand- und Hilfsbuch zur Ausführung physiko-chemischer Messungen* (The Ostwald-Luther handbook and reference book for conducting physical-chemical measurements), 3rd ed., Leipzig, 1912. MH

Owston, P. G., and K. Lonsdale, "The crystalline structure of ice," *Journal of Glaciology*, 1(3): 118–123, 1948. MHZ

Papapetrou, A., "Untersuchungen über dendritisches Wachstum von Kristallen" (Investigations of the dendritic growth of crystals), *Zeitschrift für Kristallographie, Mineralogie und Petrographie*, 92(1/2): 89–130, 1935. MHMi

Parkhomenko, S. G., "Nekotorye dannye o prirode Nizhne-Lenskogo Kraia" (Some data on the nature of the Lower Lena Region), *Akademiia Nauk SSSR, Komissiia po Izucheniiu Iakutskoi ASSR, Trudy*, Vol. 3, Part 1, Appendix III, 1929, pp. 206–246. MHZ

————, "Merzlotovedenie kak uchenie o kriofil'nykh gornykh porodakh" (Permafrostology as the science of cryophilic rocks), *Akademiia Nauk SSSR, Komitet po Vechnoi Merzloty, Trudy*, 6: 177–194, 1938. AB 31187

Paulcke, W., "Eisbildungen I. Der Schnee und seine Diagenese" (Ice formations I. Snow and its diagenesis), *Zeitschrift für Gletscherkunde*, 21(4/5): 259–282, 1934. MHZ

Perutz, M. F., "Discussion," (concerning R. U. Winterhalter) *Journal of Glaciology*, 1(1): 31, 1947. MHZ

————, "Report on problems relating to the flow of glaciers," *Journal of Glaciology*, 1(2): 47–51, 1947. MHZ

————, "A description of the iceberg aircraft carrier and the bearing of the mechanical properties of frozen wood pulp upon some problems of glacier flow," *Journal of Glaciology*, 1(3): 95–104, 1948. MHZ

————, "Direct measurement of the velocity distribution in a vertical profile through a glacier," *Journal of Glaciology*, 1(5): 249, 1949; 1(7): 382–383, 1950. MHZ

———— and G. Seligman, "A crystallographic investigation of glacier structure and the mechanism of glacier flow," *Royal Society of London, Proceedings*, Series A, 172(950): 335–360, 1939. MH

Philipp, H., "Geologische Untersuchungen über den Mechanismus der Gletscherbewegung und die Entstehung der Gletschertextur" (Geological research on the mechanism of glacier movement and the formation of glacier texture), *Neues Jahrbuch für Mineralogie, Geologie und Palaeontologie, Beilage-Band*, 43(3): 439–556, 1920. MHMi

————, "Gletscheruntersuchungen in den Ostalpen" (Glacier research in the eastern Alps), *Zeitschrift für Gletscherkunde*, 20(4/5): 233–268, 1932. MHZ

Piotrovich, V. V., "Proiskhozhdenie poloschatosti lednikovogo l'da" (The origin of glacier ice striation), *Leningrad. Gosudarstvennyi Gidrologicheskii Institut, Izvestiia*, No. 56: 38–46, 1933. SIP 1360

Plyler, E. K., "Some properties of ice crystals," in "Proceedings of the Twenty-Fourth Annual Meeting of the North Carolina Academy of Science," *Elisha Mitchell Scientific Society, Journal*, 41(1/2): 18, 1925. MHZ

Pod'iakonov, S. A., "Naledi Vostochnoi Sibiri i prichiny ikh vozniknoveniia" (Icings of East Siberia and their origin), *Geografcheskoe Obshchestvo SSSR, Izvestiia,* 39(4): 305–337, 1903. MHZ

Popov, A. I., "Osobennosti litogeneza alliuvial'nykh ravnin v usloviiakh surovogo klimata" (Lithogenesis features of alluvial plains in a severe climate), *Akademiia Nauk SSSR, Izvestiia, Seriia Geografcheskaia,* No. 2: 29–41, 1953. SIP 13983

*Popov, E. G., *Moscow. Tsentral'nyi Institut Prognozov, Trudy,* No. 9(36): 3, 1948.

Popov, M. M., *Termometriia i kalorimetriia* (Thermometry and calorimetry), 2nd revised ed.; Moscow, Izdatel'stvo Moskovskogo Universiteta, 1934. 941 pp. DLC

*Popov, O. V., "K voprosu o fizicheskoi skheme infil'tratsii vody v pochvo-gruntakh" (The physical scheme of the infiltration of water in soil-grounds), *Leningrad. Gosudarstvennyi Gidrologicheskii Institut,* No. 24(78): 47, 1950.

*Prendel', R., *Vestnik Estestvoznaniia,* 1(8): 340, 1890.

Priklonskii, V. A., and F. F. Laptev, *Rukovodstvo po izucheniiu fizicheskikh svoistv i khimicheskogo sostava podzemnykh vod* (Handbook for the study of the physical properties and chemical composition of underground waters), Moscow, Gosudarstvennoe Izdatel'stvo Geologicheskoi Literatury, 1949. 208 pp. DLC

*Pustovalov, L. V., *Petrografiia osadochnykh porod* (The petrography of sedimentary rocks), Moscow, 1940, Parts 1 and 2.

Quincke, G., "Über Eisbildung und Gletscherkorn" (Ice formation and glacier grains), *Annalen der Physik,* Leipzig, Series 4, 18(11): 1–80, 1905. AFCRL

Rakovskii, A. V., and T. V. Polianskii, "Szhatie pri adsorbtsii vody kolloidami" (Compression occurring during adsorption of water by colloids), *Zhurnal Fizicheskoi Khimii,* 2(1): 151–160, 1931. DLC

Rau, W. von, "Gefriervorgänge des Wassers bei tiefen Temperaturen" (Freezing processes at low temperatures), *Deutsche Akademie der Luft-fahrtforschung, Schriften,* 8(2): 65–84, 1944. MHMc

Reid, H. F., "The mechanics of glaciers. I," *Journal of Geology,* 4(8): 912–928, 1896. MHZ

Renaud, A., "A contribution to the study of the glacier grain," *Journal of Glaciology,* 1(6): 320–324, 1949. MHZ

Riecke, E., "Über das Gleichgewicht zwischen einem festen, homogen deformirten Körper und einer flüssigen Phase, insbesondere über die Depression des Schmelzpunctes durch einseitige Spannung" (The equilibrium of a solid, homogeneously deformed substance and a liquid phase; in particular, the depression of the melting point by unilateral tension), *Gesellschaft der Wissenschaften zu Göttingen, Mathematisch-Physikalische Klasse, Nachrichten,* No. 4: 278–284, 1894. AFCRL

Riecke, E., "Zur Erniedrigung des Schmelzpunktes durch einseitigen Zug oder Druck" (The reduction of the melting point by unilateral tension or pressure), *Zentralblatt für Mineralogie, Geologie und Palaeontologie*, No. 4: 97–104, 1912. MHZ

Rigsby, G. P., "Crystal fabric studies on Emmons Glacier, Mount Rainier, Washington," *Journal of Geology*, 59(6): 590–598, 1951. MHZ

Rinne, F., "Thermotaxie als Problem der orientierten Kristallisation" (Thermotaxy as a problem of oriented crystallization), *Zeitschrift für Kristallographie, Mineralogie und Petrographie*, 64(1/2): 71–75, 1926. MHMi

Rodebush, W. H., "Nuclei in evaporation and condensation," *Chemical Reviews*, 44(2): 269–276, 1949. MHCh

Royer, L., "Recherches expérimentales sur l'épitaxie ou orientation mutuelle de cristaux d'espèces différentes" (Experimental investigations on the epitaxy or mutual orientation of different types of crystals), *Société Française de Minéralogie, Bulletin*, 51(1/2): 7–156, 1928. MHMi

*Rymsha, V. A., "Elektricheskii metod opredeleniia soderzhaniia vody v snege" (Electrical method of determining the water content of snow), *Leningrad. Gosudarstvennyi Gidrologicheskii Institut, Trudy*, No. 4(58), 1948.

Saks, V. N., "Nekotorye dannye o vechnoi merzlote v nizov'iakh Eniseia" (Some data on permafrost in the lower Yenisei Basin), *Problemy Arktiki*, No. 1: 62–79, 1940. AB 15199

Sander, B. *Gefügekunde der Gesteine* (Structural Geology), Vienna, J. Springer, 1930. 352 pp. MHMi

——, "Glazialgeologie und Gefügekunde" (Glaciology and structural geology), *Zeitschrift für Gletscherkunde*, 22(1/5): 171–175, 1935. MHZ

——, *Einführung in die Gefügekunde der geologischen Körper. II. Die Korngefüge* (Introduction to structural geology. Part II. Grain structure), Vienna, Springer Verlag, 1950. 409 pp. MHMi

Schaefer, V. J., (a) "Use of snowflake replicas for studying winter storms," *Nature*, 149(3768): 81, 1942. AFCRL

——, (b) "New methods for preparing surface replicas for microscopic observations," *Physical Review*, 62: 495–496, 1942. MHPh

——, "Surface replicas containing dye for use in the light microscope," *Metal Progress*, 44(1): 72–74, 1943. MHMc

——, "The formation of ice crystals in the laboratory and in the atmosphere," *Chemical Reviews*, 44(2): 291–320, 1949. MHCh

——, "A new method for studying the structure of glacier ice," *Journal of Glaciology*, 1(8): 440–442, 1950. MHZ

Schlagintweit, H. von, "Verhandlungen der Gesellschaft. Protokoll der Aprilsitzung" (Transactions of the society. Report on the April session), *Deutsche Geologische Gesellschaft, Zeitschrift*, 6(2): 260, 1854. MHZ

—— and A. Schlagintweit, *Untersuchungen über die physikalische Geographie der Alpen* (Studies of the physical geography of the Alps), Leipzig, J. A. Barth, 1850. 600 pp. MHZ

Schmidegg, O., "Über geregelte Wachstumsgefüge" (Ordered growth structure), *Austria. Geologische Bundesanstalt, Jahrbuch*, 78(1/2): 1–51, 1928. MHZ

Schmidt, W., "Gefügestatistik" (Statistics on structure), *Mineralogische und Petrographische Mitteilungen*, Vol. 38, Report No. 23: 392–423, 1925. MHMi

————, *Tektonik und Verformungslehre* (Tectonics and deformation theory), Berlin, Verlag von Gebrüder Borntraeger, 1932. 208 pp. MHMi

*Schoentjes, H., *Fleurs de la glace* (Ice flowers), Ghent, 1905.

Schwarzacher, W., and N. Untersteiner, "Zum Problem der Bänderung des Gletschereises" (The problem of glacier-ice banding), *Akademie der Wissenschaften, Vienna, Sitzungsberichte, Mathematisch-Naturwissenschaftliche Klasse*, Abteilung 2a, 162(1/4): 111–145, 1953. MH

Seitz, F., *The physics of metals*, New York, McGraw-Hill Book Co., Inc., 1943. 330 pp. (Russian translation, *Fizika metallov*, Moscow, 1947).

Seliakov, N. Ia., "To what class of symmetry does ordinary ice belong?" *Akademiia Nauk SSSR, Doklady*, Novaia Seriia, 1(7): 293–294, 1936. MHZ

————, "Some remarks on α- and β-ice," *Akademiia Nauk SSSR, Doklady*, Novaia Seriia, 2(7): 227, 1937. MHZ

————, "The nature of ordinary ice," *Akademiia Nauk SSSR, Doklady*, 14(4): 183–186, 1937. MHZ

Seligman, G., *Snow structure and ski fields*, London, Macmillan and Co., Ltd., 1936. 555 pp. MH

————, "The structure of a temperate glacier," *Geographical Journal*, 97(5): 295–317, 1941. MHZ

————, "Wind slab avalanches," *Journal of Glaciology*, 1(2): 70–73, 1947. MHZ

————, "The growth of the glacier crystal," *Journal of Glaciology*, 1(5): 254–267, 1949. MHZ

————, "The growth of the glacier crystal. Some further notes," *Journal of Glaciology*, 1(7): 379–381, 1950. MHZ

————, "The specific gravity of ice," (Re: K. Lonsdale) *Journal of Glaciology*, 1(8): 442, 1950. MHZ

Seng, H., "Für das Riecke'sche Prinzip!" (In support of the Riecke principle), *Neues Jahrbuch für Mineralogie, Geologie und Palaeontologie, Beilage-Band*, Abteilung A, 73(2): 239–308, 1937. MHMi

Shakhov, A. A., "Fizicheskie protsessy v snegovom pokrove" (Physical processes in the snow cover), *Akademiia Nauk SSSR, Izvestiia, Seriia Geograficheskaia i Geofizicheskaia*, 12(3): 239–248, 1948. SIP 768

Sharp, R. P., "Deformation of a vertical bore hole in a piedmont glacier," *Journal of Glaciology*, 2(13): 182–184, 1953. MHZ

Shepelevskii, A. A., "O raspredelenii i izmenenii s techeniem vremeni plotnosti v snegovom pokrove" (The distribution and time variation of the density of a snow cover), Leningrad. *Vsesoiuznyi Arkticheskii Institut, Trudy*, 110(1): 15–31, 1938. MHZ

Sherzer, W. H., "Glaciers of the Canadian Rockies and Selkirks. Smithsonian Expedition of 1904," *Smithsonian Contributions to Knowledge*, Vol. 34, No. 1692, Article 4, 1907. 135 pp. MHZ

Shubnikov, A. V., *Kak rastut kristally* (Crystal growth), Moscow, Akademiia Nauk SSSR, Seriia Nauchno-populiarnaia, 1935. 174 pp. MHMi

——— and G. G. Laemmlein, "Ob ortotropizme rosta kristallov" (The orthotropy of crystal growth), *Akademiia Nauk SSSR, Doklady*, Seriia A, No. 4: 61–64, 1927. AFCRL

Shukevich, I. B., "O formakh snezhnykh kristallov i drugikh tverdykh gidrometeorov vypadaiushchikh v S.-Peterburge" (Forms of snow crystals and other hydrometeors observed in St. Petersburg), *Akademiia Nauk SSSR, Bulleten'* (Izvestiia), Seriia 6, 4(4): 291–302, 1910. AFCRL

*Shul'man, A. R., *Leningrad. Gosudarstvennyi Gidrologicheskii Institut, Trudy*, No. 7(61): 43, 1948.

Shumskii, P. A., (a) *Energiia oledeneniia i zhizn' lednikov* (The energy of glaciation and the life of glaciers), Moscow, Gosizdat Geograficheskoi Literatury, 1947. 58 pp. MH

———, (b) "Sovremennoe oledenenie sovetskoi Arktiki" (Contemporary glaciers of the Soviet Arctic), *Voprosy Geografii*, Sbornik 4: 11–32, 1947. MH

———, "K voprosu o passivnom orientiruiushchem vliianii tverdogo osnovaniia na narastaiushchie kristally" (The passive orienting influence of the solid base on growing crystals), *Akademiia Nauk SSSR, Doklady*, 93(1): 51–54, 1953. MHZ

Shvetsov, P. F., and V. P. Sedov, "Gigantskie naledi i podzemnye vody khrebta Tas-Khaiakhtakh" (Giant icings and subterranean waters of the Tas-Khayakhtakh Range), *Informatsionnyi Biuleten' Noveishei Literatury po Geologicheskim Naukam*, No. 1/6: 134, 1942. SIP 3519

Sirota, N. N., "O neizbezhnom gisterezise prevrashcheniia pri perekristallizatsii" (The inevitable hysteresis of conversion during perecrystallization), *Akademiia Nauk SSSR, Doklady*, 59(7): 1309–1312, 1948. MHZ

Somigliana, C., "Sulla profondità dei ghiacciai" (The depth of glaciers), *Accademia Nazionale dei Lincei, Classe di Scienze fisiche, Matematiche e Naturali, Rendiconti*, Series 5, 30(1): 291–296, 323–327, 360–364; 30(2): 3–7, 1921. AFCRL

Sorge, E., "Glaziologische Untersuchungen in Eismitte" (Glaciological studies at Eismitte Station), *Deutsche Grönland-Expedition Alfred Wegener, 1929 und 1930–31, Wissenschaftliche Ergebnisse*, Vol. 3, 1935, pp. 62–270. AB 16545

Sorge, E., "Glaziologische Untersuchungen bei 200 km Randabstand" (Glaciological studies at the 200-km boundary line), *Deutsche Grönland-Expedition Alfred Wegener, 1929 und 1930–31, Wissenschaftliche Ergebnisse,* Vol. 4, No. 2, 1939, pp. 346–355. AB 16543

Steenstrup, K. J. V., "Bidrag til kjendskab til braeerne og braeisen i Nord-Grønland" (Contribution to the knowledge of glaciers and glacier ice in North Greenland), *Meddelelser om Grønland,* 4: 69–112, 1893. MHZ

Streiff-Becker, R., "Zwanzig Jahre Firnbeobachtung" (Twenty years of firn observations), *Zeitschrift für Gletscherkunde,* 24: 31–42, 1936. MHZ

———, "Zur Dynamik des Firneises" (On the dynamics of firn ice), *Zeitschrift für Gletscherkunde,* 26(1/2): 1–21, 1938. MHZ

Stulov, N. N., "Ledianye igly" (Ice crystals), *Vsesoiuznoe Mineralogicheskoe Obshchestvo, Zapiski,* 78(2): 172–176, 1949. SIP 3966

Sukachev, V. N., "K voprosu o vliianii merzloty na pochvu" (The influence of frost on soil), *Akademiia Nauk SSSR, Bulleten' (Izvestiia),* Seriia 6, 5(1): 51–60, 1911. MHZ

Sumgin, M. I., (*a*) "Led v vechno merzlykh gruntakh" (Ice in permafrost), in Veinberg, B. P., *et al., Led. Svoistva, vozniknovenie i ischeznovenie l'da* (Ice. Its properties, appearance and disappearance), Moscow, Gostekhizdat, 1940, pp. 460–490. AB 48251

———, (*b*) "On the formation of perennial ice mounds (bulgunniakhs)," *Akademiia Nauk SSSR, Doklady,* 28(2): 156–157, 1940. MHZ

———, S. P. Kachurin, N. I. Tolstikhin and V. F. Tumel', *Obshchee merzlotovedenie* (General permafrostology), Moscow, Izdatel'stvo Akademii Nauk SSSR, 1940. 240 pp. AB 17178

Sverdrup, H. U., "Scientific results of the Norwegian-Swedish Spitsbergen Expedition in 1934. Part 6. The rise of the temperature of the firn in summer," *Geografiska Annaler,* 17(1/2): 22–88, 1935. See pp. 71–72. MHZ

———, "The eddy conductivity of the air over a smooth snow field," *Geofysiske Publikasjoner,* 11(7): 1936. 69 pp. MH

Taber, S., "The mechanics of frost heaving," *Journal of Geology,* 38(4): 303–317, 1930. MHZ

———, "Perennially frozen ground in Alaska: Its origin and history," *Geological Society of America, Bulletin,* 54(10): 1433–1548, 1943. MHZ

Tammann, G., "Über die Grenzen des festen Zustandes IV" (The limits of the solid state IV), *Annalen der Physik,* Leipzig, Series 4, 2(5): 1–31, 1900. AFCRL

———, *Aggregatzustände* (Aggregate states), 2nd ed., Leipzig, L. Voss, 1923. 292 pp. MHMi

———, "Die Bildung des Gletscherkorns" (The formation of glacier grains), *Naturwissenschaften,* 17(44): 851–854, 1929. SIP 6717

———, "Zur Molekular-Dynamik in Kristallen" (Molecular dynamics in crystals), *Gesellschaft der Wissenschaften zu Göttingen, Mathematisch-Physikalische Klasse,* No. 3: 227–254, 1930. AFCRL

Tammann, G., and A. Büchner, "Die lineare Kristallisationsgeschwindigkeit des Eises aus gewöhnlichem und schwerem Wasser" (The linear crystallization velocity of ice derived from common and heavy water), *Zeitschrift für anorganische Chemie*, 222(1): 12–16, 1935. MHCh

—— and K. L. Dreyer, "Die Rekristallisation leicht schmelzender Stoffe und die des Eises" (The recrystallization of easily melting substances and of ice), *Zeitschrift für anorganische Chemie*, 182(3): 289–313, 1929. MHCh

Tarr, R. S., and O. D. von Engeln, "Experimental studies of ice with reference to glacier structure and motion," *Zeitschrift für Gletscherkunde*, 9(2): 81–139, 1915. MHZ

—— and J. L. Rich, "The properties of ice—Experimental studies," *Zeitschrift für Gletscherkunde*, 6(4): 225–249, 1912. MHZ

Teichert, C., "Corrasion by wind-blown snow in polar regions," *American Journal of Science*, 237(2): 146–148, 1939. MHZ

Teis, R. V., "Variation in deuterium concentration in the process of melting of ice," *Akademiia Nauk SSSR, Doklady*, 53(6): 529–532, 1946. MHZ

——, "Izotopnyi sostav iskopaemykh l'dov" (The isotopic composition of fossil ice), *Akademiia Nauk SSSR, Doklady*, 62: 365–367, 1948. MIT

—— and K. P. Florenskii, "Isotopic composition of snow," *Akademiia Nauk SSSR, Doklady*, 28(1): 70–74, 1940. MHZ

Thomson, G. P., "The growth of crystals," *Physical Society of London, Proceedings*, Vol. 61, Part 5, No. 347: 403–416, 1948. MH

Thomson, J., "On crystallization and liquefaction, as influenced by stresses tending to change of form in the crystals," *Royal Society of London, Proceedings*, Series A, 11(47): 473–481, 1861. MH

Thomson, W., "On the stratification of vesicular ice by pressure," *London, Edinburgh and Dublin Philosophical Magazine and Journal of Science*, Series 4, 16(109): 463–466, 1858. MH

——, "Polar ice-caps and their influence in changing sea levels," *Geological Society of Glasgow, Transactions*, Vol. 8, Part II, Report 35: 322–340, 1888. MHZ

Tol', E. V., "Iskopaemye ledniki Novo-Sibirskikh ostrovov, ikh otnoshenie k trupam mamontov i k lednikovomu periodu, na osnovanii rabot dvukh ekspeditsii" (The fossil ice of the New Siberian Islands, its relationship to the carcasses of mammoths and to the Glacial Epoch, based on the work of two expeditions), *Geograficheskoe Obshchestvo SSSR, Zapiski po Obshchei Geografii*, Vol. 32, No. 1, 1897. 139 pp. AB 17768

Tollner, H., "Untersuchungen über die Bewegung des Eises auf 3 Spitzbergen-Gletschern" (Studies of the ice movement of three Spitsbergen glaciers), *Vienna. Naturhistorisches Museum. Archiv für Polarforschung, Jahresbericht* No. 1: 5–17, 1938. AB 17791

*Tolmachev, I. P., *Ekspeditsiia dlia raskopki mamonta v 1901 g. Nauchnye Rezul'taty* (Expedition for the excavation of the carcass of a mammoth, 1901. Scientific Results), St. Peterburg (?), Imp. Akademiia Nauk, 1903, Vol. 1, p. 125.

Tolstikhin, N. I., "Podzemnye vody Zabaikal'ia i ikh gidrolakkolity" (Subterranean waters of the Transbaikal region and their hydrolaccoliths), *Akademiia Nauk SSSR, Komitet po Vechnoi Merzlote, Trudy*, 1: 29–50, 1932. AB 17871

————, "K voprosu klassifikatsii l'dov i l'distykh porod" (The problem of classifying ice and ice-mineral complexes), *Problemy Sovetskoi Geologii*, 6(7): 628–636, 1936. MHZ

————, *Podzemnye vody merzloi zony litosfery* (The underground waters of the frozen zone of the lithosphere), Moscow, Gosizdat Geologicheskoi Literatury, 1941. 201 pp. MH

Troll, C., "Büsserschnee (nieve de los penitentes) in den Hochgebirgen der Erde" (Penitent snow in the high mountains of the earth), *Petermanns Geographische Mitteilungen, Ergänzungsheft*, No. 240: 1942. 103 pp. AB 32534

[Trouton, F. T.], "Orientierung der Krystalle gewisser Substanzen bei der Erstarrung," an abstract (by H. L. Bowman) of Trouton's article "Arrangement of the crystals of certain substances on solidification" (see next entry), *Zeitschrift für Kristallographie, Mineralogie und Petrographie*, 32(3): 292–293, 1900. MHMi

————, "Arrangement of the crystals of certain substances on solidification," *Royal Dublin Society, Scientific Proceedings*, New Series, Vol. 8, Part 6: 691–692, 1898. MH

Tsytovich, N. A., "K teorii ravnovesnogo sostoianiia vody v merzlykh gruntakh" (Equilibrium theory of water in frozen ground), *Akademiia Nauk SSSR, Izvestiia, Seriia Geograficheskaia i Geofizicheskaia*, 9(5/6): 493–502, 1945. AB 26822

———— and M. I. Sumgin, *Osnovaniia mekhaniki merzlykh gruntov* (Principles of frozen ground mechanics), Moscow, Izdatel'stvo Akademii Nauk SSSR, 1937. 423 pp. AB 18061

Tushinskii, G. K., *Laviny, vozniknovenie i zashchita ot nikh* (Avalanches, their formation and protection against them), Moscow, Gosudarstvennoe Izdatel'stvo Geograficheskoi Literatury, 1949. 213 pp. AB 32563

Tyndall, J., "On some physical properties of ice," *Royal Society of London, Philosophical Transactions*, 148(1): 211–229, 1858. MHZ

————, *Al'piiskie ledniki*, Moscow, 1866. A Russian translation of *The glaciers of the Alps*, Boston, Ticknor and Fields, 1861. 446 pp. MHZ

Vadilo, P. S., "Methods for the investigation of the structure of ice," *Akademiia Nauk SSSR, Doklady*, 23(4): 343–344, 1939. MHZ

*————, *Kishinev, Universitet, Uchenye Zapiski*, 3(1): 195, 1951.

Vareschi, V., "Blütenpollen im Gletschereis" (Flower pollen in glacier ice), *Zeitschrift für Gletscherkunde*, 23(4/5): 255–276, 1935. MHZ

Vareschi, V., "Die pollenanalytische Untersuchung der Gletscherbewegung" (Pollen analysis study of glacier movement), *Geobotanisches Institut Rübel in Zürich, Veröffentlichungen*, No. 19, 1942. 144 pp. MHBot

Veinberg (Weinberg), B. P., "O vnutrennem trenii l'da" (The internal friction of ice), *Russkoe Fiziko-Khimicheskoe Obshchestvo, Zhurnal, Chast' Fizicheskaia*, 38: 186–224, 250–281, 289–328, 329–364, 1906. SIP 7626

———, *Sneg, inei, grad, led i ledniki* (Snow, rime, hail, ice and glaciers), 2nd ed., Moscow, Ob"edinenie Nauchno-Tekhnicheskikh Izdatel'stv, 1936. MAB 6, p. 883

———, "The role of regelation in the condensation of the snow cover," *International Geodetic and Geophysical Union, Association of Scientific Hydrology, Bulletin*, 23: 493–508, 1938. SIP 2649

———, V. Ia. Al'tberg, V. E. Arnol'd-Aliab'ev, and M. P. Golovkov, *Led. Svoistva, vozniknovenie i ischeznovenie l'da* (Ice. Its properties, appearance and disappearance), Moscow, Gosudarstvennoe Izdatel'stvo Tekhniko-Teoreticheskoi Literatury, 1940. 524 pp. AB 48711

*Vernadskii, V. I., *Istoriia mineralov zemnoi kory. 2. Istoriia prirodnykh vod* (History of the minerals of the earth's crust. 2. History of natural waters), Vol. 1, No. 1, 1933; Vol. 1, No. 2, 1934.

Visser, P. C., "Glaziologie" (Glaciology), *Niederländische Expeditionen in den Karakorum, Wissenschaftliche Ergebnisse*, Leiden, E. J. Brill, 1938, Vol. 2, Part 1. 216 pp. SIP 8437

Volmer, M., *Kinetik der Phasenbildung* (The kinetics of phase formation), Dresden, T. Steinkopf, 1939. 220 pp. AFCRL

Vul'f, G. V., "K voprosu o skorostiakh rosta i rastvoreniia kristallicheskikh granei" (The rates of growth and dissolution of crystal faces), *Warsaw, Universitet, Izvestiia*, No. 7, Report 7, pp. 1–16, 1895. DLC

Wade, F. A., "The physical aspects of the Ross Shelf ice," *American Philosophical Society, Proceedings*, 89(1): 160–172, 1945. MHZ

Wallerant, F., "Sur une nouvelle modification cristalline de la glace" (A new crystalline modification of ice), *Société Française de Minéralogie, Bulletin*, 31(6): 217–218, 1908. MHMi

Ward, H., "Glaciology" in "Baffin Island Expedition, 1950: a preliminary report," *Arctic*, 3(3): 131–149, 1950. See pp. 141–143. AFCRL

Washburn, H. B., and R. P. Goldthwait, "Movement of the South Crillon Glacier, Crillon Lake, Alaska," *Geological Society of America, Bulletin*, 48(11): 1653–1663, 1937. MHZ

Weickmann, H., "Die Eisphase in der Atmosphäre" (The ice phase in the atmosphere), *Germany. Deutscher Wetterdienst in der U. S. Zone, Berichte*, Vol. 1, No. 6, 1949. 54 pp. SIP 5944

Whitman, W. G., "Elimination of salt from sea-water ice," *American Journal of Science*, Series 5, 11: 126–132, 1926. MHZ

Wilson, W. T., "An outline of the thermodynamics of snow-melt," *American Geophysical Union, Transactions*, 22(1–B): 182–195, 1941. AFCRL

Winterhalter, R. U., [see Perutz, M. F., *Journal of Glaciology*, 1(1): 31, 1947.] MHZ

Wright, C. S., and R. E. Priestley, "Glaciology," *British (Terra Nova) Antarctic Expedition 1910–1913, Scientific Report*, London, Harrison & Sons, Ltd., 1922. 581 pp. MHZ

*Zamorskii, A. D., *Leningrad. Glavnaia Geofizicheskaia Observatoriia, Trudy*, No. 13(75): 1948. N.B.: pp. 52 and 61.

——, "Atmosfernyi led" (Atmospheric ice), *Priroda*, 40(1): 24–32, 1951. MHZ

Zubov, N. N., *L'dy Arktiki* (Arctic ice), Moscow, Izdatel'stvo Glavsevmorputi, 1944. 359 pp. MHZ

SUBJECT INDEX

Ablation, differential, 378; radiational, 426

Ablation region of a glacier, 313, 378, 429, 430, 437, 439, 442, 448

Accumulation region of a glacier, 313, 431, 442, 444, 448

Active layer (zone) of ice formation, 288, 291, 401–4, 406, 412–14, 415, 417–19, 421–22, 424–27, 429, 436

Adsorption, 211

Air bubbles in ice, 89–90, 138, 174–77, 234, 238, 255, 268, 284, 294, 298, 351

Air pressure in ice, 89–90, 140–44, 178, 180, 268, 274–76, 284, 295, 299, 306, 346–48, 351, 359, 365, 443

Albedo of the snow cover, 408, 418, 432

Allotriomorphism, 131, 171, 178

Anatexis, 84

Anisotropy: of mechanical properties of ice, 41–42, 180; of rates of crystal growth, 65, 146, 161, 165–66; of viscosity of ice, 44

Annealing, 242, 247

Atmospheric ice, 3, 11, 58, 69–74, 84, 95, 230–31, 442

Autometamorphism, 232

Avalanches, 270, 373, 423, 441; loose-snow, 270, 309; wet-snow, 290, 309, 374; windslab, 270, 273, 309

Axial angle of crystals, 22, 46–47, 120, 125, 133–34, 350, 353

Baidzharakhs, 199

Bands in glaciers, 354, 360, 362–73, 375; blue, 360, 362–73; dirt, 363

Barchans, snow, 236

Bergschrund, 311

Bertin's law, 155–57

Birefringence of ice, 45

Block slipping of glaciers, 315–16, 323–26, 328, 361

Bottom ice, 81, 151–52, 185

Bottom zone of folded strata and thrusts, 444

Boundary of accumulation and ablation regions, 423, 430–31, 435, 447

Bravais's law, 27, 42, 62, 64

Breaking strength of ice, 44

Breccia, flow, 309, 373; friction, 360, 362, 365

Brine ice, 15, 23, 95–97

Brittleness of ice, 39, 43, 252, 304, 307

Bulgunniakhs (pingos), 226–28

Buried ice, 438, 457

Cataclasis of ice, 251–53, 338, 348–53, 372, 375, 441

Cavern (cave) ice, 16, 74–75

Centers of crystallization, 51, 54, 56–59, 150, 153, 171, 178–79, 215, 217, 284, 295–97

Centers of freezing, 59–60

Chemical composition of ice, 6, 15–16

Chionosphere, 410, 447–48

Classification of glaciers (geophysical), 275, 396

Classification of ice (genetic, petrographic), 81–85, 383

Classification of snow, 268

Classification of snowflakes, 69

Cleavage, ice, 42

Clouds, altostratus and altocumulus, 71, 446; cirrostratus, 71; cirrus, 28, 71, 445; convective cirrus, 71; nacreous, 10; nimbostratus, 71, 446; water, 58, 60, 287

Coefficient of lateral pressure, 306–8, 327

Cold layer of the atmosphere, 2

Cold of crystallization, latent, 421, 430–32, 447

Cold reserve of winter freezing, 277, 279, 287, 289, 398, 400, 403, 411–14, 417, 419–23, 427, 430, 447

Composition of ice, 103–5

Condensation of water vapor, 402–3; capillary, 60, 71; spontaneous, 59

Congelation zone of ice formation, 424, 435–40, 443, 447–48, 450–53; seasonal, 423–24, 437–40, 446–47

Conglomerate, flow, 309, 373; ice tectonic, 184, 353, 441

Conoscopic figure, 120, 122

Continental ice, 80

Coordination number, 25, 36

Creep of snow and firn, downhill, 256, 269, 285

Crevasses (cracks), glacier, 74–75, 105, 185, 194, 252, 321, 330–32, 361, 364, 429, 441–42